M

SERIES

Work Out

Chemistry

'O' Level and GCSE

The titles in this series

For examinations at 16+

Biology

Chemistry

Computer Studies

English Language

French

German

Mathematics

Physics

Principles of Accounts

Spanish

Statistics

For examinations at 'A' level

Applied Mathematics

Biology

Chemistry

English Literature

Physics

Pure Mathematics

Statistics

MACMILLAN
MASTER
SERIES

Work Out

Chemistry

'O' Level and GCSE

A. L. Barker

and

K. A. Knapp

MACMILLAN

First published 1986
Reprinted 1986

Published by
MACMILLAN EDUCATION LTD
Houndmills, Basingstoke, Hampshire RG21 2XS
and London
Companies and representatives
throughout the world

Typesetting and Illustration by TecSet Ltd,
Sutton, Surrey
Printed in Great Britain by The Bath Press, Avon

British Library Cataloguing in Publication Data
Barker, A.L. (Alan Lewis)
Work out chemistry — (Macmillan
master series) — (Macmillan work
out series)
1. Chemistry—Examinations, questions, etc.
I. Title   II. Knapp, K.A.
540'.76   QD42
ISBN 0-333-38996-4

Contents

Acknowledgements

The author and publishers wish to thank the following who have kindly given permission for the use of copyright material:

The Associated Examining Board, the Northern Ireland Schools Examination Council, the Scottish Examination Board, the Southern Universities' Joint Board, the University of Cambridge Local Examinations Syndicate, the University of London School Examinations Board and the University of Oxford Delegacy of Local Examinations for questions from past examination papers.

Every effort has been made to trace all the copyright holders, but if any have been inadvertently overlooked the publishers will be pleased to make the necessary arrangement at the first opportunity.

The University of London Entrance and School Examinations Council accepts no responsibility whatsoever for the accuracy or method in the answers given in this book to actual questions set by the London Board.

Acknowledgement is made to the Southern Universities' Joint Board for School Examinations for permission to use questions taken from their past papers but the Board is in no way responsible for answers that may be provided and they are solely the responsibility of the authors.

The Associated Examining Board, the University of Oxford Delegacy of Local Examinations, the Northern Ireland Schools Examination Council, and the Scottish Examination Board wish to point out that worked examples included in the text are entirely the responsibility of the author and have neither been provided nor approved by the Board.

Groups Responsible for Examinations at 16+

In the United Kingdom, examinations are administered by four examining groups and three examination boards. Syllabuses and examination papers can be ordered from the addresses given here.

Northern Examining Association

Joint Matriculation Board
    Publications available from:
John Sherratt and Son Ltd
78 Park Road, Altrincham
Cheshire WA14 5QQ (JMB)
Yorkshire and Humberside
    Regional Exam Board
Scarsdale House
136 Derbyshire Lane
Sheffield S8 8SE
North West Regional Exam Board
Orbit House, Albert Street
Eccles, Manchester M30 0WL

Northern Regional Exam Board
Wheatfield Road, Westerhope
Newcastle upon Tyne NE5 5JZ

Associated Lancashire Schools Exam Board
12 Harter Street Manchester M1 6HL

Midland Examining Group

**University of Cambridge Local
    Examinations Syndicate**
Syndicate Buildings, Hills Road
Cambridge CB1 2EU (UCLES)
Southern Universities Joint Board
Cotham Road
Bristol BS6 6DD (SUJB)
West Midlands Regional Exam Board
Norfolk House, Smallbrook
Queensway, Birmingham B5 4NJ

**Oxford and Cambridge Schools
    Examination Board**
10 Trumpington Street
Cambridge CB2 1QB
East Midlands Regional Exam Board
Robins Wood House, Robins Wood Road
Aspley, Nottingham NG8 3NR

London and East Anglian Group

**University of London School
    Examinations Board**
University of London Publications Office
52 Gordon Square, London WC1E 6EE (L)
East Anglian Regional Exam Board
The Lindens, Lexden Road
Colchester, Essex CO3 3RL

London Regional Exam Board
Lyon House
104 Wandsworth High Street
London SW18 4LF

Southern Examining Group

The Associated Examining Board
Stag Hill House
Guildford, Surrey GU2 5XJ (AEB)
Southern Regional Examining Board
Avondale House, 33 Carlton Crescent
Southampton, Hants SO9 4YL

**University of Oxford Delegacy of
    Local Examinations**
Ewert Place, Summertown
Oxford OX2 7BZ (OLE)
**South-Western Regional Examining
    Board**
23–29 Marsh Street, Bristol BS1 4BP

Scottish Examination Board (SEB)
  Publications available from:

Robert Gibson & Sons (Glasgow) Ltd
17 Fitzroy Place, Glasgow G3 7SF
(SEB)

Welsh Joint Education Committee
245 Western Avenue
Cardiff CF5 2YX (WJEC)

**Northern Ireland Schools Examination
    Council**
Examinations Office
Beechill House, Beechill Road
Belfast BT8 4RS (NISEC)

Introduction

How to Use this Book

This book is intended for use towards the end of a Chemistry course leading to examinations for GCSE, GCE'O' level, Scottish 'O' Grade, or BTEC. Its purpose is to help you with your revision and to improve your examination performance.

Each chapter begins with a short revision section which deals briefly with the topics that you will need to know. For more detailed background reading you should use a textbook such as the authors' *Chemistry – A Practical Approach*.

The revision section is followed by worked examples from past examination questions. These enlarge upon the topics presented in the revision section and help you to see how to present your answers. Further explanation and advice are given occasionally and enclosed in 'boxes' to separate them from the answers.

Finally, there is a section of questions on which you can practise your skills and test your knowledge. Answers are given at the end of each chapter but you should not look at them until you have *written* your own.

If you work carefully and sensibly through the three sections of each chapter you should gain both knowledge and understanding of chemistry and an awareness of what your examiner will require you to do.

Revision

The first thing you must do is to obtain a copy of the syllabus and some past examination papers from your Examination Board so that you know exactly what you have to learn. Many topics are common to the syllabuses of all of the Boards but there is no point at this stage in your course in learning things that you will not be asked about. The addresses of the Examination Boards are given on page *x*.

Next, you should make a revision plan to cover the last few months before the examination. Having made the plan, you must keep to it!

Your revision should be active – try to write out definitions, equations and key points from memory. Every 20 minutes or so, get up and stretch: this may sound silly but it really does help you to concentrate and revise more effectively. Shorten your notes to a few headings, definitions and equations for each topic and learn them thoroughly. There is no excuse for losing marks through not knowing a definition.

Work through questions from past papers in the same way as you do for the self test sections of this book. You may well find that extra practice, using the authors' *Structured Questions in Chemistry*, will be helpful at this stage.

Remember that advanced planning is always better than last-minute cramming.

The Examination

Pack everything you need on the night before the examination and avoid the temptation to stay up late trying to revise. Get up early enough the next morning to enable you to get to the examination room without rushing and becoming flustered.

If the examiner gives you a choice of questions, read the paper carefully before deciding which ones to answer – you may regret it if you choose in a hurry. In all papers, keep an eye on the time and do not spend too long on a difficult question. It is better to leave it and try again later. If you finish early, check your paper carefully — there is always room for improvement.

Types of Question

The Examination Boards use various types of questions. You must check to find which ones your Board uses.

Multiple choice questions require you to choose one correct answer from four or five alternatives. Take your time and read **all** of the possible answers given before making your choice. It is very easy to make mistakes in these questions, either by not reading all of the alternatives or by misreading one of them. If you are not sure of the correct answer, you can usually eliminate two or three that are definitely wrong. You can then make a guess from the remainder with a better chance of being right. *Never* leave an answer blank.

Multiple completion questions involve choosing one or more correct answers from several alternatives and then using a grid of the type below to choose an answer A–E. Question 1.3 is an example of a multiple completion question.

A	B	C	D	E
1, 2, 3 all correct	1, 2 only correct	2, 3 only correct	1 only correct	3 only correct

Grid 1

Assertion–reason questions give two statements linked by the word 'because' (see Question 3.5). Each statement may be true or false and if both are true the second may or may not be a correct explanation of the first. Careful thought is needed before using Grid 2 to choose an answer A–E.

	First statement	Second statement	
A	True	True	Reason is a correct explanation
B	True	True	Reason is **NOT** a correct explanation
C	True	False	
D	False	True	
E	False	False	

Grid 2

In any papers containing these three types of question you should first answer the questions which you find easy. Then go back and tackle the more difficult ones if you have time.

Structured questions consist of a series of questions, usually related to one another and requiring short answers (see Example 2.7). Clues to the length of answer and the detail required can be found in the amount of space allowed on the paper for you to write and by the number of marks allocated, which is quoted in a bracket. For example, if 5 marks are to be awarded, a one-word answer is bound to be insufficient.

Free response questions require longer answers (see Example 4.1) and it is worth making a check-list of main points and an outline plan before beginning.

In the last two types of question it is especially important to keep to a time schedule. Draw diagrams only if they are asked for or if they really clarify a point. Draw them neatly but do not spend too long on them as they are rarely worth many marks. Give equations wherever possible because they often earn marks, even when they are not specifically mentioned in the question.

Always answer the question which is asked! This may sound obvious advice but many candidates throw away marks through not paying attention to the wording of the question. If you are asked to *name* a substance, then giving its formula will earn you nothing. If you are asked to *describe* a reaction, the examiner will expect you to mention colour change, fizzing, production of heat, etc. Finally, do not 'waffle' — in other words do not write a great deal on a topic just because you know it well. The examiner will award you marks only if you write what has been asked for.

Passing examinations requires time and effort. Take note of the advice given by your teachers and by this book. Be prepared to make sacrifices, work steadily, and you should be rewarded by success.

We wish you luck!

A.L.B.
K.A.K.

1 Some Simple Ideas

1.1 Elements, Compounds and Mixtures

An **element** is a substance which cannot be split up into two or more simpler substances by chemical means, e.g. aluminium and sulphur (see Question 1.1).

There are over 100 elements which are grouped into two main classes — metals and non-metals. The differences between the classes are investigated in later chapters (13–17) and a summary appears in Example 13.4.

A **compound** is a substance which consists of two or more elements chemically combined together, e.g. copper(II) sulphate crystals, $CuSO_4.5H_2O$, contain copper, sulphur, oxygen and hydrogen.

Synthesis is the building up of a compound from simpler substances, often its elements.

A **mixture** consists of two or more elements or compounds which have not been chemically combined, e.g. water and ethanol, aluminium and sulphur.

The main differences between compounds and mixtures are summarised in Table 1.1.

Table 1.1

	Compound	*Mixture*
Composition	Fixed	Variable
Heat change	Heat usually produced or absorbed when compound made	Usually no heat change on making mixture
Appearance	Different from constituent elements	'Average' of constituents
Properties	Different from constituent elements	Similar to constituents
Separation	Cannot be separated into constituent elements by physical means	Can be separated into constituents by physical means

The acronym 'CHAPS' should help you to remember the table.

1.2 Symbols

A system of symbols was developed so that chemical reactions could be written down in shorthand form. The initial letter, or the initial plus one other letter, of an element is used to represent one atom of it, e.g. C is the symbol for carbon and Ca is the symbol for calcium. In some cases, the latin names are used, e.g. Fe is the symbol for iron (ferrum). A full list of symbols is given on page 228.

1.3 Chemical and Physical Changes

When a new substance is made we say that a **chemical change** has taken place or that a chemical reaction has occurred.

A **physical change** is one where no new substance is formed.

The differences between chemical and physical changes are given in Example 1.2.

1.4   The Separation of Mixtures

The separation of mixtures is generally comparatively easy, the method chosen depending on the nature of the substances to be separated.

(a) To Obtain a Solute from a Solution

(i)   *Evaporation*

A *solution* consists of a *solute* dissolved in a *solvent*, e.g. sea water is a solution of salt (the solute) in water (the solvent). If sea water is heated in the apparatus shown in Fig. 1.1 (a), the water evaporates and salt is left. The final heating may be carried out using a steam bath (Fig. 1.1 (b)) to avoid loss of salt by spitting.

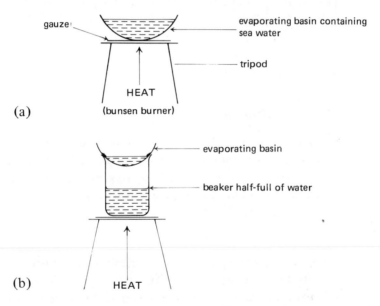

Fig. 1.1

(ii)   *Crystallisation*

The main disadvantage of evaporating all of the solvent from a solution in order to obtain the solute is that if there are any dissolved impurities present, they will be obtained with the solid at the end of the experiment. This problem is avoided if crystallisation is carried out. The solution is evaporated to crystallisation point, i.e. the point at which crystals of solute will form on cooling the solution to room temperature. Drops of solution are removed at intervals and allowed to cool; the formation of crystals in one of these drops indicates that the solution is at crystallisation point. If the solution is allowed to cool, crystals form and can then be filtered out, washed and dried.

(b) To Separate a Solid from a Liquid

(i) *Filtration*

This method uses the apparatus shown in Fig. 1.2 to separate a solid from a liquid. The solid is left on the filter paper as the residue while the liquid passes through and is collected in the evaporating basin as the filtrate.

Fig. 1.2

A centrifuge can also be used. A tube of mixture is spun round at high speed. The solid settles to the bottom of the tube and the liquid may then be removed using a dropping pipette.

(c) To Separate Two Solids

(i) *Sublimation*

Sublimation is the direct conversion of a solid to a vapour on heating and of a vapour to a solid on cooling, without going through the liquid state.

Since only a few solids sublime, (e.g. ammonium chloride, anhydrous aluminium chloride) this method of separation is very limited.

(ii) *Paper Chromatography*

Paper chromatography is used to separate a mixture of similar solids dissolved in a solvent (see Example 1.4). The separation depends on differences in (a) the solubilities of the dyes in the water and (b) the tendencies of the dyes to stick to the surface of the paper. Chromatography can also be used to separate colourless substances but in this case the paper must be developed by spraying it with another chemical so that the position of the solids can be seen (see also Example 19.8).

(d) To Separate a Solvent from a Solution

(i) *Distillation*

For this separation the apparatus shown in Fig. 1.3 is used.

When the solution is boiled, the solvent changes to vapour. The vapour passes down a condenser where it is converted back to liquid and is collected as the distillate in the beaker.

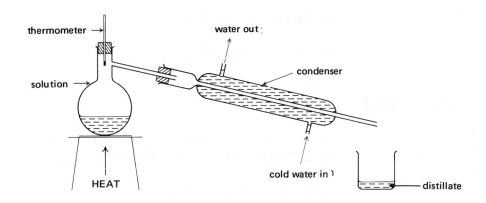

Fig. 1.3

(e) To Separate Two Liquids

(i) *Separating Funnel*

If two liquids are *immiscible* (i.e. they separate into two distinct layers) then the simplest way to separate them is to use a separating funnel (see Question 1.5). The lower layer may be run into a beaker and the upper layer tipped into another container.

(ii) *Fractional Distillation*

Miscible liquids (i.e. they mix together completely and do not form layers) may be separated by fractional distillation provided that their boiling points are different. When a mixture of two such liquids is heated to boiling in the apparatus shown in Fig. 1.4 the vapour of the more volatile component (i.e. the liquid with the lower boiling point) travels up the column more easily. The vapour of the component with the higher boiling point condenses more readily. Eventually the vapour escaping to the condenser consists of the more volatile component only.

  Important applications of fractional distillation include:

(a) the separation of liquid air into oxygen, nitrogen, etc. (see Section 10.2);
(b) the separation of crude oil into petrol, paraffin, etc. (see Section 19.5);
(c) the manufacture of spirits (e.g. gin, whisky, brandy).

Fig. 1.4

(f) To Separate Two Gases

Diffusion (see Section 2.3) can be used to separate two gases of differing densities.

1.5   Tests for Purity

Pure substances usually have definite sharp melting points and boiling points and the addition of only a trace of an impurity will alter these values. The presence of dissolved solid impurities raises the boiling point of a liquid and lowers the melting point of a solid, making it less sharp.

1.6   Worked Examples

Example 1.1

Which one of the following groups consists only of compounds?

A Cl_2 HCl $MgCl_2$ C_6H_5Cl
B $CaSO_4$ H_2S S_8 Na_2S
C MnO_2 PH_3 XeF_4 O_2
D $KMnO_4$ H_2SO_4 HNO_3 HCl
E NH_3 N_2 $NaNO_3$ CH_3NH_2

The answer is **D**.

Cl_2, S_8, O_2 and N_2 are all the formulae for elements because each one consists of atoms of the same type.

Example 1.2

Give four ways in which a chemical change differs from a physical change.   **(4 marks)**
Do you think that the following are physical or chemical changes? (a) The boiling of water, (b) the magnetisation of a strip of iron, (c) the decaying of plants on a compost heap, (d) the heating of copper in air. Give reasons for your answers.   **(6 marks)**

Table 1.2 shows how a chemical change differs from a physical change.

Table 1.2

Chemical change	Physical change
New substance formed with different chemical properties	No new substance formed
Heat usually produced or absorbed	No heat change, usually
Generally difficult to reverse	Generally easy to reverse
Mass of residue often differs from that of starting material	Mass of residue usually same as that of starting material

(a) Physical change. No new substance has been formed: the water has changed to steam but this is no different chemically. It still consists of H_2O molecules.
(b) Physical change. The iron has not become a new substance.

(c) Chemical change. The plants rot on a compost heap and become totally new substances.

(d) Chemical change. When heated in air, copper becomes coated with a layer of black copper(II) oxide, a new substance.

Example 1.3

(a) Name the chemical technique which could be used successfully to separate:
   (i) iodine crystal from sand;   (1 mark)
Sublimation (see section 1.4).

Iodine sublimes when heated whereas sand does not.

   (ii) petrol from crude oil.   (1 mark)
Fractional distillation (see Section 1.4).

Crude oil consists of a number of different fractions including petrol. These have different boiling points and so must be separated by fractional distillation.

(b) A pupil decides to separate powdered calcium carbonate from powdered calcium chloride by shaking the mixture with water and then filtering. Would this procedure succeed? Explain your answer.   (2 marks)
                                                                            (OLE)
This procedure would succeed. Calcium carbonate is insoluble in water whereas calcium chloride is very soluble. On filtering the mixture, calcium carbonate would remain on the filter paper whereas calcium chloride solution would pass through.

Example 1.4

(a) In earlier times a retort was used for carrying out distillations (see figure).

HEAT

   (i) Explain what is meant by *distillation* and state why it is an important process in chemistry.   (8 marks)
   (ii) Write down, with a few words of explanation, **two** ways in which a modern distillation set is an improvement on the above apparatus.   (2 marks)
(b) Describe an experiment based on chromatography which would successfully separate a **named** mixture of your own choosing. Would this kind of experiment be successful in separating ethanol from a mixture of ethanol and water? Explain your answer.
                                                                            (10 marks)
                                                                            (OLE)

(a) (i) Distillation occurs when a liquid is heated to form a vapour which is then condensed to reform the liquid. It is an important process in chemistry since it provides a means of purifying liquids.

(ii) Today, distillation would be carried out using the apparatus shown in Fig. 1.3. The thermometer enables the boiling point of the distillate to be found and hence the purity of the distillate can be checked (see Section 1.5). The cold water in the condenser ensures that all the vapour changes to liquid — the yield of product is maximised.

(b) Chromatography can be used to separate the dyes in ink. Using a dropping pipette with a fine jet, a small drop of black ink is placed in the centre of a piece of filter paper and allowed to dry. A strip of filter paper about 3 cm wide is rolled up to make a wick and pushed through a hole in the centre of the ink spot. The apparatus is set up as shown in Fig. 1.5, with the wick just dipping into the water and left until the water has reached the edge of the filter paper. The dyes separate into rings of different substances. The paper is then removed and allowed to dry.

Fig. 1.5

Ethanol and water could not be separated in this way. Ethanol and water are both colourless liquids. Paper chromatography is generally used to separate two or more solids dissolved in a solvent.

Example 1.5

Name the methods you would use to carry out each of the following separations, explaining briefly the principles upon which your methods rely:

(i) a sample of elderberry wine from a mixture of it with solid yeast residues; **(2 marks)**

Filtration (see Section 1.4). The elderberry wine will pass through the filter paper but the yeast residues, being insoluble, will remain in the filter paper.

(ii) reasonably pure ethanol from elderberry wine. **(3 marks)**

(OLE)

Elderberry wine will contain ethanol and water together with a number of other substances. Since these substances have different boiling points they may be separated by fractional distillation (see Section 1.4).

Example 1.6

(i) Name two physical measurements that can be used to demonstrate that a substance is pure. **(2 marks)**

(ii) Will (A) a compound and (B) a mixture behave in the same way when those measurements are made? **(2 marks)**

(i) melting point, boiling point.

(ii) A compound will have a definite sharp melting point and boiling point. The melting point of a mixture will not be sharp and its value will depend on the relative proportions of the components in the mixture. Although the boiling point of a mixture will be sharp, its value will vary.

1.7 Self-Test Questions

Question 1.1

Which of the substances **A** to **E** is most likely to be an element?
A Changes colour and loses oxygen rapidly on gentle heating.
B Burns in air to form carbon dioxide and water.
C Conducts electricity as a solid and also when molten.
D Produces several fractions when distilled.
E On heating evolves a gas leaving a solid residue. ✓

(L)

Question 1.2

(a) Name the chemical technique which could usefully be used to separate:
(i) the mixture of soluble dyes used to colour 'blackcurrant' sweets; *distilation*
(ii) water from a solution of sodium chloride in water. **(1 mark)**

(b) A pupil decides to separate a mixture of the solids calcium hydroxide and ammonium chloride by shaking the mixture with hot water and then filtering. Will this procedure work? Explain your answer. *No, because both substances would* **(3 marks)** *filter*
For Questions 1.3, 1.4 and 1.5 use grid 1 on page 2 to choose an answer A–E.
through the paper

(OLE)

Question 1.3

Benzene and water are two liquids which do not mix. If placed together in a test tube they form two separate layers.
It would be possible to identify the water layer:
1 by adding a little more water
2 by adding a little more benzene
3 given the densities of the two liquids.

(L)

Question 1.4

Filtration is a method of separating:
1 one insoluble solid from another
2 a solute from its solvent
3 an insoluble solid from a liquid.

(AEB)

Question 1.5

Two liquids A and B are placed in a separating funnel and separated as shown in the figure.

It can be deduced that liquid A:
1 Has a higher density than liquid B.
2 Is water.
3 Has a lower boiling point than liquid B.

1.8 Answers to Self-Test Questions

1.1 C

If substance A loses oxygen on heating, it must contain oxygen and something else. Substance B combines with oxygen from the air to give carbon dioxide and water and therefore must contain at least carbon and hydrogen. Pure substances do not produce several fractions when distilled and therefore substance D must be a mixture. Substance E splits up on heating; elements cannot be split up into simpler substances.

1.2 (a) (i) chromatography;
      (ii) distillation.
  (b) This procedure will not work. Ammonium chloride is very soluble in hot water but calcium hydroxide is slightly soluble too. Thus, although most of the calcium hydroxide would remain on the filter paper, some would dissolve and contaminate the ammonium chloride in the filtrate.

1.3 A.

1.4 E.

Do not make the mistake of thinking that option 2 is correct − the solute will be dissolved in the solvent and so cannot be separated in this way.

1.5 D.

2 Atoms and Molecules

2.1 Introduction

Matter consists of tiny particles — either atoms or groups of atoms called molecules (see Example 2.1).

An **atom** is the smallest particle of an element that can exist and still retain the ordinary chemical properties of that element.

Many elements consist of groups of atoms joined together, e.g. oxygen, O_2, sulphur, S_8. In addition, atoms of different elements may join together in groups to form particles of a compound. These groups of atoms are called molecules.

A **molecule** is the smallest particle of an element or compound that can exist naturally and still retain the ordinary chemical properties of that element or compound.

The results of many experiments can be explained in terms of the particle theory of matter and hence they provide evidence to support it, e.g. the dissolving of a solid in a liquid or the mixing of two gases may be interpreted in terms of the intermingling of the particles of the various substances. Crystals of a particular compound all have more or less the same shape. This can easily be understood if we assume that every crystal consists of layers of particles packed together in a regular pattern.

2.2 The States of Matter

Table 2.1 summarises some differences in the structure and properties of solids, liquids and gases.

Table 2.1

	Solid	Liquid	Gas
Compressibility	Difficult to compress	Difficult to compress	Easy to compress
Molecular packing	Close	Close	Sparse
Shape	Fixed	Variable	Variable
Molecular movement	Vibrate and rotate about fixed points	Free to move	Free to move
Attractive forces	Relatively high	Relatively high	Very small
Diffusion	Very slow	Slow	Rapid

When the temperature of a solid is raised, the particles vibrate more and more violently until they are moving to such an extent that they can no longer be held in an ordered arrangement by the forces of attraction. When this happens the solid melts. Raising the temperature of a liquid increases the speed of movement of the particles until their kinetic energy is sufficient to overcome the forces of attraction between them. At this point the liquid boils. On cooling the reverse changes occur. The particles of the gas gradually slow down as the temperature falls until the forces of attraction are able to condense them together and form a liquid. Cooling the liquid causes further loss of kinetic energy until eventually the particles settle into a solid crystal where they vibrate and rotate about fixed points (see Examples 2.3 and 2.4).

2.3 Diffusion

Gases have a tendency to spread in all directions and this can be explained by the idea that gases are made up of moving particles (see Examples 2.5 and 2.6). The process of spreading is known as diffusion. In general, the denser the gas the slower the diffusion process.

2.4 The Chemical Laws

(a) The Law of Conservation of Mass

Matter can neither be created nor destroyed during the course of a chemical reaction (see Example 2.7).

(b) The Law of Constant Composition

All pure samples of the same chemical compound contain the same elements combined in the same proportion by mass (see Example 2.8 and Question 2.2).

2.5 Atomic Structure

Atoms consist of a minute nucleus, where all the positive charge and most of the mass of the atom is concentrated, surrounded by electrons. The nucleus is made up of two types of particle: protons and neutrons.

A **proton** is a positively charged particle, with mass approximately equal to that of a hydrogen atom.

A **neutron** is a neutral particle, with mass approximately equal to that of a hydrogen atom.

The **electron** is a negatively charged particle, its charge being equal but opposite to that of a proton, and its mass approximately 1/1840 of that of a proton.

Since atoms are electrically neutral, the numbers of protons and electrons in an atom must be equal.

The number of protons in the nucleus of an atom is its **atomic number** and gives its position in the periodic table.

The total number of protons and neutrons in an atom is its **mass number**.

Information about the atomic number and mass number of an element can be given with its symbol. Thus $^{12}_{6}C$ represents an atom of carbon with an atomic number of 6 and a mass number of 12.

(a) Arrangement of Electrons (see Question 2.3)

The electrons surround the nucleus and are found at varying distances from it in groups known as energy levels or 'shells'. Each shell contains electrons with similar energies and can contain up to a certain maximum number. The first shell, nearest the nucleus, can contain up to two electrons, the second up to eight and the third up to 18. For example, a potassium atom, atomic number 19, will have the electron arrangement shown in Fig. 2.1.

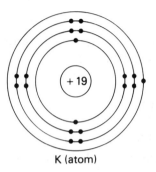

K (atom)

Fig. 2.1

There is a special stability associated with having eight electrons in a shell. Thus, in a potassium atom, there are eight electrons in the third shell and one in the fourth shell even though the third is not full.

Table 3.1 (page 28) shows the atomic structures of the most common isotopes of the first 20 elements.

(b) Isotopes (see Example 2.9)

It is the number of protons in the nucleus of an atom which identifies it. However, it is possible to have atoms of the same element with different numbers of neutrons in their nuclei. They are called **isotopes**, e.g.

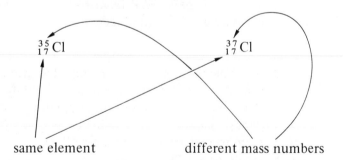

$^{35}_{17}Cl$ $^{37}_{17}Cl$

same element   different mass numbers

2.6   Radioactivity

All atoms with atomic number greater than 83, together with some of the lighter ones, are radioactive. This means that their nuclei are unstable and split up, emitting radiation which is of three distinct types — α, β and γ.

1. α-particles. These are positively charged helium nuclei (i.e. made up of two protons and two neutrons).
2. β-particles. These are negatively charged electrons.

15

3. γ-rays. When either an α- or a β-particle is emitted, the remaining nucleus usually has an excess amount of energy. This extra energy is given out in the form of γ-rays, which are like X-rays but with even shorter wavelength. When the nucleus of a radioactive atom gives off an α- or a β-particle an atom of a new element is formed. If this new atom is stable the disintegration process stops, but if it is radioactive then the splitting-up process continues, e.g.

$$^{238}_{92}U \rightarrow \, ^{234}_{90}Th + \, ^{4}_{2}He$$

$$^{234}_{90}Th \rightarrow \, ^{234}_{91}Pa + \, ^{0}_{-1}e$$

Further disintegration occurs until finally a stable $^{206}_{82}Pb$ atom is left (see Example 2.13 and Question 2.5).

(a) Half-life

The **half-life** of an isotope is the time taken for the mass of radioactive material to be reduced to half its initial value (see Example 2.10).

(b) The Uses of Radioactive Isotopes

1. Nuclear power stations generate electricity from the energy produced when isotopes like uranium-235 decay. Uranium-235 absorbs neutrons to form uranium-236 and then nuclear fission occurs according to the following equation:

$$^{1}_{0}n + \, ^{235}_{92}U \rightarrow [^{236}_{92}U] \rightarrow \, ^{90}_{38}Sr + \, ^{143}_{54}Xe + 3\,^{1}_{0}n$$

The neutrons emitted can cause the fission of more uranium atoms and so produce more and more neutrons. The controlled production of neutrons releases a considerable amount of heat energy which can be used to generate electricity.

2. In living animals and plants the percentage of the radioactive isotope $^{14}_{6}C$ remains constant because it is continually being replaced from the carbon dioxide in the air and from food. In dead tissue this does not happen so the percentage of $^{14}_{6}C$ gradually decreases as the isotope decays. Hence by comparing the percentage of carbon-14 in a dead sample with that in living matter the age of the sample can be found.

3. If radioactive compounds are injected into a patient the functioning of glands and the flow of blood around the body may be checked by means of a Geiger counter or some other detecting device.

4. Cancer may be cured in some cases by killing the cancerous cells by exposing them to radiation (see Example 2.9).

5. γ-radiation will completely destroy bacteria and so can be used to sterilise surgical equipment.

6. Radioactive sources also have a number of industrial uses, e.g. to test for leaks in pipelines by allowing a solution of a radioactive isotope to flow through the pipe and measuring the radioactivity of the surrounding soil.

(c) The Dangers of Radiation

Radiation kills all living cells. The most penetrating type is γ-radiation but all radioactive sources must be handled with care; they are generally stored and transported in lead containers.

2.7   Worked Examples

Example 2.1

A solution of 0.1 cm^3 of oil in 1 dm^3 of petroleum ether was made up. A loop of cotton was floated on water and drops of the oil solution were allowed to fall on the surface of the water inside the loop. The loop filled out and became circular and after three drops of the oil solution had been added it no longer dented when touched. Its diameter was 14 cm.

In a separate experiment it was found that 20 drops of the oil solution had a volume of exactly 1 cm^3.

(a) When the oil solution was added to the water the petroleum ether evaporated. What happened to the oil?   **(1 mark)**

The oil stayed on the surface of the water inside the loop.

(b) Why did the loop no longer dent after three drops of oil solution had been added?
                                                                        (1 mark)

The oil was now filling the space inside the loop.

(c) What was the volume of one drop of oil solution?   **(1 mark)**
20 drops = 1 cm^3
1 drop = 1/20 = 0.05 cm^3

(d) What volume of oil was present in 1 cm^3 of solution?   **(1 mark)**
1000 cm^3 of solution contains 0.1 cm^3 of oil.
1 cm^3 of solution contains 0.1/1000 cm^3 = 0.0001 cm^3

(e) What volume of oil was present in one drop of solution?   **(1 mark)**
Volume of one drop of solution = 0.05 cm^3
Volume of oil in one drop = 0.05 × 0.0001 = 0.000005 cm^3

(f) What volume of oil was present inside the loop?   **(1 mark)**
There were three drops of oil inside the loop.
Therefore volume of oil inside the loop = 0.000015 cm^3.

(g) What was the area of the loop?   **(2 marks)**
The loop was circular; its area is given by π × radius^2 = π × 7^2
Area of the loop = 154 cm^2.

(h) What was the approximate thickness of the oil film inside the loop?   **(2 marks)**
Thickness = volume/area = 0.000015/154 cm
Thickness of the oil film = 0.0000001 cm.

(i) How is the thickness of the oil film related to the diameter of an oil molecule? What assumption must be made in answering this question?   **(2 marks)**
The thickness of the oil film is approximately equal to the diameter of an oil molecule. This assumes that the oil film is one molecule thick.

(j) How could you tell if insufficient oil had been added?   **(1 mark)**
If insufficient oil had been added it would be possible to dent the loop on touching it.

(k) Would it be easy to tell if too much oil had been added? Explain.   **(2 marks)**
It would not be easy to tell if too much oil had been added. The molecules are very small and the same effects would be observed even if the oil film were several molecules thick.

Example 2.2

(a) Why is it that in a cinema the projector beam becomes much more obvious when people in the audience begin to smoke? **(2 marks)**

(b) What do you see when smoke is lit by a beam of light and examined under a microscope? Explain your answer. **(2 marks)**

(a) Smoke consists of particles. In clean air the projector beam is invisible but when smoke is present, the beam of light collides with the particles of smoke and some light is scattered in all directions, thus making the beam visible from the side.

(b) The smoke particles reflect the light and bright specks are seen moving around continually in a random manner. The effect is due to air molecules, themselves too small to be seen, colliding with the smoke particles and causing them to bounce around in all directions.

This sort of motion was first observed by the botanist, Robert Brown, when he looked through a microscope at pollen grains suspended in water — hence the name, Brownian motion.

Example 2.3

Give TWO ways in which the ions in an ionic lattice may be made free to move. **(2 marks)**
(SUJB)

Melting the ionic solid or dissolving it in water enable the ions to move.

Example 2.4

This question is about changing naphthalene from solid to liquid. Naphthalene, $C_{10}H_8$, is a white crystalline solid. 6.4 g of naphthalene crystals were weighed and placed in a test tube together with a thermometer. The tube was placed in a beaker of boiling water and a stop-clock was started. The water was kept boiling and the naphthalene crystals stirred continuously with the thermometer. The temperature of the naphthalene was recorded every 15 seconds. The results are shown on the graph.

(a) What was the boiling point of the water? **(1 mark)**

99°C.

The maximum constant temperature obtained must be the boiling point of the water.

(b) What was the melting point of the naphthalene? **(1 mark)**

80°C.

(c) Explain why the temperature of the naphthalene remained constant from 105 seconds to 165 seconds even though the water was kept boiling. **(2 marks)**

Since the water was kept boiling heat was being supplied to the naphthalene. This was used up in overcoming the forces holding the particles together in the solid lattice (i.e. energy is used up in pulling the particles apart). The temperature remained constant until all of the solid had melted.

(d) Describe how the movement of the naphthalene molecules changes within the crystals during the first 30 seconds of heating. **(2 marks)**

As the temperature increases the naphthalene molecules vibrate more vigorously about fixed points.

Fig. 1

(e) On Fig. 1 sketch the curve you would expect to obtain if the test tube and naphthalene were removed from the beaker of boiling water and placed in a beaker of water at 20°C, the temperature of the naphthalene being recorded at regular intervals of time. Begin your graph at time = 0 s. **(3 marks)**

The answer is given in Fig. 2.2.

(f) Calculate the number of moles of naphthalene molecules used in the experiment. (Relative atomic masses: C = 12, H = 1.) **(2 marks)**

(L)

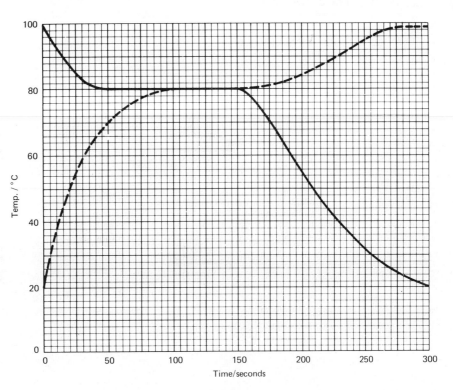

Fig. 2.2

Molas mass of naphthalene ($C_{10}H_8$) $= 10 \times 12 + 8 \times 1$
$$= 128 \ g \ mol^{-1}$$
Moles of naphthalene $= \dfrac{mass}{molar \ mass}$
$$= \dfrac{6.4}{128}$$
$$= 0.05$$

Example 2.5

Tube 1 shows the result of an experiment to investigate the formation of ammonium chloride by the counter-diffusion of ammonia gas and hydrogen chloride. If a similar experiment were set up as in tube 2 to investigate the reaction between ammonia gas and hydrogen bromide, at which one of the five positions shown is the solid most likely to form?
M_r (HCl) = 36.5; M_r (HBr) = 81. (AEB)

The answer is **E**.

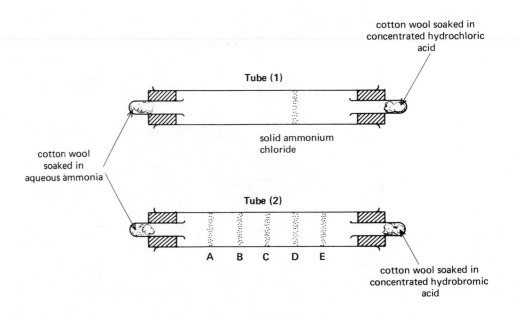

Hydrogen bromide has a higher molar mass and a higher density than hydrogen chloride and hence it will diffuse more slowly.

Example 2.6

A certain volume of carbon monoxide diffuses in 30 s. Which one of the following is the time required for an equal volume of nitrogen to diffuse, under exactly the same conditions? (Relative atomic masses: C = 12, N = 14, 0 = 16.)

A 20 s
B 28 s
C 30 s
D 32 s
E 40 s

The answer is **C**.

Both carbon monoxide and nitrogen have the same relative molecular mass. Since densities are proportional to relative molecular mass, their densities will be equal and hence they will diffuse at equal rates.

Example 2.7

(a) The apparatus shown in the figure may be used to illustrate the law of conservation of mass.

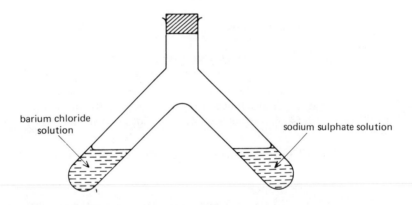

(i) Explain what would be observed if the apparatus were turned upside down, illustrating your answer by means of an equation.   **(2 marks)**

A white precipitate of barium sulphate is obtained when the two solutions mix.

$$BaCL_2(aq) + Na_2SO_4(aq) \rightarrow BaSO_4(s) + 2NaCl(aq)$$

(ii) If the apparatus was weighed before and after the above inversion, what change in mass (if any) would be noted?   **(1 mark)**

None.

Since the apparatus is sealed, there cannot possibly be any change in mass — see Law of Conservation of Mass, Section 2.4.

(b) A sample of ethanol is burnt in an open dish placed on a top-pan balance.
(i) State how the balance readings would change as the combustion took place.
                                   (2 marks)

The balance readings would decrease.

      (ii) Discuss whether or not these observations conflict with the law stated in (a) above.

(2 marks)

(OLE)

On combustion, ethanol combines with oxygen from the air to give gaseous products.

$$C_2H_5OH(l) + 3O_2(g) \rightarrow 2CO_2(g) + 3H_2O(g)$$

These products will pass into the atmosphere and will not be weighed. If a known mass of oxygen is combined with a known mass of ethanol and the mass of the products is found, then the law stated in (a) will be found to be obeyed.

Example 2.8

  (a) State the Law of Constant Composition. **(4 marks)**
  (b) The mass of copper(II) oxide obtainable from a known mass of copper can be determined as follows:
      Place the copper in a hard glass test tube and then add concentrated nitric acid, a few drops at a time, until all the copper metal has disappeared. Now place a loose plug of glass wool in the mouth of the test tube and heat the tube, gently at first until no more liquid remains, and then more strongly until the mass of the tube and its contents is constant.

     (i) Describe what you would see during this conversion of copper to copper(II) oxide and give an equation for one of the reactions taking place. **(5 marks)**
     (ii) Why was the concentrated acid added as described? **(1 mark)**
     (iii) What was the purpose of the plug of glass wool? **(1 mark)**
     (iv) How would you ensure that the mass of the tube and its contents was constant? **(3 marks)**
     (v) List in their correct sequence the weighings required in this experiment. **(4 marks)**
  (c) Briefly describe another method by which copper(II) oxide could be obtained from a suitable named copper compound. **(3 marks)**
  (d) In an experiment similar to the one described, 1 g of metal M, of relative atomic mass 64, was converted into 1.25 g of its oxide. Deduce the formula of the oxide. **(4 marks)**

(OLE)

(a) All pure samples of the same chemical compound contain the same elements combined in the same proportion by mass.
(b) (i) Copper reacts vigorously with concentrated nitric acid to give brown fumes of nitrogen dioxide and blue/green copper(II) nitrate solution.

$$Cu(s) + 4HNO_3(aq) \rightarrow Cu(NO_3)_2(aq) + 2H_2O(l) + 2NO_2(g)$$

When the tube is heated water is lost and then the copper(II) nitrate decomposes to give more brown fumes of nitrogen dioxide and black copper(II) oxide.

   The equation is given below but only one equation need be given in your answer.

$$2Cu(NO_3)_2(s) \rightarrow 2CuO(s) + 4NO_2(g) + O_2(g)$$

    (ii) The acid must be added slowly because the reaction is vigorous — loss of copper(II) nitrate must be avoided if good results are to be obtained.
    (iii) The glass wool was needed to prevent any loss of solution by spitting.
    (iv) The tube is allowed to cool down and is then weighed. The heating, cooling and weighing process is repeated until a constant value is obtained.

     (v) The weighings needed are:

        Mass of test tube

        Mass of test tube + copper

        Mass of test tube + copper(II) oxide (constant mass).

(c) Copper(II) oxide may be obtained by the action of heat on copper(II) carbonate. The green solid turns black.

$$CuCO_3\,(s) \rightarrow CuO(s) + CO_2\,(g)$$

Copper(II) sulphate or copper(II) hydroxide will do equally well in place of the copper(II) carbonate.

(d)

	M	:	O
ratio of g	1	:	0.25 (mass of oxygen = 1.25–1 g)
ratio of mol	$\dfrac{1}{64}$	:	$\dfrac{0.25}{16}$

$$= 0.016 : 0.016$$
$$= 1 \ : \ 1$$

Therefore the empirical formula of the oxide is MO.

See Section 5.1.

Example 2.9

(a) Chlorine has two common isotopes with symbols $^{35}_{17}Cl$ and $^{37}_{17}Cl$.

    (i) Using chlorine as an example, explain the meaning of the term *isotope*. **(2 marks)**

Isotopes are atoms of the same element with different numbers of neutrons in their nuclei. Thus both $^{35}_{17}Cl$ and $^{37}_{17}Cl$ have 17 protons and 17 electrons but $^{35}_{17}Cl$ has 18 neutrons whilst $^{37}_{17}Cl$ has 20 neutrons.

    (ii) Explain why chlorine, whether as the element or in its compounds, always has relative atomic mass of about 35.5. **(2 marks)**

The relative atomic mass is the average mass of one of the atoms and has to take into account the relative abundances of the various isotopes. Natural chlorine always contains about 3/4 $^{35}_{17}Cl$ and 1/4 $^{37}_{17}Cl$.

Therefore, relative atomic mass = $(\tfrac{3}{4} \times 35) + (\tfrac{1}{4} \times 37)$
$= 35.5$

(b) Some radioactive isotopes are playing increasingly important roles in medicine. Write down the name of **one** such isotope and briefly describe its use in medicine. **(2 marks)**

                                                                 (OLE)

Cobalt-60 gives off intense γ-radiation which can be used to destroy cancerous growths.

Example 2.10

In a radioactivity experiment the background count was found to be 14 counts per minute. At the start a radioactive specimen gave a count rate of 174 counts per minute (including background radiation). Half an hour later the count was found to be 94 counts per minute. What would be the count rate in counts per minute (including background radiation) 1 hour after the beginning of the experiment?

A 14
B 28
C 40
D 54
E 80

(L)

The answer is **D**.

> The background count must be subtracted from each reading. Initially, the count rate due to the radioactive material will be 160 counts per minute. This drops to 80 counts per minute after half an hour. (Therefore the half-life = 1/2 hour.) After another half an hour, the actual count rate = 80/2 + 14 counts per min.

Examples 2.11–2.14 concern an experiment to determine the half-life of protactinium-234 in which a small quantity of a solution of a uranium compound is placed in a separating funnel, acidified with concentrated hydrochloric acid, and then shaken with ethyl ethanoate. The mixture is allowed to settle into two layers and the lower, aqueous layer is transferred to a beaker. A sample of the other layer, which contains the protactinium-234, is transferred to a liquid counter and counts for 5 second periods are recorded at 15 second intervals. A graph of counts per second against time is plotted. The half-life of protactinium is found to be about 70 seconds.

Example 2.11

In addition to a Geiger–Müller tube and counter, which of the following measuring instruments is *essential* for this experiment?

A Ruler
B Teat pipette
C Stop-watch
D Voltmeter
E Measuring cylinder

(L)

The answer is **C**.

Example 2.12

Which of the following curves most closely represents the decay of protactinium-234?   (L)

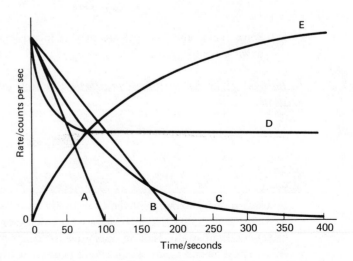

The answer is **C**.

Example 2.13

Protactinium-234 atoms are formed from $^{238}_{92}U$ atoms, which decay by loss of an alpha particle followed by a beta particle. What is the atomic number of protactinium?

A 88
B 89
C 90
D 91
E 92   (L)

The answer is **D**.

> Loss of an α-particle means that the atomic number of the new element is 2 less and its mass number is 4 less than that of the original element. Loss of a β-particle results in the atomic number of the new element being 1 more than that of the original one but its mass number will be the same.

Example 2.14

If the protactinium sample has an initial count rate of 2400 counts per minute, the count rate after 4 half-lives will be:

A 600
B 400
C 300
D 200
E 150   (L)

The answer is **E** (see Section 2.6).

2.8 Self-Test Questions

Question 2.1

Use grid 1 on page 2 to choose an answer A–E.

If the apparatus shown on the next page is standing in air, which of the following gases when placed in the porous pot would cause the level of mercury at Q to rise?

1 Air
2 Carbon dioxide
3 Hydrogen   ✓   (AEB)

Question 2.2

A new jar of pure anhydrous copper(II) sulphate contains a white solid The solid in an older much used jar is pale blue and, on analysis, is found to contain 37.6% by mass of copper.

(a) Calculate the % mass of copper in pure anhydrous copper(II) sulphate.   **(3 marks)**
(b) Which law appears to have been broken?   **(1 mark)**
(c) Explain what has happened.   **(2 marks)**
                                                                                   (OLE)

porous pot

Q

mercury

Question 2.3

The element silicon has three isotopes with mass numbers 28, 29 and 30. An accurate value for the relative atomic mass of natural silicon is 28.09.

(a) Which isotope do you consider to be most abundant? Explain your answer. **(3 marks)**

(b) For each of the isotopes, give the composition of its nucleus. **(5 marks)**

    (i) ^{28}Si

    (ii) ^{29}Si

    (iii) ^{30}Si

(c) Give the electronic structure of the isotope $^{30}_{14}$Si. **(1 mark)**

(d) From your answer to (c), would you expect silicon to form *ionic* or *covalent* compounds? Explain your answer. **(2 marks)**

            (OLE)

Question 2.4

An atom contains 11 electrons, 11 protons and 12 neutrons. What is its mass number?

A 11

B 12

C 22

D 23 ✓

E 34

Question 2.5

What are the particles x and y in the following changes?

$$^{238}_{92}U + x \rightarrow {}^{239}_{92}U \rightarrow {}^{239}_{93}Np + y$$

	x	y
A	Neutron	Electron
B	Proton	Electron
C	Electron	Proton
D	Proton	Neutron
E	Neutron	Proton

            (L)

2.9   Answers to Self-Test Questions

2.1. **E**

The hydrogen is less dense than air and will diffuse out of the pot faster than the air diffuses into the pot.

2.2 (a) Anhydrous copper(II) sulphate has the formula $CuSO_4$.

Relative molecular mass = $64 + 32 + 4 \times 16$

$$= 160$$

$$\% \text{ copper} = \frac{64}{160} \times 100$$

$$= 40$$

(b) The law of constant composition.

(c) The pale blue solid in the older jar has absorbed atmospheric moisture and now contains some hydrated copper(II) sulphate, $CuSO_4.5H_2O$, so that the average relative molecular mass will be greater than 160. Thus the % of copper in the sample will be lower than 40%.

2.3 (a) The isotope with mass number 28 will be the most abundant. The relative atomic mass is found from the average masses of the three isotopes, taking into account the relative abundances. Since the other two have masses greater than 28, they must be present to a small extent only.

(b) (i) 14 protons, 14 neutrons.

(ii) 14 protons, 15 neutrons.

(iii) 14 protons, 16 neutrons.

Silicon has an atomic number of 14 and therefore has 14 protons. The mass number gives the number of protons + the number of neutrons and hence by subtraction the number of neutrons can be found.

(c) Silicon has 14 electrons and has the electronic structure 2.8.4.

(d) Silicon will form covalent compounds. For silicon to form ionic compounds, four electrons must be lost or gained so that silicon can have an outer shell of eight electrons. This requires too much energy and so silicon will share electrons and form covalent compounds (see Section 4.1).

2.4 **D.**

2.5 **A.**

The equations are

$$^{238}_{92}U + ^{1}_{0}n \rightarrow ^{239}_{92}U \qquad (238 + 1 = 239; 92 + 0 = 92)$$

$$^{239}_{92}U \rightarrow ^{239}_{93}Np + ^{0}_{-1}e \qquad (239 = 239 + 0; 92 = 93 - 1)$$

---

3 The Periodic Table

3.1 Introduction

The periodic table is obtained by arranging the elements in order of increasing atomic number and placing them in rows so that similar elements fall into vertical columns (see page 230). The horizontal rows are called *periods* and the vertical columns are called *groups*.

Table 3.1 shows that atoms of similar elements, such as sodium and potassium, have the same numbers of electrons in their outermost shells.

For the outer blocks of the periodic table the number of electrons in the outermost shells of the atoms is the same as the number of the group in which they are found.

Hydrogen and helium do not fit properly into any of the groups and are usually separated from the rest of the table.

When element 21 is reached the electronic structures of the atoms become more complicated and a centre block of *transition elements* has to be added.

Several of the groups have 'family' names: group I elements are called the *alkali metals*, group II elements are the *alkaline earths*, group VII elements are the *halogens* and group 0 (plus helium) the *noble gases*.

Table 3.1

Element	Atomic number	Number of neutrons	Mass number	Electronic arrangement
Hydrogen	1	0	1	1
Helium	2	2	4	2
Lithium	3	4	7	2,1
Beryllium	4	5	9	2,2
Boron	5	6	11	2,3
Carbon	6	6	12	2,4
Nitrogen	7	7	14	2,5
Oxygen	8	8	16	2,6
Fluorine	9	10	19	2,7
Neon	10	10	20	2,8
Sodium	11	12	23	2,8,1
Magnesium	12	12	24	2,8,2
Aluminium	13	14	27	2,8,3
Silicon	14	14	28	2,8,4
Phosphorus	15	16	31	2,8,5
Sulphur	16	16	32	2,8,6
Chlorine	17	18 or 20	35 or 37	2,8,7
Argon	18	22	40	2,8,8
Potassium	19	20	39	2,8,8,1
Calcium	20	20	40	2,8,8,2

3.2 Trends in Properties Going Across a Period (Outer Blocks Only)

Going across a period, the elements change from metals to non-metals.

The valencies (see Section 5.1) of the elements in groups I–IV are equal to the group numbers: for the elements in groups V–VII they are equal to 8 minus the group number (e.g. for magnesium, in group II, the valency is 2; for nitrogen, in group V, the valency is $8 - 5 = 3$). If you use oxidation numbers rather than valencies, the appropriate sign must be added.

In a particular period the reactivity of the outer block elements is connected with the number of electrons which must be lost or gained to reach the same electronic structure as a noble gas. Thus sodium, which needs to lose only one electron per atom to obtain the same electronic structure as neon, is more reactive than magnesium, which needs to lose two. Similarly chlorine, which needs to gain one electron per atom to reach the argon configuration, is more reactive than sulphur, which needs to gain two.

The oxides of the elements on the left of the table are basic (e.g. magnesium oxide) and those of elements on the right are acidic (e.g. sulphur dioxide). Somewhere in between these two extremes are oxides which are *amphoteric* (both acidic and basic – e.g. aluminium oxide).

This section is summarised in Table 3.2.

Table 3.2

Element	Sodium	Magnesium	Aluminium	Silicon	Phosphorus	Sulphur	Chlorine	Argon
Appearance	Silvery metal	Silvery metal	Silvery metal	Black solid	Yellow solid	Yellow solid	Greenish gas	Colourless gas
Electronic structure	2,8,1	2,8,2	2,8,3	2,8,4	2,8,5	2,8,6	2,8,7	2,8,8
Most common oxidation number	+1	+2	+3	+4	−3	−2	−1	0
Most common valency	1	2	3	4	3	2	1	0
Oxide	Na_2O	MgO	Al_2O_3	SiO_2	P_4O_{10}	SO_3	Cl_2O_7	–
Highest possible oxidation number	+1	+2	+3	+4	+5	+6	+7	–
Melting point of oxide/K (°C)	1466 (1193)	3348 (3075)	2318 (2045)	2001 (1728)	836 (563)	303 (30)	182 (−91)	–
Bonding and structure of oxide	← Giant ionic lattice →			Giant atomic lattice (covalent)	← Covalent molecules →			–
Nature of oxide	← Decreasingly basic →			Amphoteric	← Increasingly acidic →			–

3.3 Trends in Properties Going Down a Group

The changes found on going down a group are less marked than those seen in going across a period, since all members of a particular group have the same number of electrons in the outermost shells of their atoms. There are three important trends:

(1) The metallic nature of the elements increases as a group is descended. This is most noticeable in group IV, which starts with the non-metal carbon and ends with the metal lead.
(2) The reactivity of *metals* increases down a group (see Example 3.2).
(3) The reactivity of *non-metals* decreases down a group (see Example 3.2).

3.4 The Transition Elements

These are all metals but, except for the first and last members of each row, they differ from the outer block metals in a number of important ways:

(1) They have relatively high melting points and densities.
(2) They form coloured compounds (e.g. copper(II) sulphate).
(3) They can have more than one valency or oxidation number (e.g. iron(II) and iron(III)).
(4) Both the metals and their compounds can act as catalysts (e.g. platinum in the oxidation of ammonia and manganese(IV) oxide in the decomposition of hydrogen peroxide).

3.5 Worked Examples

Example 3.1

Consider the following information about an imaginary new element named bodium, symbol Bo, which has recently been discovered.

Bodium is a solid at room temperature but is easily cut with a knife to reveal a shiny surface which rapidly tarnishes. It reacts vigorously with water liberating a flammable gas and forming a solution with a high pH value. When bodium reacts with chlorine, it forms a white solid containing 29.5% by mass of chlorine.
$A_r(Bo) = 85$.

(a) Calculate the empirical formula of bodium chloride. **(3 marks)**
(b) To which group in the Periodic Table should bodium be assigned? **(1 mark)**
(c) What type of bonding is likely to be present in bodium chloride? **(1 mark)**
(d) If concentrated aqueous bodium chloride was electrolysed, what would be the main products discharged at carbon electrodes? Write equations for the reactions which take place. **(4 marks)**
(e) Write an equation and name the products for the reaction between bodium and water. **(2 marks)**
(f) Write the formula for (i) bodium nitrate and (ii) bodium carbonate. For each of these compounds, state whether it would be expected to decompose at bunsen burner temperature. Name any product(s) and write an equation for any reaction which occurs. **(5 marks)**
(AEB)

(a)   Bo : Cl

ratio of g   70.5 : 29.5

ratio of mol $\dfrac{70.5}{85} : \dfrac{29.5}{35.5}$

        = 0.829 : 0.831

        =   1 : 1

∴ empirical formula of bodium chloride is BoCl.

(b) Bodium should be assigned to group I.

(c) Ionic bonding will be present in bodium chloride.

(d) At the anode the product would be chlorine.

$$2Cl^-(aq) - 2e^- \rightarrow Cl_2(g)$$

At the cathode the product would be hydrogen.

$$2H^+(aq) + 2e^- \rightarrow H_2(g)$$

(e) $2Bo(s) + 2H_2O(l) \rightarrow 2BoOH(aq) + H_2(g)$

The products are bodium hydroxide solution and hydrogen.

(f) (i) $BoNO_3$. Bodium nitrate would decompose at bunsen burner temperature into bodium nitrite and oxygen.

$$2BoNO_3(l) \rightarrow 2BoNO_2(l) + O_2(g)$$

(ii) Bo_2CO_3. Bodium carbonate would not decompose at bunsen burner temperatures.

From the information given, bodium is similar to potassium and sodium. Answers (b)–(f) are obtained by considering what would happen in corresponding circumstances to potassium, sodium and their compounds. The two metals are in group I of the periodic table, their chlorides are ionic (Section 4.1) and electrolysis of their aqueous chlorides gives chlorine and hydrogen (Section 7.2). Their reactions with water and the effect of heat on their nitrates and carbonates are given in Sections 13.1 and 13.2.

Example 3.2

(a) Magnesium, calcium and strontium are in Group II of the Periodic Table and have atomic numbers 12, 20 and 38 respectively.

   (i) Write down the electronic configuration of magnesium and calcium. Deduce the number of electrons in the outer shell (energy level) of a strontium atom.

   (ii) Write an equation for the reaction which would be expected to occur between strontium (symbol Sr) and water. Name the products of the reaction, and state how the reactivity of strontium would compare with that of calcium.

   (iii) Explain what would be observed if aqueous sodium carbonate was added to aqueous strontium chloride. Write an equation for the reaction. **(10 marks)**

(b) Chlorine, bromine and iodine are three members of Group VII in the Periodic Table.

   (i) How many electrons are there in the outer shell (energy level) of a bromine atom?

   (ii) What type of bonding would be present in the compound formed between calcium and bromine? Explain briefly the changes in electronic structure which would occur if these two elements were to chemically combine.

   (iii) Name a halogen which would react more vigorously than bromine. **(9 marks)**

(c) Silicon is a non-metal and its atomic number is 14.

   (i) Draw a diagram to show the arrangement of **outer shell** electrons in a molecule of silicon tetrachloride, $SiCl_4$. (Use a small cross x to represent an electron of a silicon atom and a small circle o to represent an electron of a chlorine atom.)

   (ii) Name the type of bonding present in the molecule, silicon tetrachloride, and state **one** physical property usually associated with compounds bonded in this way.

(5 marks)

(AEB)

(a) (i) Mg 2, 8, 2; Ca 2, 8, 8, 2. As strontium is also in group II it, too, must have two electrons in the outer shells of its atoms.

Electronic configurations are explained in Section 2.5.

    (ii) $Sr(s) + 2H_2O(l) \rightarrow Sr(OH)_2(aq) + H_2(g)$
Products are strontium hydroxide solution and hydrogen.
Strontium would be more reactive than calcium.
    (iii) On adding aqueous sodium carbonate to aqueous strontium chloride a white precipitate of strontium carbonate would be formed.

$$SrCl_2(aq) + Na_2CO_3(aq) \rightarrow SrCO_3(s) + 2NaCl(aq)$$

Strontium will resemble calcium in its reactions and compounds (see Section 13.3). Metal atoms react by losing their outermost electrons and becoming positive ions (Section 4.1). Since atoms become larger on going down any group, the outermost electrons are at increasing distances from the nucleus and therefore less strongly attracted to it. It follows that, as the group is descended, the metal atoms more readily lose electrons to form positive ions (i.e. become more metallic) and their reactivity increases.

(b) (i) Since bromine is in group VII it must have 7 electrons in the outer shell of its atoms.
    (ii) Ionic bonding would be present. Each calcium atom would lose its two outermost electrons and become a Ca^{2+} ion with the same electronic configuration as the nearest noble gas in the periodic table (argon, 2, 8, 8). Bromine atoms would each gain one electron to become Br^- ions with a stable octet of electrons in their outermost shells. Two Br^- ions would be needed for each Ca^{2+} ion.
    (iii) Chlorine would be more reactive than bromine.

Ionic bonding is dealt with in Section 4.1. Non-metal atoms react by gaining electrons and becoming negative ions. Since the outermost shell of electrons is further from the nucleus on going down a group, extra electrons are less strongly held. Therefore as the group is descended the non-metallic elements less readily form negative ions and become *less* reactive (compare with metals in (a)).

(c) (i) Fig. 3.1.
    (ii) Covalent bonding would be present. Compounds bonded in this way do not conduct electricity, either when molten or in solution.

Silicon has 14 electrons, arranged 2, 8, 4 and forms four covalent bonds in order to complete its octet. This is explained in Section 4.1 and Question 2.3.

Example 3.3

Three elements X, Y, and Z, are in the same period of the periodic table. The table on the next page gives some data concerning the elements and their oxides. One of the elements forms another oxide in addition to that listed.

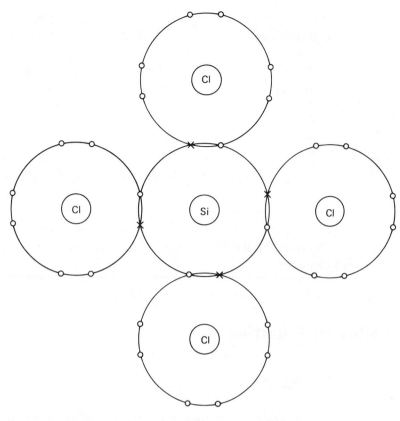

Fig. 3.1

Element	X	Y	Z
Appearance	Shiny black solid	Silvery solid	Yellow crystals
Oxide	White solid, XO_2	White solid, YO	White solid, ZO_3

Use the letters, X, Y, Z, in answering the following questions. Do not try to identify the elements.

(a) What is the valency of each element in its oxide? **(3 marks)**

Valencies are: X = 4, Y = 2, Z = 6

(b) Write the letters X, Y, and Z in the order in which the elements appear in the period.

(1 mark)

Y, X, Z.

Because valency = group number (Section 3.2).

(c) To which groups do the elements belong? **(3 marks)**

Y is in group II, X is in group IV, Z is in group VI.

(d) Write the formulae of the compounds which the elements would form with hydrogen.

(3 marks)

YH_2, XH_4, ZH_2.

(e) Which element would be the best conductor of electricity? **(1 mark)**

Y.

Because it is in group II and therefore is a metal.

(f) Which oxide is most likely to be ionic? **(1 mark)**

The oxide of Y.

Because Y is a metal.

Example 3.4

The Group in the Periodic Table which contains the element with eleven protons in its nucleus is

A 1
B 2
C 3
D 5
E 7

The answer is **A**.

Because the atoms have eleven electrons, arranged 2, 8, 1 and the number of electrons in the outermost shell gives the group number for the outer block elements.

3.6   Self-Test Questions

Question 3.1

A section of the Periodic Table is shown below for elements with atomic numbers from 3 to 18. Some of the elements are represented by letters but the letters are **not** the usual symbols for the elements.

A 3	4	5	6	7	D 8	E 9	G 10
J 11	L 12	13	M 14	15	R 16	17	18

(a) Use the letter given in the table to identify the element which:
  (i) is a noble gas   **(1 mark)**
  (ii) is a halogen   **(1 mark)**
  (iii) would react most readily with chlorine.   **(1 mark)**
(b) Write down the electronic configuration of:
  (i) element D   8, 8, 9   2, 8, 0   **(1 mark)**
  (ii) element J.   **(1 mark)**
What would be the formula of the compound formed if D and J were to react and what type of bonding would be present?   **(2 marks)**
(c) Draw a diagram to show the electron arrangement in a molecule of the hydride of element R. (OUTER SHELLS only need be shown. Use a small cross (x) to represent an electron of an atom of R and a small circle (o) to represent an electron of a hydrogen atom.)   **(3 marks)**

For questions 3.2 and 3.3 used grid 1 on page 2 to choose an answer A–E.

Question 3.2

An element whose atoms each contain 17 protons:
1 is a non-metal
2 has a valency of 1
3 is in Group VII of the Periodic Table.

34

Question 3.3

Zirconium is a transition metal. It is therefore likely to:
1 not react with cold water
2 form a coloured chloride
3 float on water.

Question 3.4

Use grid 2 on page 2 to choose an answer A-E.

Sodium and calcium are in the same group of the Periodic Table

BECAUSE

both sodium and calcium atoms each have two electrons in their outer shells

(AEB)

3.7   Answers to Self-Test Questions

3.1 (a) (i) G (ii) E (iii) J.

Because the most reactive metals are found on the *left* of the periodic table and at the *bottom* of their groups (see Section 3.2 and Example 3.2).

(b) (i) 2, 6 (ii) 2, 8, 1. Formula $J_2 D$, ionic bonding (metal + non-metal — see Section 4.1).
(c) Fig. 3.2.

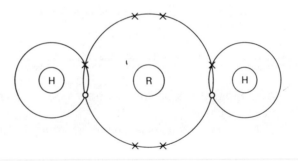

Fig. 3.2

3.2 **A.**

The element has 17 electrons, arranged 2, 8, 7, and therefore is in group VII, with valency 1 (oxidation number −1).

3.3 **B.**

See Section 3.4.

3.4 **E.**

See Section 3.1.

4 Bonding and Structure

4.1 Introduction

Bonds are formed between atoms when electrons are redistributed among those atoms to give each one the stable electronic configuration of the nearest noble gas in the periodic table. Usually this results in the formation of an octet of electrons.

An **ionic (electrovalent) bond** is formed when one or more electrons is transferred from an atom of an element on the left-hand side of the periodic table (i.e. a metal) to an atom of one on the right-hand side (i.e. a non-metal). Ionic compounds are made up of ions (see Example 4.1).

An **ion** is an electrically charged particle formed from an atom or group of atoms by the loss or gain of one or more electrons.

The charge on an ion is equal to its oxidation number. The number of electrons lost or gained by an atom in forming an ion is often called its valency. For metals outside the centre block of the periodic table, the number of electrons lost per atom is equal to the group number; for non-metals, the number of electrons gained by each atom is equal to (8 minus group number).

A **covalent bond** is formed when a pair of electrons is shared between two atoms which both need to gain electrons (i.e. non-metals).

Covalent compounds are made up of molecules (see Example 4.1).

The number of electron pairs shared by an atom is often called its valency.

4.2 The Shapes of Covalent Molecules

Any molecule consisting of only two atoms must be linear, i.e. the atoms must be in a straight line.

In working out the shape of other covalent molecules, we assume that the electron pairs of the outermost shell of the central atom repel one another and take up positions in which they are as far apart as possible. In the determination of molecular shape, a double bond behaves in the same way as a single one.

Example 4.7 shows the structure of a tetrachloromethane molecule and a water molecule. If we wish to show the structure of a molecule more simply, we usually indicate a covalent bond by a line joining the two atoms concerned, e.g.

$$
\begin{array}{c}
\text{Cl} \\
| \\
\text{Cl} - \text{C} - \text{Cl} \\
| \\
\text{Cl}
\end{array}
$$

The nitrogen atom in an ammonia molecule has four pairs of electrons in its outer shell but only three of these are bonding pairs. Although the arrangement of the electron pairs is tetrahedral, the shape of the molecule (i.e. the distribution of its atoms) is pyramidal.

4.3   Crystal Structure

The ways in which the particles are arranged in a solid can be determined by X-ray diffraction. A crystal consists of particles arranged in a repeating pattern extending in three dimensions. Such three-dimensional arrangements are called lattices.

(a) Giant Ionic Lattices

The sodium chloride lattice is shown in Fig. 4.1.

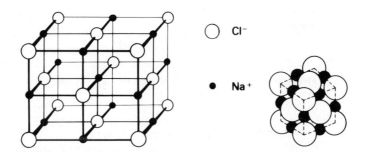

Fig. 4.1

This arrangement extends throughout the crystal, involving millions of ions. Each cube is joined to its neighbours and the whole crystal is thus a continuous giant structure of ions or giant ionic lattice (see Example 4.4).

(b) Giant Metallic Lattices

Metals consist of an array of positively charged ions embedded in a 'sea' of electrons. It is the forces of attraction between the positive ions and these electrons which hold the lattice together.

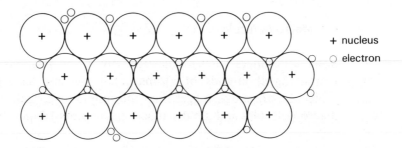

Fig. 4.2

(c) Molecular Lattices

Most covalent compounds are gases, liquids or solids which crystallise with a molecular lattice. The particles are molecules, linked by very weak attractive forces. It must be emphasised that the individual atoms *within* the molecule are joined together by strong covalent bonds. For example, in solid carbon dioxide, there are only weak forces acting between separate molecules but each carbon dioxide molecule contains a carbon atom linked by strong covalent bonds to two oxygen atoms.

(d) Giant Atomic Lattices (Sometimes Called Giant Molecular Lattices)

There are a number of substances such as silicon(IV) oxide, diamond and graphite, which have very high melting points. They consist of giant atomic lattices with strong covalent bonds acting throughout the whole crystal. The particles in these cases are atoms so they must be held together by covalent bonds but there can be no separate molecules or the melting points would be much lower (see Example 14.1).

The properties shown by the main structural types are summarised in Table 4.1 (see Examples 4.1, 4.4 and 4.5).

Table 4.1

Property	Giant structures			Molecular structures
	Metallic	Ionic	Atomic	
m.p. & b.p.	← High →			Low
Solubility in organic solvents	← Generally insoluble →			Generally soluble
Solubility in water	Insoluble	Generally soluble	Insoluble	Generally insoluble
Conductors of electricity (molten)	← Yes →		← No →	
Conductors of electricity (solid)	Yes	← No →		
Conduction of heat	Good	← Bad →		

(e) Macromolecules

Some substances such as plastics, fibres and proteins are made up of molecules containing thousands of atoms. They do not have giant structures but their molecules are much bigger than the simple ones dealt with earlier. They are called macromolecules and are discussed in Chapters 15 and 19.

4.4 Oxidation Number

The **oxidation number** of an ion is equal to the charge on it. Table 5.1 (page 50) shows the oxidation numbers of some common ions.

4.5 Oxidation and Reduction

Oxidation is:

1. the addition of oxygen to a substance;
2. the removal of hydrogen from a substance;

3. any change in which there is a loss of one or more electrons; or
4. any change in which the oxidation number of an atom or ion increases.

Reduction is the opposite of oxidation (see Example 4.9). It is:

1. the removal of oxygen from a substance;
2. the addition of hydrogen to a substance;
3. any change in which there is a gain of one or more electrons; or
4. any change in which the oxidation number of an atom or ion decreases.

Electrons cannot simply disappear and hence if one particle loses electrons (i.e. is oxidised), another must gain them (i.e. be reduced). In other words, oxidation cannot occur without reduction. Reactions involving changes of this type are often known as **redox** (*red*uction–*ox*idation) reactions.

Common oxidising agents include oxygen, chlorine, nitric acid, acidified potassium manganate(VII) and acidified potassium dichromate(IV). Common reducing agents include hydrogen, sulphur dioxide, hydrogen sulphide and carbon monoxide.

4.6   Worked Examples

Example 4.1

(a) Name an ionic and a covalent compound and explain how each structure is formed from its elements. **(6 marks)**
(b) Show how each type of bonding influences the properties of the compound in terms of physical appearance, melting point, solubility in water and electrical conductivity.
(9 marks)
(SUJB)

(a) Sodium chloride, NaCl, is an ionic compound. Each sodium atom (electron configuration 2,8,1) has one electron in its outermost shell while each chlorine atom (2,8,7) has seven. If the outer electron is transferred from an atom of sodium to one of chlorine, then both will have a stable octet of electrons in their outermost shells (see Fig. 4.3).

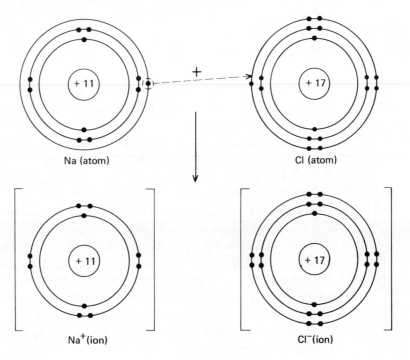

Fig. 4.3

When the sodium atom has lost its electron it is left with a net positive charge of 1 unit since it has 11 protons (i.e. 11 positive charges) but now has only 10 electrons (i.e. 10 negative charges). Similarly, the chlorine atom acquires unit negative charge since it contains the original 17 protons but now has 18 electrons. These charged particles, called ions, strongly attract one another, the Na^+ and Cl^- ions being arranged in a repeating pattern in three dimensions (see Section 4.3).

Methane, CH_4, is an example of a covalent compound. Carbon (electron configuration 2,4) has 4 electrons in its outermost shell and would have to form the C^{4+} ion in order to attain the stable electronic configuration of helium. So much energy is required to form the C^{4+} ion that the carbon and hydrogen atoms combine by an easier method — they share pairs of electrons. Each atom contributes one electron to a shared pair and in this way they all achieve stable octets (Fig. 4.4).

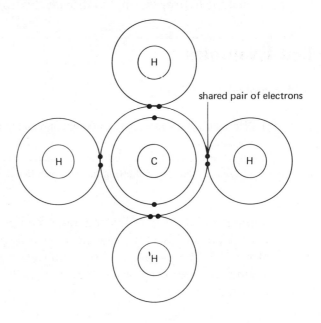

shared pair of electrons

Fig. 4.4

The atoms are held together by the attraction of the two nuclei for the shared pair of electrons. The particles formed are molecules which are free to move in all directions.

(b) Sodium chloride is a solid with a high melting point because a large amount of energy has to be provided to overcome the strong forces of electrostatic attraction holding the oppositely charged ions together. On the other hand, the forces of attraction between neighbouring methane molecules are weak and so the melting point is low — methane is a gas at room temperature.

Before we can consider the solubility of a compound in water, we need to know something about the water molecule. Oxygen is very electronegative. This means that an oxygen atom attracts electrons and tends to pull them towards itself in any molecule in which it is found. Thus the electron pairs making up the covalent bonds between the oxygen atom and the two hydrogen atoms in a water molecule are not shared equally but are displaced towards the oxygen. The molecule is polar, with a small negative charge on the oxygen atom and small positive charges on the hydrogen atoms.

$$\underset{H}{\delta+}\diagdown\overset{\overset{\textstyle\delta-}{O}}{}\diagup\underset{H}{\delta+}$$

The 'δ' indicates that the charges are much smaller than on ions but it has no specific value.

When sodium chloride is placed in water, the negative part of each water molecule (i.e. the oxygen atom) will be attracted to the Na^+ ions on the surface of the solid. Similarly, the positively charged hydrogen atoms in the water molecules will be attracted to the Cl^- ions. The attraction between the ions and the water molecules is strong enough to overcome the forces holding the ions together in the crystal, so sodium chloride dissolves and the ions are carried off into solution surrounded by a 'jacket' of water molecules.

Methane is insoluble in water because the attraction of the water molecules for one another is far greater than their attraction for non-polar methane molecules.

Organic solvents, e.g. methylbenzene, do not generally dissolve ionic solids. The molecules of these solvents are non-polar or only slightly polar and hence the forces of attraction between them and the ions in the crystal are weak. For a covalent solid, the forces of attraction between the individual molecules in the lattice are comparable with those between the solvent molecules. The lattice is easily penetrated by the solvent molecules and a solution is formed. You need to remember the phrase 'like dissolves like'. A highly polar solvent such as water dissolves polar (ionic) solids, whereas a non-polar solvent such as methylbenzene dissolves non-polar (covalent) solids.

Sodium chloride does not conduct an electric current when solid because the ions are only able to vibrate about fixed positions in the crystal lattice and cannot migrate towards the electrodes. When sodium chloride is melted or dissolved in water, the ions are free to move and hence carry an electric current. Covalent compounds cannot conduct an electric current because they do not contain ions.

Example 4.2

Element X has an atomic number of 12. The formula of its chloride will be
A X_2Cl
B XCl
C XCl_2
D XCl_3
E XCl_4
(AEB)
The answer is C.

The electron configuration of X must be 2,8,2. This means that X must lose two electrons in order to attain a stable octet, but each atom of chlorine (2,8,7) can only accept one. Hence the X atom must give its two electrons to two chlorine atoms as illustrated in Fig. 4.5.

Example 4.3

In which one of the following compounds are both ionic and covalent bonding present?
A lithium chloride
B hydrogen chloride
C ammonium chloride

D tetrachloromethane

E methane.

The answer is **C**.

Ammonium chloride consists of ammonium ions, NH_4^+, and chloride ions, Cl^-, but within the ammonium ion, the nitrogen atom is covalently bonded to the hydrogen atoms, i.e.

$$\left[\begin{array}{c} H \\ | \\ H-N-H \\ | \\ H \end{array} \right]^+$$

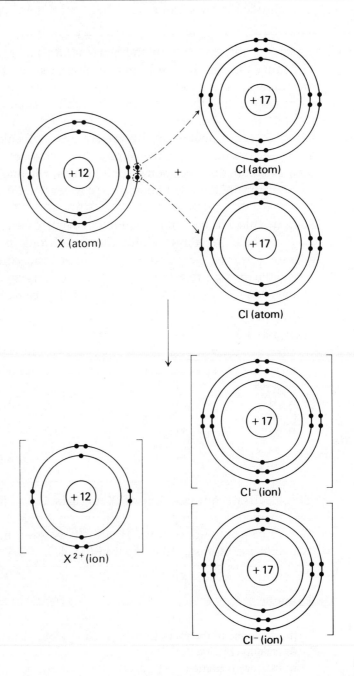

Fig. 4.5

Example 4.4

The properties of materials may be explained in terms of the particles present. Such explanations often relate to the *movement*, *energy*, and *arrangement* of the particles.
(a) Explain each of the following situations.
   (i) Molten sulphur becomes more viscous when the free-flowing liquid which is first formed is further heated.

See Example 16.5.

   (ii) Solid iodine changes to iodine vapour on gentle heating.

Solid iodine contains I$_2$ molecules which are linked together by weak attractive forces known as van der Waals' forces. Little heat is required to overcome these forces and produce I$_2$ vapour.

   (iii) Metals such as copper have a high density compared to most non-metals.

Copper has a giant metallic lattice in which the ions pack together very closely indeed and so copper has a high density. Most non-metals consist of molecules which do not pack closely together.

   (iv) More energy is required to vaporize 1 mole of water molecules than 1 mole of hexane molecules. **(6 marks)**

Water molecules are polar (see Example 4.1) and so the forces of attraction between individual molecules are much greater than between the non-polar hexane molecules. Hence more energy is needed to overcome the forces of attraction between water molecules than between hexane molecules.

(b) Using ● to represent a sodium ion and ⊕ to represent a chlorine ion, complete the FRONT FACE (ABCD) of the diagram below to represent the structure of solid sodium chloride. (L)

Fig. 4.6 shows the sodium chloride lattice although this question only requires that the front face be drawn out.

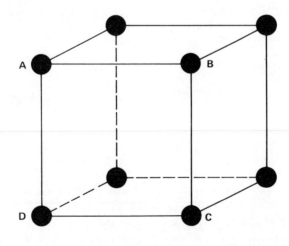

Fig. 4.6

Example 4.5

The table on the next page gives some data for elements *A* to *E*. These letters are not the chemical symbols for the elements.
(a) Which of these elements do you think are composed of simple molecules? **(1 mark)**

A and C.

Element	Melting point /°C	Boiling point /°C	Heat of fusion /kJ mol^{-1}	Heat of vaporisation /kJ mol^{-1}
A	− 219	− 183	0.22	3.4
B	650	1117	8.95	128.7
C	− 7	58	5.29	15.0
D	232	2687	7.20	290.4
E	1540	2887	15.36	351

(b) Give TWO of the elements which could be metals. **(1 mark)**
*Any two of **B**, **D** and **E**.*

(c) The element copper has a giant structure and its ions are arranged in a face-centred cubic (cubic close packed) lattice. Explain this arrangement in words (using a diagram if necessary). **(2 marks)**
The ions are packed together as closely as possible as shown in the diagram. Notice that there is a copper ion at the centre of each face (this has been shaded in).

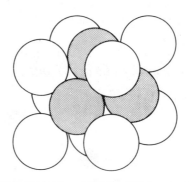

Fig. 4.7

(d) Pure copper will not withstand a great bending force. What modification of the grain structure of copper will increase its strength? **(1 mark)**
Copper is flexible because the layers of ions can slide past one another without greatly altering the forces of attraction between them and the mobile 'sea' of electrons. Areas of close packing (i.e. where there are perfect rows of atoms) are called grains. Copper will not bend easily if the grains are small. Grains can be broken up by cooling the molten metal suddenly or by introducing a few atoms of a different size.

(e) Explain why copper is a good conductor of electricity. Suggest two reasons for using aluminium instead of copper for high-voltage overhead power cables. **(3 marks)**
The 'sea' of electrons normally moves in the lattice with random motion but if a potential difference is applied, they will move through the metal in one direction, this flow of electrons being an electric current.
Aluminium is much cheaper than copper. It is also of lower density.

Example 4.6

Each of the sets of properties (a)–(c) refers to a different substance. Complete the table by giving the name of **one** substance whose properties fit the description given and state the type of bonding present.   (AEB)

Structure of substance	Name	Type of bond
(a) Consists of molecules containing only two atoms which are <u>different</u> from each other	(i)	(ii) (2)
(b) A giant molecule. The attractive forces are between atoms within the giant molecule and are symmetrical	(iii)	(iv) (2)
(c) The forces of attraction are between positive ions and electrons	(v)	(vi) (2)

    (i) Hydrogen chloride.   (ii) Covalent.
  (iii) Diamond.   (iv) Covalent.
   (v) Magnesium.   (vi) Metallic.

Example 4.7

Show by means of diagrams the three-dimensional structures or shapes of the following substances: a tetrachloromethane molecule, a water molecule, and part of a sodium chloride crystal.   **(6 marks)**

A tetrachloromethane molecule is shown in Fig. 4.8.

Fig. 4.8

The carbon atom has four bonding pairs of electrons and mutual repulsion causes these to take up a tetrahedral distribution around it. Thus the molecule consists of four chlorine atoms at the corners of a regular tetrahedron with the carbon atom at its centre.

Fig. 4.9 shows the structure of a water molecule.

Fig. 4.9

Once more, there are four electron pairs arranged tetrahedrally around the central atom but this time only 2 of them are bonding pairs. The molecule is thus V-shaped.

For the structure of a sodium chloride crystal, see Fig. 4.1.

Example 4.8

(a) Describe the processes of oxidation and reduction in terms of electron transfer.

(2 marks)

Oxidation is any change in which there is a loss of one or more electrons.
Reduction is any change in which there is a gain of one or more electrons.

(b) Give **one** equation in each case to illustrate the following conversions. State whether the process is an oxidation or a reduction.
(i) Non-metal ions to a molecule.

Equation   (2 marks)
$2Br^-(aq) + Cl_2(aq) \rightarrow Br_2(aq) + 2Cl^-(aq)$
Type of process   (1 mark)
Oxidation of Br^- ions

(ii) Metal ion to metal ion of higher charge.

Equation   (2 marks)
$2Fe^{2+}(aq) + Cl_2(aq) \rightarrow 2Fe^{3+}(aq) + 2Cl^-(aq)$
Type of process   (1 mark)
Oxidation of Fe^{2+} ions   (AEB)

Example 4.9

(a) Name **two** gaseous reducing agents.   (2 marks)
(b) For each, give one reaction to show the gas behaving in this manner.   (2 marks each)

(a) Sulphur dioxide, hydrogen.
(b) Sulphur dioxide answers the usual tests for reducing agents, turning acidified potassium manganate(VII) solution from purple to colourless, acidified potassium dichromate(VI) solution from orange to green and orange iron(III) ions to pale green iron(II) ions in aqueous solution. Any one of these is a suitable answer.
Hydrogen reduces black copper(II) oxide to reddish/brown copper on heating.

4.7   Self-Test Questions

Questions 4.1–4.6 concern the following elements and compounds:
A lead bromide
B neon
C rhombic sulphur
D aluminium
E diamond.

Which substance:

Question 4.1

Is composed of a giant structure of positive and negative ions? E

Question 4.2

Has the lowest melting point?   C

Question 4.3

Will have a similar structure to that of silicon? *aluminium*

Question 4.4

Consists of separate atoms? *neon*

Question 4.5

Conducts electricity when molten but not when solid? *aluminium*

Question 4.6

When melted and allowed to cool slowly, gives needle shaped crystals which revert to the original substance after a few days?

diamond

Question 4.7

Substance **X** has a molecular lattice and substance **Y** has an ionic lattice. Which one of the following statements about **X** and **Y** is probably correct?
A **Y** has a lower melting point than **X**.
B **Y** is more volatile than **X**.
C Molten **Y** conducts electricity but molten **X** does not.
D **Y** is insoluble in water but **X** is soluble.
E **Y** is soluble in tetrachloromethane but **X** is insoluble.   (AEB)

Question 4.8

Iodine and naphthalene are examples of substances that exist as molecules.
(i) State two liquids in which they would be expected to dissolve readily.   **(2 marks)**
(ii) Would the same solvents be expected to dissolve sodium chloride? Give a reason for your answer.   **(2 marks)**

Question 4.9

Which one of the following changes is **NOT** an example of reduction?
A $Zn \rightarrow Zn^{2+}$
B $Fe^{3+} \rightarrow Fe^{2+}$
C $Cu^{2+} \rightarrow Cu$
D $Cl_2 \rightarrow 2Cl^-$
E $S \rightarrow S^{2-}$

4.8 Answers to Self-Test Questions

4.1 A.

4.2 B.

47

4.3 **E.**

4.4 **B.**

4.5 **A.**

4.6 **C.**

4.7 **C.**

4.8 (i) Iodine and naphthalene have molecular lattices and dissolve in organic solvents, e.g. methylbenzene, petroleum spirit.
(ii) No. Sodium chloride is ionic and so requires a polar solvent (see Example 4.1).

4.9 **A.**

5 Moles, Formulae and Equations

5.1 Introduction

The **relative atomic mass**, A_r, of an element is the number of times that the average mass of one of its atoms is greater than $1/12$ of the mass of an atom of $^{12}_{6}C^*$. Since it is a ratio, relative atomic mass has no units. Values of relative atomic masses are given on page 228.

A **mole** of any substance is the amount of it which contains as many particles (atoms, molecules, etc.) as there are carbon atoms in 12 g of $^{12}_{6}C^*$. The abbreviation for mole is 'mol'.

The number of particles per mole of any substance is called the **Avogadro Constant**, L. Its value is 6.02×10^{23} mol^{-1} (mol^{-1} means 'per mol').

The **molar mass** of a substance, M, is the mass of one mole of it. The units are g mol^{-1} (or g/mol).

For practical purposes, particularly in calculations, remember that one mole of *atoms* of any element:

(a) contains 6.02×10^{23} atoms;

(b) has a mass in grams which is numerically equal to the relative atomic mass of the element.

From (a) it follows that to convert an amount in moles to a number of atoms we must multiply by 6.02×10^{23},

i.e. **number of atoms = mol** $\times$ **L** – see Example 5.3.

To convert a number of atoms to an amount in mol we must divide by 6.02×10^{23},

i.e. **mol = number of atoms/L**.

From (b), conversion of a mass in grams to an amount in moles involves dividing by the molar mass,

i.e. **mol = mass/molar mass** – see Examples 5.1 and 5.3.

Conversion of an amount in moles to a mass in grams involves multiplying the amount in moles by the molar mass,

i.e. **mass = mol** $\times$ **molar mass** – see Example 5.2.

The **empirical formula** of a compound shows the simplest ratio of the numbers of atoms of the different elements in it.

A **radical** is a group of atoms which occurs in compounds but which cannot exist on its own. For example, the sulphate radical, SO_4, is found in all sulphates but there is no substance which is just called 'sulphate'.

Empirical formulae can be calculated from experimental results (see Example 5.4), or worked out using oxidation numbers or valencies (see Example 5.7). The

*For an explanation of the figures in $^{12}_{6}C$, see page 14.

oxidation number of an ion (Section 4.1) shows its combining power, and combination between ions takes place in such proportions that the oxidation numbers add up to zero (i.e. cancel out). For example, in aluminium nitrate the ratio of aluminium ions (oxidation number +3) to nitrate ions (oxidation number −1) is 1:3, making the empirical formula $Al(NO_3)_3$.

$$Al(NO_3)_3$$

oxidation numbers $+3 + (3 \times -1) = 0$

Notice that if a radical appears more than once in a formula it must be enclosed in a bracket.

Valencies are the same as oxidation numbers but have no sign. The sum of the valencies of the positive ions or hydrogen atoms in a formula must *equal* the sum of the valencies of the negative ions or non-metal atoms (see Question 5.2(g)).

Table 5.1 shows the oxidation numbers of the commonly encountered ions.

Table 5.1

Metal or other positive ion		*Oxidation number*		*Non-metal or other negative ion*	
Ammonium	NH_4^+			Br^-	Bromide
Hydrogen	H^+			Cl^-	Chloride
Potassium	K^+	+1	−1	OH^-	Hydroxide
Silver	Ag^+			I^-	Iodide
Sodium	Na^+			NO_3^-	Nitrate
Barium	Ba^{2+}				
Calcium	Ca^{2+}				
Copper (in copper(II) compounds)	Cu^{2+}			CO_3^{2-}	Carbonate
Iron (in iron(II) compounds)	Fe^{2+}	+2	−2	O^{2-}	Oxide
Lead (in lead(II) compounds)	Pb^{2+}			SO_4^{2-}	Sulphate
Magnesium	Mg^{2+}				
Zinc	Zn^{2+}				
Aluminium	Al^{3+}				
Iron (in iron(III) compounds)	Fe^{3+}	+3	−3	PO_4^{3-}	Phosphate(V)

The **relative molecular mass**, M_r, of an element or compound is the number of times that the average mass of one of its molecules is greater than 1/12 of the mass of an atom of $^{12}_6C$. Like relative atomic mass, this is a ratio and has no units.

The relative molecular mass of a substance may be calculated by adding together the relative atomic masses of the individual atoms in one molecule of it, e.g. the relative molecular mass of carbon dioxide, CO_2, is $(12 + 16 + 16) = 44$.

For compounds with giant structures of atoms or ions (see Section 4.3) the term 'relative molecular mass' applies to a *formula unit* of the substance. Thus for potassium chloride, empirical formula KCl, the relative molecular mass is $(39 + 35.5) = 74.5$.

The **molecular formula** of a compound shows the actual numbers of atoms of the different elements in one molecule of it. For example, a molecule of hydrogen peroxide consists of two hydrogen atoms and two oxygen atoms and so its molecular formula is H_2O_2. (Note that its *empirical* formula is HO.) Unlike relative molecular mass, the term 'molecular formula' must be applied *only* to substances that consist of separate molecules.

The definitions of the mole and Avogadro constant given on page 49 apply to molecules and formula units, as well as to atoms. Thus, just as a mole of atoms of an element contains 6.02×10^{23} atoms and has a mass in grams which is numerically equal to its relative atomic mass, so a mole of a *compound* contains 6.02×10^{23} *molecules* (or formula units) and its mass in grams is numerically equal to its relative *molecular* mass. Conversions between masses, moles and numbers of particles follow the same paths as those given for atoms (see Examples 5.1, 5.3 and 5.6).

5.2 Chemical Equations

A chemical equation shows the relative numbers of atoms and molecules taking part in a chemical reaction. It can also show whether the various substances involved are in the solid (s), liquid (l) or gaseous (g) state, or are dissolved in water (aq). To write an equation you should:

1. *Know* what the reactants and products are.
2. Write down the formulae and states of the reactants and products, leaving space in front of each formula for balancing.
3. Work through the equation from left to right, checking that the same numbers of atoms of the various elements appear on both sides.

For example, when magnesium burns in oxygen it forms magnesium oxide. Applying step (2) we have:

$$Mg(s) + O_2(g) \rightarrow MgO(s)$$

The magnesium atoms balance but there are two oxygen atoms on the left and only one on the right. Therefore we try a 2 in front of the MgO(s).

$$Mg(s) + O_2(g) \rightarrow 2MgO(s)$$

The 2 in front of the MgO(s) doubles the number of magnesium atoms as well as the number of oxygen atoms so, in order to balance the whole equation we need a 2 in front of the Mg(s), giving:

$$2Mg(s) + O_2(g) \rightarrow 2MgO(s)$$

5.3 Ionic Equations

These include only those ions that *change* in some way during a reaction. Ions that do not change are called *spectator ions* and are omitted.

A useful working rule to remember when writing ionic equations is that *metallic compounds, ammonium compounds* and *dilute acids* are ionic, all other compounds being covalent. (This is an oversimplification but will suffice at this level.) You should also remember that the charges on the ions in *solids* are usually omitted, though they are still there.

To write an ionic equation you should:

1. Write a normal chemical equation for the reaction.
2. Write the equation in terms of ions, remembering that in aqueous solution the ions are completely separate from one another.
3. Rewrite the equation, omitting the spectator ions.

For example, when aqueous solutions of magnesium sulphate and barium chloride are mixed, a white precipitate of barium sulphate is formed and a solution of magnesium chloride remains. Applying the steps above, we have:

1. $BaCl_2(aq) + MgSO_4(aq) \rightarrow BaSO_4(s) + MgCl_2(aq)$
2. $Ba^{2+}(aq) + 2Cl^-(aq) + Mg^{2+}(aq) + SO_4^{2-}(aq) \rightarrow BaSO_4(s) + Mg^{2+}(aq) + 2Cl^-(aq)$
3. Clearly, the $Mg^{2+}(aq)$ and $Cl^-(aq)$ ions are spectator ions and take no part in the reaction. The ionic equation is therefore

$$Ba^{2+}(aq) + SO_4^{2-}(aq) \rightarrow BaSO_4(s)$$

Note For simple precipitation reactions of this kind you may find it easier simply to write first of all the formula of the precipitate on the right-hand side and then the formulae of the ions which go to make it up on the left-hand side, thus missing out steps (1) and (2) entirely (see Example 20.5(a), parts (i), (ii) and (iii)).

5.4 Calculating Reacting Masses from Equations

The steps in this type of calculation are as follows:

1. Write a balanced equation for the reaction.
2. Pick out the substances involved in the calculation and write down the ratio of moles of each as they appear in the equation. Always write down the ratio so that the substance whose mass is *known* is on the *left* and the one whose mass is *required* is on the *right*. Convert the ratio, if necessary, so that only *one* mole of the first substance is involved (see Example 5.8).
3. Set out the calculation as shown in Example 5.8.

5.5 Worked Examples

Example 5.1

If 0.5 mol of a hydrated salt contains 63 g of water, how many moles of water of crystallisation are contained in 1 mol of salt?
$M_r(H_2O) = 18$.

A 1
B 2
C 3
D 7
E 10   (AEB)

The answer is **D**.

0.5 mol of hydrated salt contains 63 g H_2O
$\therefore$ 1 mol of hydrated salt contains 126 g H_2O
Molar mass of water = 18 g mol^{-1}
$\therefore$ Mol H_2O per mol of salt = 126/18 = 7 (amount in mol = mas/molar mass — see Section 5.1)

Example 5.2

How many grams of nitrogen gas, N_2, contain as many atoms as there are in two moles of oxygen gas, O_2? (N = 14).

A 70
B 56

C 42
D 35
E 28   (NISEC)
The answer is **B**.

In 2 mol of O_2 there are 4 mol of O atoms
Molar mass of N atoms = 14 g mol^{-1}
Mass = mol × molar mass (see Section 5.1)
∴ 4 mol of N atoms has mass 4 × 14 = 56 g.

Example 5.3

  (a) The Avogadro constant, L, is interpreted as the number of specified particles in 1 mol of a substance. State, in terms of L, the number of:

      (i) atoms in 20 g of argon   **(1 mark)**

0.5L

No of atoms = mol of atoms × L = 20/40 × L
(molar mass of Ar = 40 g mol^{-1})

      (ii) molecules in 20 g of hydrogen   **(1 mark)**

10L

No of molecules = mol of H_2 × L = 20/2 × L
(molar mass of H_2 = 2 g mol^{-1})

      (iii) hydrated protons in 1 dm^3 of aqueous sulphuric acid of concentration 1 mol/dm^3.
                                                            (1 mark)

2L

---

1 mol of H_2SO_4 gives 2 mol of H$^+$(aq)

      (iv) electrons needed to discharge 1 mol of Cu^{2+} ions.   **(1 mark)**

2L

Each Cu^{2+} ion needs 2 electrons to discharge it.

  (b) (i) 2.3 g of a metal **T** (A_r(**T**) = 69) displaced 3.2 g of copper from excess aqueous copper(II) sulphate. Calculate the number of moles of each metal involved in the reaction and hence determine the charge on an ion of metal **T**.   **(4 marks)**

Mol of Cu = mass/molar mass = 3.2/64 = 1/20; mol of T = 2.3/69 = 1/30
1/20 mol Cu is displaced by 1/30 mol T
∴ 3 mol Cu are displaced by 2 mol T
3 mol Cu^{2+} ions require 6 mol electrons for discharge
∴ 2 mol T atoms supply 6 mol electrons
∴ 1 T atom must supply 3 electrons and the charge on an ion of T is 3+

      (ii) Write an ionic equation for the reaction.   **(1 mark)**
2T(s) + 3Cu^{2+}(aq) → 3Cu(s) + 2T^{3+}(aq)
                                                                    (AEB)

Example 5.4

2.38 g of tin was converted to 3.02 g of tin oxide. What is the formula of the oxide?
$A_r(Sn) = 119; A_r(O) = 16$.

A Sn_4O
B Sn_2O
C SnO
D SnO_2
E SnO_4 (AEB)

The answer is **D**.

Mass of oxygen combined with 2.38 g of tin = $(3.02 - 2.38) = 0.64$ g

$$\text{Sn} : \text{O}$$
$$\text{ratio of g } 2.38 : 0.64$$
$$\text{ratio of mol } \frac{2.38}{119} : \frac{0.64}{16} \quad \text{(No of mol = mass/molar mass)}$$
$$= 0.02 : 0.04 \quad \text{(Divide by smallest to convert to whole numbers)}$$
$$= 1 : 2$$

$\therefore$ Empirical formula is SnO_2

Example 5.5

(a) A hydrocarbon contains 82.8% carbon. Determine the empirical (i.e. simplest) formula for this compound.   **(5 marks)**

A hydrocarbon is made up of hydrogen and carbon only, so if the percentage of carbon is 82.8, the rest (17.2%) must be hydrogen.

$$C : H$$
$$\textit{ratio of mol } \frac{82.8}{12} : \frac{17.2}{1}$$
$$= 6.90 : 17.2$$
$$= 1 \qquad 2.49 \approx 2 : 5 \therefore \textit{Empirical formula is } C_2H_5.$$

(b) A rough estimate puts the relative molecular mass of this hydrocarbon between 50 and 60. What is the actual value? Explain your answer.   **(3 marks)**
(OLE)

Relative mass of $C_2H_5 = (24 + 5) = 29$
Molecular formula must be a whole number $\times C_2H_5$, i.e. C_2H_5, C_4H_{10}, etc.
$\therefore M_r$ must be a whole number $\times 29$. In this case it must be 58.

Example 5.6

On heating 8.0 g of hydrated copper(II) sulphate, $CuSO_4.xH_2O$, 5.1 g of anhydrous salt remained. The formula of the hydrated salt was

A $CuSO_4.2H_2O$
B $CuSO_4.3H_2O$
C $CuSO_4.4H_2O$
D $CuSO_4.5H_2O$
E $CuSO_4.7H_2O$.

The answer is **D**.

The mass of water of crystallisation evolved = (8.0 − 5.1) = 2.9 g
Molar mass of anhydrous $CuSO_4$ = (63.5 + 32 + 64) = 159.5 g mol.

Molar mass of water = (16 + 2) = 18 g mol^{-1}

$$\begin{array}{ccc} & CuSO_4 & : & H_2O \\ \text{ratio of mol} & \dfrac{5.1}{159.5} & : & \dfrac{2.9}{18} \\ & = 0.032 & : & 0.16 \\ & = 1 & : & 5 \end{array}$$

∴ Empirical formula is $CuSO_4 . 5H_2O$

Example 5.7

Metal M, with atomic number 3, has an oxide with formula:
A M_3O_2
B M_2O
C M_2O_3
D MO_2
E MO_3

The answer is **B**.

M has the electronic configuration 2,1 and therefore is in group I of the periodic table with oxidation number +1 (valency 1). Oxygen has oxidation number −2 (valency 2).

Example 5.8

2.8 g of iron reacted completely with chlorine according to the equation

$2Fe(s) + 3Cl_2(g) \rightarrow 2FeCl_3(s)$ (Fe = 56; $FeCl_3$ = 162.5)

The mass of iron(III) chloride formed would be about:
A 2.8 g
B 4.0 g
C 5.6 g
D 8.1 g
E 16.2 g   (L)

The answer is **D**.

$$\begin{aligned} \text{mol Fe} : \text{mol } FeCl_3 &= 2 : 2 = 1 : 1 \quad \text{(A)} \\ \text{g Fe} &= 2.8 \\ \text{mol Fe} &= \frac{2.8}{56} \\ \text{mol } FeCl_3 &= \frac{2.8}{56} \times 1 \quad \text{(from A)} \\ \text{g } FeCl_3 &= \frac{2.8}{56} \times 162.5 \\ &\approx 8.1 \end{aligned}$$

5.6   Self-Test Questions

Question 5.1

Use grid 1 on page 2 to choose an answer **A–E**.
6.02×10^{23} is the number of:
1 molecules in 1.0 g of hydrogen gas
2 chloride ions in 58.5 g of sodium chloride
3 molecules in 16 g of methane

Question 5.2

Some iodine was added to a weighed sample of powdered metal, M, in a test tube and the combined mass found. Ethanol was added and the metal and iodine were seen to react. When the reaction had finished, all of the iodine had gone but some metal was left in the bottom of the tube. The ethanol was removed and the metal washed with fresh ethanol. It was then dried and weighed.

The results were

Mass of test tube + M at beginning = 14.77 g
Mass of test tube + M + iodine   = 15.27 g
Mass of test tube + metal at end   = 14.64 g
A_r (M) = 65; A_r(I) = 127.
(a) What happened to the compound formed by the reaction?   (1 mark)
(b) What mass of M reacted with the iodine?   (1 mark)
(c) What fraction of a mole of M atoms is this?   (2 marks)
(d) What mass of iodine reacted?   (1 mark)
(e) What fraction of a mole of iodine atoms is this?   (2 marks)
(f) Write down the empirical formula of the compound formed between M and iodine.
                                                                           (2 marks)
(g) What is the oxidation number (valency) of M?   (1 mark)

Question 5.3

Use grid 2 on page 2 to choose an answer **A–E**.
Magnesium oxide has the formula MgO

BECAUSE

Magnesium oxide is formed by the combination of 1 mol of magnesium atoms with 1 mol of oxygen molecules.

Question 5.4

A compound of relative molecular mass 180 and empirical formula CH_2O has the molecular formula:
A CH_2O
B $C_2H_4O_2$
C $C_3H_6O_3$
D $C_4H_8O_4$
E $C_6H_{12}O_6$
$(A_r(H) = 1;\ A_r(O) = 16)$

Question 5.5

The percentage by mass of water of crystallisation in hydrated sodium sulphate, $Na_2SO_4.10H_2O$, is about

A 10
B 20
C 28
D 56
E 70

Question 5.6

A metal M forms a chloride MCl_2 of relative formula mass 95. It reacts with aqueous sodium hydroxide to give a precipitate of metal hydroxide. What is the relative formula mass of the hydroxide? (H = 1, O = 16 and Cl = 35.5)

A 24
B 40
C 41
D 58
E 95

(NISEC)

5.7 Answers to Self-Test Questions

5.1 C.

1 g of hydrogen contains 1 mol of H atoms but only $\frac{1}{2}$ mol H_2
58.5 g is 1 mol of NaCl, containing 1 mol Na^+ and 1 mol Cl^-.
Methane is CH_4, so 16 g is 1 mol.

5.2 (a) It dissolved in the ethanol and was removed.
(b) (14.77 − 14.64) = 0.13 g
(c) 0.13/65 = 0.002 mol
(d) (15.27 − 14.77) = 0.50 g
(e) 0.50/127 = 0.0039 mol
(f) mol M : mol I = 0.002 : 0.0039 ≈ 1 : 2. ∴ empirical formula is MI_2.
(g) oxidation number of M is +2 because oxidation number of I is −1.
(valency of M is 2 because valency of I is 1)

5.3 C.

1 mol of magnesium atoms combines with 1 mol of oxygen *atoms*, not O_2 molecules.

5.4 E.

Relative empirical formula mass of CH_2O is (12 + 2 + 16) = 30
Relative molecular mass is 180, which is 6 × 30
∴ Molecular formula is 6 × empirical formula.

5.5 D.

M_r $(Na_2SO_4.10H_2O) = (2 \times 23) + 32 + (4 \times 16) + (10 \times 18) = 322$

Percentage of water $= \dfrac{10 \times 18}{322} \times 100 = 55.9 \approx 56.$

5.6 D.

A_r (metal) must be $95 - (2 \times 35.5) = 24$

If the chloride is MCl_2, the hydroxide must be $M(OH)_2$

M_r $(M(OH)_2)$ is $24 + 2 \times (16 + 1) = 58.$

6 Gas Volumes

6.1 Introduction

Gas volumes are often quoted at **standard temperature and pressure**, or s.t.p. Standard temperature is 273 K (0°C); standard pressure is 101 325 Pa (760 mm of mercury, i.e. 1 atmosphere. 1 Pa (pascal) is equal to 1 newton per square metre).

Avogadro's principle states that equal volumes of all gases at the same temperature and pressure contain the same number of molecules.

Thus if two *volumes* of gas A combine with one *volume* of gas B (measured at the same temperature and pressure), then two *molecules* of gas A must combine with one *molecule* of gas B (see Examples 6.1 and 6.3).

The **molar volume** of a gas is the volume of one mole of it. Since one mole of *any* gas contains the same number of molecules (6.02×10^{23}), all gases must have the same molar volume, at the same temperature and pressure. At s.t.p. the molar volume of a gas is 22.4 dm³ mol⁻¹ (or 22.4 1/mol); at room temperature and pressure the value is usually taken to be 24 dm³ mol⁻¹.

Just as dividing the *mass* of a substance by its molar *mass* gives the amount of the substance in moles (Section 5.1), so dividing the *volume* of a gas by its molar *volume* also gives an amount in moles (see Example 6.2).

Multiplying an amount of gas in moles by its molar volume gives the volume of the gas.

The **atomicity** of an element is the number of atoms in one molecule of it, e.g. hydrogen, H_2, oxygen, O_2 and nitrogen, N_2 are **diatomic**; the noble gases, helium, He, neon, Ne, argon, Ar, etc. are **monatomic**.

6.2 Worked Examples

Example 6.1

Ethene reacts with oxygen according to the equation:

$$C_2H_4(g) + 3O_2(g) \rightarrow 2CO_2(g) + 2H_2O(g)$$

15.0 cm³ of ethene were mixed with 45.0 cm³ of oxygen and the mixture was sparked to complete the reaction. If all volumes were measured at a pressure of one atmosphere and a temperature of 120°C, the volume of the products would be

A 30 cm³
B 45 cm³
C 60 cm³
D 75 cm³
E 90 cm³

(NISEC)

The answer is C.

$$C_2H_4(g) + 3O_2(g) = 2CO_2(g) + 2H_2O(g)$$

1 molecule 3 molecules 2 molecules 2 molecules

By Avogadro's principle 1 vol 3 volumes 2 volumes 2 volumes

                15 cm^3 45 cm^3 30 cm^3 30 cm^3

                                       60 cm^3

Note Usually volumes are measured at *room* temperature and pressure, in which case the water would condense and its volume (though not the number of molecules) would be *negligible*. Remember, Avogadro's principle applies *only* to gases, not to liquids or solids.

Example 6.2

What is the minimum mass of sodium hydrogencarbonate which on heating will produce 3 dm^3 of carbon dioxide measured at room temperature and pressure? (H = 1, C = 12, O = 16, Na = 23 and one mole of carbon dioxide at room temperature and pressure occupies 24.0 dm^3.) The equation for the reaction is

$$2NaHCO_3 = Na_2CO_3 + H_2O + CO_2$$

A 7 g

B 14 g

C 21 g

D 84 g

E 168 g

The answer is **C**.

(NISEC)

$$2NaHCO_3 = Na_2CO_3 + H_2O + CO_2$$

$$\text{mol } CO_2 : \text{mol } NaHCO_3 = 1 : 2 \qquad \text{(A)}$$

$$\text{dm}^3\, CO_2 = 3$$

$$\text{mol } CO_2 = \frac{3}{24} \quad \text{(no of mol = volume/molar volume)}$$

$$\text{mol } NaHCO_3 = \frac{3}{24} \times 2 \quad \text{(from A)}$$

$$\text{g } NaHCO_3 = \frac{3}{24} \times 2 \times 84 \quad \text{(mass = no of mol} \times \text{molar mass)}$$

$$= 21$$

Compare this method of setting out with that given in Example 5.8.

Example 6.3

Use grid 1 on page 2 to choose an answer **A–E**.

Which of the gaseous hydrocarbons listed below would burn in oxygen to produce a mixture of carbon dioxide and steam having a volume equal to three times the volume of the original hydrocarbon? (All volumes measured at the same temperature and pressure.)

1 C_2H_2

2 CH_4

3 C_2H_6

The answer is **B**.

Since the relative numbers of molecules in the reactions are the same as the relative volumes of the gases, by Avogadro's principle:
1 volume of C_2H_2 produces 2 volumes of CO_2 + 1 volume of steam
1 volume of CH_4 produces 1 volume of CO_2 + 2 volumes of steam
1 volume of C_2H_6 produces 2 volumes of CO_2 + 3 volumes of steam

6.3   Self-Test Questions

Question 6.1

100 cm^3 of nitrogen oxide gas (NO) combine with 50 cm^3 of oxygen to form 100 cm^3 of a single gaseous compound, all volumes being measured at the same temperature and pressure. Which of the following equations fits these facts?

A $NO(g) + O_2(g) \rightarrow NO_3(g)$
B $NO(g) + 2O_2(g) \rightarrow NO_5(g)$
C $2NO(g) + O_2(g) \rightarrow 2NO_2(g)$
D $2NO(g) + O_2(g) \rightarrow N_2O_4(g)$
E $2NO(g) + 2O_2(g) \rightarrow N_2O_6(g)$

(L)

Question 6.2

A sample of gas, mass 0.39 g, was enclosed in a gas syringe and the volume of the gas was recorded at various temperatures but at a constant pressure of 101.3 kPa (101.3 kPa is equivalent to 1 atm); the results are shown in the table below.

Temperature (°C)	20	40	60	80	100
Volume (cm^3)	241	258	274	291	308

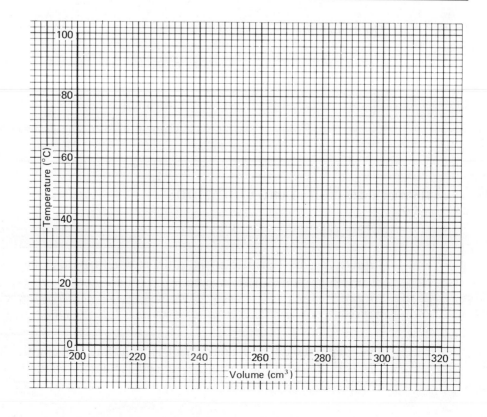

(a) Plot the data on the grid provided and draw the best straight line through the points; extend the line so that it cuts the horizontal axis. **(3 marks)**

(b) Read from the graph the volume of the gas at $0°C$. **(2 marks)**

(c) Calculate the mass of gas which would have a volume of $22\,400\ cm^3$ at $0°C$. **(2 marks)**

(d) What is the relative molecular mass of the gas? **(1 mark)**

(AEB)

Question 6.3

What volume of hydrogen is produced at room temperature and pressure, when 0.6 g of magnesium reacts with excess 1 M sulphuric acid?

$$Mg(s) + 2H^+(aq) \rightarrow Mg^{2+}(aq) + H_2(g)$$

(Relative atomic mass: Mg = 24; 1 mole of any gas occupies $24\,000\ cm^3$ at room temperature and pressure.)

A $240\ cm^3$

B $600\ cm^3$

C $1000\ cm^3$

D $14\,400\ cm^3$

E $24\,000\ cm^3$ (L)

For questions 6.4 and 6.5 use grid 2 on page 2 to choose an answer **A–E**.

Question 6.4

When stating the volume of a gas, the pressure and temperature should also be given

BECAUSE

The volume of a fixed mass of gas increases when the temperature is increased and decreases when the pressure is increased.

(L)

Question 6.5

The volume of 1 mole of hydrogen molecules is twice the volume of 1 mole of helium atoms at the same temperature and pressure

BECAUSE

Hydrogen gas consists of diatomic molecules but helium is monatomic.

(L)

6.4 Answers to Self-Test Questions

6.1 C.

From Avogadro's principle, the ratio of reacting molecules is the same as that of reacting volumes, i.e. 2 : 1 : 2.

6.2 (a)

The graph should be a single, neat straight line, cutting the horizontal axis at $224\ cm^3$ and with the points clearly and accurately marked.

(b) 224 cm^3.

(c) 224 cm^3 of gas at 0°C and 1 atm has a mass of 0.39 g.

∴ 22 400 cm^3 of gas at 0°C and 1 atm has a mass of 39 g.

(d) 39

---

22 400 cm^3 of gas at s.t.p. is 1 mol of the gas.

6.3 **B**.

$Mg(s) + 2H^+(aq) \rightarrow Mg^{2+}(aq) + H_2(g)$

mol Mg : mol H$_2$ = 1 : 1   (A)

         g Mg = 0.6

$$\text{mol Mg} = \frac{0.6}{24} \qquad (\text{mol = mass/molar mass})$$

$$\text{mol H}_2 = \frac{0.6}{24} \times 1 \quad (\text{from A})$$

$$\text{cm}^3 \text{ H}_2 = \frac{0.6}{24} \times 1 \times 24\,000 \; (\text{volume = mol} \times \text{molar volume})$$

$$= 600$$

6.4 **A**.

6.5 **D**.

The molar volume is the *same* for all gases at the same temperature and pressure.

---

7 Electrochemistry

7.1 Introduction

Substances that allow electricity to pass through them are known as **conductors**: those that do not are called **insulators**.

Metallic elements conduct electricity when solid or molten but are not decomposed by it (compare with electrolytes below). The current is carried by loosely held electrons, which move from one atom to the next.

Non-metallic elements do not conduct electricity because their electrons cannot move from one atom to the next (graphite is an exception).

An **electrolyte** is a compound which, when molten and/or in solution, conducts an electric current and is decomposed by it (compare with metals above). The current is carried by ions, which are free to move through the liquid to the oppositely charged electrodes where they are discharged. Acids, alkalis and salts are examples of electrolytes (see Example 7.2).

A **non-electrolyte** is a compound which does not conduct an electric current, either when molten or in solution, because no ions are present. Sugar and ethanol are non-electrolytes. Most metal compounds, particularly salts, have giant ionic lattices (see Section 4.3). When they are dissolved in water the ions separate and diffuse throughout the liquid, thus providing a solution which is a good conductor of electricity. Such substances are examples of *strong electrolytes*.

Covalent substances are generally non-electrolytes. However, when the covalent gas, hydrogen chloride, dissolves in water it forms hydrochloric acid, which is a strong electrolyte. The water reacts with the gas molecules, changing them into ions.

$$HCl(g) + H_2O(l) \rightarrow H_3O^+(aq) + Cl^-(aq)$$

Sulphuric acid and nitric acid molecules also react with water in this way.

Some other covalent substances, such as ammonia and ethanoic acid, have similar reactions with water but form far fewer ions. They are examples of *weak electrolytes*, their solutions being poor conductors of electricity. e.g.

$$NH_3(aq) + H_2O(l) \rightleftharpoons NH_4^+(aq) + OH^-(aq)$$

7.2 Electrolysis

Electrolysis is the decomposition of an electrolyte by the passage of an electric current through it.

During electrolysis negatively charged ions are attracted to the **anode** (positive electrode) and so are called **anions**; positively charged ions are attracted to the **cathode** (negative electrode) and are called **cations**. A useful mnemonic is:

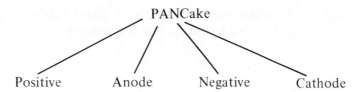

PANCake

Positive   Anode   Negative   Cathode

Since electrons are removed at the anode, the process taking place is oxidation; at the cathode, electrons are added and so reduction is occurring (see Section 4.5).

(a) The Electrolysis of Lead(II) Bromide (Fig. 7.1)

Fig. 7.1

Solid lead(II) bromide does not conduct electricity because its ions are fixed in the crystal lattice. When the solid is melted the ions are free to move and travel to the oppositely charged electrodes. At the anode, electrons are removed from the bromide ions giving bromine atoms, which combine in pairs to form molecules; reddish brown bromine gas is given off. At the cathode, electrons are added to the lead ions, forming lead atoms, and a bead of molten lead collects at the bottom of the cell.

At anode

$$2Br^-(l) \longrightarrow 2Br(g) + 2e^-$$

$$\downarrow$$

$$Br_2(g)$$

(oxidation)

At cathode

$$2e^- + Pb^{2+}(l) \longrightarrow Pb(l)$$

(reduction)

(b) The Electrolysis of Aqueous Solutions

Water is a very weak electrolyte; one molecule in about 550 million ionises as shown:

$$H_2O(l) \rightleftharpoons H^+(aq) + OH^-(aq)$$

65

Consider the electrolysis of dilute sulphuric acid in the apparatus shown in Fig. 7.2. The following ions are present.

Fig. 7.2

	Ions attracted to anode	*Ions attracted to cathode*
From sulphuric acid	SO_4^{2-}(aq)	$2H^+$(aq)
From water (very few)	OH^-(aq)	H^+(aq)

At the anode, hydroxide ions are discharged in preference to sulphate ions, forming water and oxygen: hydrogen ions are discharged at the cathode, giving hydrogen gas.

The equations show why the volume of hydrogen collected is found to be twice that of the oxygen (Avogadro's principle — see Section 6.1).

(c) Predicting the Products of the Electrolysis of Aqueous Solutions

Firstly, all of the ions in the solution should be listed under the electrodes to which they are attracted, as in the above example. The ions which will be discharged may, in most cases, be predicted from two simple rules:

1. At the anode, hydroxide ions will be discharged and the products will be oxygen and water, unless:
   (a) chloride, bromide or iodide ions are present (see Example 7.4); or

(b) the anode dissolves or reacts with the oxygen formed from the hydroxide ions (see Examples 7.1 and 7.3).

2. At the cathode, the ions of the element which is lowest in the electrochemical series will be discharged, unless the cathode is made of mercury (see Example 18.4). For practical purposes, the electrochemical series may be taken to be the same as the metal reactivity series (see Section 13.1), with hydrogen coming between lead and copper (see Question 7.1).

(d) Applications of Electrolysis

1. The manufacture of elements. Examples include sodium, aluminium and chlorine (see Section 18.1).
2. The manufacture of compounds, e.g. sodium hydroxide (see Section 18.2).
3. Purification of metals. Copper is purified by electrolysing aqueous copper(II) sulphate solution with blocks of impure copper as anodes and thin sheets of the pure metal as cathodes. Pure copper is transferred from the anode to the cathode (see Example 7.3).
4. Electroplating. The article to be plated is made the cathode in the electrolysis cell, the anode is made of the plating metal and the electrolyte is a solution containing its ions. When a current passes, the plating metal is transferred from the anode to the cathode, as in the purification of copper.

7.3   Electrolysis Calculations

Faraday's first law of electrolysis states that the mass of substance liberated at an electrode during electrolysis is proportional to the quantity of electricity which passes through the electrolyte (see Example 7.5).

Quantity of electricity is measured in coulombs, one coulomb being passed when a current of one amp flows for one second. In general:

$$\text{Quantity of electricity passed} = \text{current} \times \text{time}$$

i.e.   coulombs $= \text{amps} \quad \times \text{seconds}$

The **Faraday constant** is the quantity of electric charge carried by one mole of electrons. Its value is 96 500 coulombs per mole (C mol^{-1}).

96 500 coulombs is often referred to as one Faraday.

From the definition of the Faraday constant, it can be seen that dividing the quantity of electricity passed through the circuit by 96 500 gives us the number of moles of electrons involved in the electrolysis.

7.4   Worked Examples

Example 7.1

(a) From the following list of substances: zinc bromide, paraffin wax, hydrogen chloride, copper, potassium chloride and iodine, name those that:
(i) conduct electricity in the solid state,

Copper.

(ii) conduct electricity when molten,

Zinc bromide, copper, potassium chloride.

(iii) conduct electricity in aqueous solution,

Zinc bromide, hydrogen chloride, potassium chloride.

(iv) do not readily conduct under any conditions. **(5 marks)**

Paraffin wax, iodine.

Check with Section 7.1 if you are uncertain about these answers.

(b) The electrolysis of an aqueous solution of calcium hydroxide was investigated using carbon electrodes.

(i) Which gas would you expect to be produced at the anode?

Oxygen.

Only OH^- ions (from both the calcium hydroxide and the water) are present at the anode. Therefore the electrode equation is

$$4OH^- (aq) \longrightarrow 4OH(aq) + 4e^-$$
$$\downarrow$$
$$2H_2O(l) + O_2(g)$$

(ii) During the electrolysis the anode decreases in mass and the solution round it becomes milky. Explain these observations. **(3 marks)**

The oxygen produced reacts with the carbon electrode to give carbon dioxide which will turn calcium hydroxide solution (limewater) milky, owing to the formation of insoluble calcium carbonate.

(c) The apparatus was set up as shown in the figure and after some time a yellow substance was produced in the position shown.

(i) Give the formulae of the ions present in the lead nitrate and potassium iodide solutions.

From $Pb(NO_3)_2$ *$Pb^{2+}(aq)$ and $NO_3^-(aq)$*
From KI   *$K^+(aq)$ and $I^-(aq)$*
From water   *$H^+(aq)$ and $OH^-(aq)$*

(ii) What is the yellow substance? Write an ionic equation to show its formation.

Lead iodide
$Pb^{2+}(aq) + 2I^-(aq) \rightarrow PbI_2(s)$

(iii) Explain how the yellow compound is formed. **(7 marks)**

The lead ions are attracted to the cathode while the iodide ions are attracted to the anode. Where they meet insoluble lead(II) iodide is formed.

Example 7.2

Use grid 1 on page 2 to choose an answer **A–E**.
The circuit shown below was set up and adjusted so that the lamp glowed faintly.

6–12 volt d.c.

The behaviour of the lamp was studied when different solutions, all of them having concentration 1 mol dm^{-3}, were placed in the beaker. Which of the following sets of results would be obtained?

Lamp glows brightly	Lamp does not glow at all
1. dilute sulphuric acid	sugar in water
2. hydrogen chloride in water	hydrogen chloride in methylbenzene
3. dilute ethanoic acid	copper(II) sulphate solution

The answer is **B**.

Dilute sulphuric acid, hydrogen chloride in water and copper(II) sulphate solution are strong electrolytes (good conductors of electricity) and thus the lamp glows brightly when they are in the beaker. Ethanoic acid and aqueous ammonia solution are weak electrolytes and will cause the lamp to glow faintly. Sugar in water and a solution of hydrogen chloride in methylbenzene are non-conductors and so the lamp will not glow at all. Thus 1 and 2 only are correct.

Example 7.3

(a) Copper may be purified by electrolysis of aqueous copper(II) sulphate solution.
   (i) Describe briefly how this is done, giving the name, charge and material of each electrode. Write ion-electron half equations for the reactions that take place at each electrode. Explain which reaction is an oxidation. **(8 marks)**
   (ii) Aqueous copper(II) sulphate may be regarded as an *electrolyte*. Explain why solid copper is not regarded as an electrolyte although it conducts electricity. **(4 marks)**
   (iii) Explain why it is not possible to purify aluminium in a similar way. **(2 marks)**
   (iv) Calculate how many Faradays of electricity must be passed to deposit 1.27 g of copper. **(3 marks)**
   (OLE)

(i) Copper is purifed by the electrolysis of copper(II) sulphate solution, using a block of impure copper as the positively charged anode and a thin sheet of pure copper as the negatively charged cathode. At the anode, electrons are removed from copper atoms, forming Cu^{2+} ions which go into solution. Impurities dissolve or sink to the bottom of the container. At the cathode, Cu^{2+} ions gain electrons, forming copper atoms and so the cathode becomes coated with pure copper. The overall result is the transfer of copper atoms from the impure anode to the cathode.

	At anode		At cathode

$$\text{Cu(s)} \longrightarrow \text{Cu}^{2+}\text{(aq)} + \boxed{2e^-} \quad \Big| \quad \longrightarrow 2e^- + \text{Cu}^{2+}\text{(aq)} \longrightarrow \text{Cu(s)}$$

The reaction at the anode is oxidation because each copper atom loses two electrons here.

	Ions attracted to anode	Ions attracted to cathode
From $CuSO_4$	SO_4^{2-} (aq)	Cu^{2+} (aq)
From H_2O (very few ions)	OH^- (aq)	H^+ (aq)

No gases are given off during this electrolysis. At the anode it requires less energy to remove electrons from the copper atoms of the anode itself than to remove them from the OH^- or SO_4^{2-} ions. At the cathode Cu^{2+} ions are discharged in preference to H^+ ions because copper is below hydrogen in the electrochemical series.

(ii) Electrolytes conduct electricity only when molten or in solution, and are decomposed by it. The current is carried by ions. In solid copper the current is carried by loosely held electrons and the metal remains chemically unchanged. Therefore it is not an electrolyte.

(iii) It is not possible to purify aluminium in a similar way to that described in (i). Hydrogen ions and aluminium ions would both be present at the cathode but the hydrogen ions would be discharged, since hydrogen is below aluminium in the electrochemical series (see Section 7.2). The aluminium ions would remain in solution.

(iv)

Always start by writing out the equation.

$$Cu^{2+}(aq) + 2e^- \rightarrow Cu(s)$$
$$\text{mol Cu(s) : mol } e^- = 1 : 2$$
$$\text{g Cu} = 1.27$$
$$\text{mol Cu} = \frac{1.27}{63.5} = 0.02 \qquad (A_r(Cu) = 63.5)$$
$$\text{mol } e^- = 0.02 \times 2$$
$$= 0.04$$

Thus 0.04 Faradays of electricity must pass through the external circuit.

Example 7.4

The apparatus shown in the figure was assembled and the circuit completed. Immediately bubbles of gas were seen at the cathode (negative electrode), but there was little apparent reaction at the anode. After some time it was noticed that the solution around the cathode had turned blue while the area near the anode was colourless; there were now some bubbles at the anode.

(a) Name the particles responsible for carrying the current in (i) a wire, and in (ii) an electrolyte. **(2 marks)**

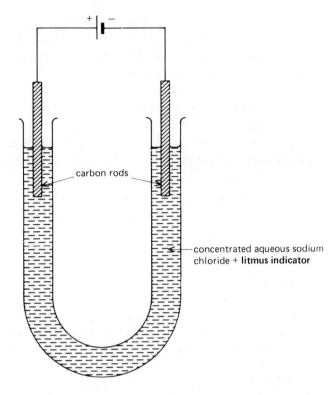

carbon rods

concentrated aqueous sodium
chloride + litmus indicator

(b) (i) Name the gas evolved at the **anode** and write an ionic equation to show how it was formed.
(ii) Why were bubbles of this gas not observed immediately when the circuit was completed?
(iii) Explain briefly the reason why the litmus indicator around the anode became colourless. **(8 marks)**

(c) (i) Name the gas evolved at the **cathode** and write an ionic equation to show how it was formed. Give **one** test to identify this gas.
(ii) Explain why the litmus solution around the cathode turned blue. **(8 marks)**

(d) Name the sodium compound which is manufactured by the electrolysis of brine and describe briefly its importance in the chemistry of soap production. **(6 marks)**

(a) (i) Electrons. (AEB)
    (ii) Ions.

(b) (i) Chlorine is evolved at the anode.

$$2Cl^-(aq) \rightarrow 2Cl(g) + 2e^-$$
$$\downarrow$$
$$Cl_2(g)$$

	Ions attracted to anode	Ions attracted to cathode
From NaCl	$Cl^-(aq)$	$Na^+(aq)$
From H_2O (very few ions)	$OH^-(aq)$	$H^+(aq)$

Chloride ions are always discharged in preference to hydroxide ions from concentrated solutions (see Section 7.2).

(ii) Chlorine is moderately soluble in aqueous sodium chloride solution and so at first the gas dissolves.
(iii) Chlorine will bleach coloured compounds by oxidising them to colourless products (see Example 17.7).

(c) (i) The gas is hydrogen.
$$2e^- + 2H^+(aq) \rightarrow 2H(g)$$
$$\downarrow$$
$$H_2(g)$$

> At the cathode, hydrogen ions are discharged in preference to sodium ions since hydrogen is much lower in the electrochemical series than sodium.

        Hydrogen could be identified by collecting a tubeful of gas and applying a flame — a 'pop' could be clearly heard.
(ii) The removal of hydrogen ions from the water molecules around the cathode leaves an excess of hydroxide ions and these turn the litmus blue.
(d) Sodium hydroxide is manufactured by the electrolysis of brine (see Example 18.4). Animal fats and vegetable oils are esters of long-chained carboxylic acids and propane-1,2,3-triol. When boiled with sodium hydroxide solution they are hydrolysed to propane-1,2,3-triol and the sodium salt of the acid, which is soap.

Example 7.5

The same quantity of electricity is passed through two solutions in series. The first one is silver nitrate solution, the second one is an aqueous solution of $M_2(SO_4)_3$. If 1.08 g silver is deposited from the first solution, the mass of M deposited is

A 0.16 g
B 0.48 g
C 1.08 g
D 1.44 g
E 2.16 g
$A_r(Ag) = 108 \quad A_r(M) = 48$.

The answer is **A**.

$e^- + Ag^+(aq) \rightarrow Ag(s)$
$\text{mol Ag} : \text{mol } e^- = 1 : 1$
$\quad\quad\quad \text{g Ag} = 1.08$
$\quad\quad\quad \text{mol Ag} = \dfrac{1.08}{108} = 0.01$
$\quad\quad\quad \text{mol } e^- = 0.01$

In the salt $M_2(SO_4)_3$ the formula of the metal ion must be M^{3+}. Therefore the electrode equation is

$3e^- + M^{3+}(aq) \rightarrow M(s)$
$\text{mol } e^- : \text{mol M} = 3 : 1 = 1 : \frac{1}{3}$
$\quad\quad\quad \text{mol } e^- = 0.01$
$\quad\quad\quad \text{mol M} = 0.01 \times \frac{1}{3}$
$\quad\quad\quad \text{g M} = 0.01 \times \frac{1}{3} \times 48 = 0.16$

7.5 Self-Test Questions

Question 7.1

A concentrated solution of copper(II) chloride was electrolysed using inert electrodes.
    After 10 mins, a pink substance was deposited on one electrode and a gas which bleached moist universal indicator paper was evolved at the other electrode.
    After 1 hour, the same products were being formed but the solution was paler in colour.
    After 2 hours, the pink substance was no longer being deposited: instead, a colourless gas

was evolved. At the other electrode, the bubbles of gas no longer bleached moist universal indicator paper.

After 3 hours, the liquid could no longer conduct electricity.

(a) Give the formulae of all ions present in the copper(II) chloride solution. (2 marks)
(b) (i) At which electrode was the pink substance deposited?
   (ii) Which gas is first discharged at the other electrode? (2 marks)
(c) Why did the colour of the copper(II) chloride solution fade? (2 marks)
(d) Name the two gases being evolved after two hours. Write ion–electron equations for each reaction and describe the tests you would carry out to confirm the identity of each gas. (6 marks)
(e) Why did the electrolysis stop after 3 hours? (1 mark)
(f) How many coulombs of electricity were passed if a current of 2 A flowed for 2 hours? (2 marks)

Questions 7.2–7.5

Directions. This group of questions deals with laboratory situations. Each situation is followed by a set of questions. Select the best answer for each question.

The apparatus below was used to investigate the electrolysis of lithium chloride, LiCl. The crucible contained molten lithium chloride. The U-tube contained an aqueous solution of lithium chloride. The bulb lit when the switch was closed.

Question 7.2

What were the products at the two cathodes in this experiment?

	At the cathode in molten lithium chloride	At the cathode in aqueous lithium chloride solution
A	Lithium	Hydrogen
B	Chlorine	Oxygen
C	Hydrogen	Hydrogen
D	Lithium	Lithium
E	Chlorine	Chlorine

(L)

Question 7.3

What would happen in the experiment described on the previous page if the heat supply under the crucible were to be removed and the contents allowed to cool to room temperature?

	Bulb	Electrolysis in the crucible	Electrolysis in the U-tube
A	Stays alight	Continues	Continues
B	Stays alight	Stops	Continues
C	Stays alight	Continues	Stops
D	Goes out	Stops	Continues
E	Goes out	Stops	Stops

(L)

Question 7.4

What apparatus is ESSENTIAL, in addition to that shown in the diagram, in an experiment to measure the number of coulombs used in the experiment?

A Ammeter, clock and thermometer
B Ammeter and gas syringe only
C Variable resistor only
D Ammeter and thermometer only
E Clock and ammeter only

(L)

Question 7.5

What is the number of moles of lithium atoms produced by electrolysis when a current of 0.1 amperes flows for 20 minutes?
(1 mole of electrons (one faraday) = 96 500 coulombs)

A $\dfrac{20 \times 60}{0.1 \times 96\,500}$

B $\dfrac{96\,500 \times 0.1}{20 \times 60}$

C $0.1 \times 20 \times 60 \times 96\,500$

D $\dfrac{0.1 \times 20 \times 60}{96\,500}$

E $\dfrac{96\,500}{0.1 \times 20 \times 60}$

(L)

For Questions 7.6 and 7.7 use grid 1 on page 2 to choose an answer **A-E**.

Question 7.6

When copper(II) sulphate is electrolysed using inert electrodes:
1 oxygen is liberated at the anode
2 the cathode becomes coated with copper
3 the anode loses mass.

Question 7.7

When aqueous sodium hydroxide is electrolysed using carbon electrodes
1 oxygen is obtained at the anode
2 hydrogen is obtained at the cathode
3 the concentration of the sodium hydroxide solution increases.

Question 7.8

Use the information in the table below to deduce which element forms an X^{2-} ion. (1 F is equivalent to 96 500 C.)

Element	Electrode at which the element is discharged	Number of coulombs transferred in discharging 1 mol of the element
A	anode	48 250
B	anode	96 500
C	anode	193 000
D	cathode	96 500
E	cathode	193 000

7.6 Answers to Self-Test Questions

7.1 (a)

	Ions attracted to anode	Ions attracted to cathode
From $CuCl_2$	Cl^- (aq)	Cu^{2+} (aq)
From H_2O (very few ions)	OH^- (aq)	H^+ (aq)

(b) (i) The pink deposit is copper formed at the cathode.
   (ii) Chlorine.
(c) The copper ions are responsible for the colour of the solution. These ions are steadily removed as copper atoms and so the colour becomes paler.
(d) The products are oxygen (relights a glowing splint) and hydrogen (pops in a flame).

Anode

$$4OH^-(aq) \longrightarrow 4OH(aq) + 4e^-$$

$$2H_2O(1) + O_2(g)$$
(oxidation)

Cathode

$$4e^- + 4H^+(aq) \longrightarrow 4H(g)$$

$$2H_2(g)$$
(reduction)

After 2 hours, there are very few copper or chloride ions left in solution, so hydrogen ions are discharged at the cathode and hydroxide ions are discharged at the anode.

(e) After 3 hours, there are no copper or chloride ions left to carry the current. Pure water is a very poor conductor of electricity because hardly any ions are present.
(f) coulombs = amps × seconds
              = 2 × 2 × 60 × 60 = 14400

7.2 **A.**

Since hydrogen is below lithium in the electrochemical series.

7.3 **E.**

Lithium chloride solidifies; ions can no longer travel to the electrodes.

7.4 **E.**

Coulombs = current in amps × time in seconds.

7.5 **D.**

Coulombs ÷ 96 500 gives mol of electrons; mol e^- = mol Li^+ discharged.

7.6 **B.**

1 and 2 are both correct. Do not be trapped into thinking that part 3 is also correct — this would be true if the anode were made of copper or carbon but it is not.

7.7 **A.**

In effect, the water is being electrolysed. Thus, although the quantity of sodium hydroxide is unchanged, its concentration increases as the water is used up.

7.8 **C.**

X^{2-} must travel to the anode; 1 mol X^{2-} loses 2 mol of electrons i.e. 2 × 96 500 C.

8 Energy Changes in Chemistry

8.1   Introduction

Energy is usually defined as the capacity for doing work. It can be neither created nor destroyed (Law of conservation of energy) but it can be converted from one form to another. For example, the chemical energy stored up in petrol can be converted to heat energy and kinetic energy (energy associated with movement) in a car engine.

Most of the energy which we use today is obtained from 'fossil fuels' — gas, oil and coal. Supplies of these fuels will not last forever and they must not be wasted. They can be supplemented by nuclear energy (see Section 2.6), energy from wind, flowing water and from the sun but these last three energy sources do not contribute very greatly to world supplies at the moment. Combustion of fossil fuels causes air pollution (see Section 10.1), while nuclear reactors give rise to radioactive waste. Choice of fuel depends largely upon availability, convenience and cost. Only fairly recently has large-scale concern about pollution had any bearing on the matter.

During almost all chemical changes energy is exchanged with the surroundings: if it is given out by the reaction the change is said to be *exothermic*, if it is absorbed the reaction is *endothermic*. The reason that the energy changes occur is that bonds between atoms or ions in the reactants have to be broken and new ones formed in the products. Bond breaking absorbs energy but bond making releases it. The overall energy change that occurs results from the difference between the energy supplied for the breaking of the reactant bonds and that evolved in the making of the product bonds.

The symbol for heat change occurring at constant pressure is ΔH, where Δ (delta) means 'change of' and H is the 'heat content' or *enthalpy* of the system. ΔH is *negative* for an exothermic change because the system *loses* energy to the surroundings: in an endothermic reaction ΔH is *positive* because the system *gains* energy from the surroundings. These enthalpy changes (often simply called 'heat changes') may be represented on *energy level diagrams* as shown in Fig. 8.1 (see also Question 8.6).

The unit of energy is the joule (J) or, more conveniently, the kilojoule (kJ), which is 1000 joules. One **joule** is the energy required to raise the temperature of 1 g of water by

$$\frac{1}{4.18} \text{ K} \left(\frac{1}{4.18} \text{ °C} \right);$$

thus 4.18 joules will raise the temperature of 1 g of water by 1 K (1°C).

The **enthalpy change of reaction (heat of reaction)**, ΔH, is the heat change which occurs when the numbers of moles of reactants indicated by the equation react together. This information is often included in the equation. For instance

$$C(s) + O_2(g) \rightarrow CO_2(g) \qquad \Delta H = -394 \text{ kJ mol}^{-1}$$

means that when 1 mole of carbon burns in excess oxygen, the heat *evolved* is 394 kJ.

Fig. 8.1

When a solid melts energy is absorbed in order to overcome the forces holding the particles together in the lattice (see Section 2.2). Measurement of the energy needed to overcome the forces for the same number of particles of different substances gives us a comparison of the forces themselves.

The **molar enthalpy change of melting** is the heat required to change one mole of solid into liquid at its melting point. The values for hydrogen chloride and sodium chloride are 1.99 and 28.9 kJ mol^{-1} respectively, showing that ionic bonds are much stronger than intermolecular forces (see Question 8.4).

The **molar enthalpy change of vaporisation** is the heat required to change one mole of liquid into vapour at its boiling point.

8.2 Measurement of Enthalpy Changes (Heat Changes)

The **enthalpy change (heat) of combustion** of a substance is the heat change which occurs when one mole of it is completely burned in excess oxygen.

Fig. 8.2

The enthalpy change of combustion of a liquid such as ethanol can be measured by burning a *known* mass of it and using the heat produced to raise the temperature of a *known* mass of water in the apparatus shown in Fig. 8.2. Heat losses must be allowed for by using a liquid of known enthalpy change of combustion first and calculating the *heat capacity* of the apparatus and contents (i.e. the heat required to raise the temperature by 1°C) (see Example 8.3).

The **enthalpy change (heat) of neutralisation** is the heat change which occurs when one mole of hydrated hydrogen ions from an acid reacts with one mole of hydrated hydroxide ions from an alkali.

The apparatus of Fig. 8.3 may be used to measure the temperature rise when a known volume of acid, concentration also known, is neutralised by a known

expanded polystyrene cup

250 cm³ beaker

Fig. 8.3

volume of alkali. The enthalpy change of neutralisation is calculated from the result. Heat losses in this case are negligible (see Example 8.4).

The **enthalpy change (heat) of solution** of a substance is the heat change that occurs when one mole of it dissolves in water to make a dilute solution.

Measurement may be carried out using the apparatus in Fig. 8.3. Energy must be supplied to overcome the forces of attraction acting between the atoms, molecules or ions of the substance. The particles form new bonds with the water molecules, thus releasing *hydration energy*. If the hydration energy is greater than that needed to separate the particles, the dissolving will be exothermic; if it is smaller, then the dissolving will be endothermic (see Fig. 8.4).

The **enthalpy change (heat) of precipitation** of a substance is the heat change that occurs when one mole of it is precipitated from aqueous solution. The apparatus of Fig. 8.3 may be used to measure this enthalpy change too.

8.3   Electrical Cells

Electrical cells enable electrical energy to be obtained from chemical reactions. This is the reverse of what happens during electrolysis, where chemical reactions

Fig. 8.4

are brought about by the use of electrical energy. The simplest type of cell consists of two metals dipping into an electrolyte (see Section 7.1) and connected to one another by a wire.

In the Daniell cell a zinc rod dips into a solution of zinc sulphate and a copper plate dips into a solution of copper(II) sulphate. The two solutions are separated by a porous partition. This prevents a displacement reaction (see Section 13.1) from taking place directly between the zinc rod and the copper(II) sulphate solution but allows ions to travel through it to complete the circuit. Fig. 8.5 shows the apparatus. Zinc, being more reactive than copper, forms ions more readily and so its atoms each give up two electrons and go into solution as Zn^{2+} ions. The electrons flow through the wire to the copper plate where Cu^{2+} ions from the solution take them to become Cu atoms.

Fig. 8.5

At zinc $\qquad\qquad\qquad$ $Zn(s) \rightarrow Zn^{2+}(aq) + 2e^-$
At copper $\quad Cu^{2+}(aq) + 2e^- \rightarrow Cu(s)$

Adding $\qquad \overline{Cu^{2+}(aq) + Zn(s) \rightarrow Cu(s) + Zn^{2+}(aq)}$ (overall change)

Clearly, the overall chemical change taking place is the same as that which occurs when zinc is dipped into copper(II) sulphate solution, i.e. displacement, but the cell enables us to obtain electrical energy from the reaction.

8.4 Light Energy in Chemistry

Light energy can be produced by a chemical reaction (e.g. in a flame) or can be absorbed (e.g. in the reaction between hydrogen and chlorine (see Example 17.3), in photography and very importantly, in photosynthesis (see Section 10.4)).

8.5 Worked Examples

Examples 8.1 and 8.2 concern the following graphs of a quantity Y plotted against a quantity X.

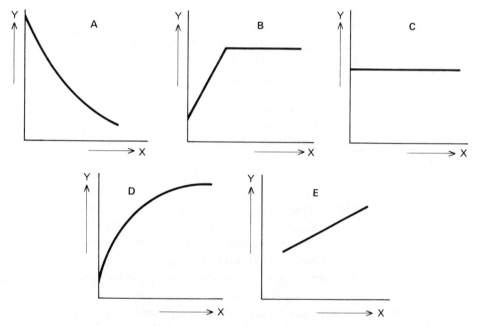

Select, from A to E, the graph which best represents the way Y changes with X, when Y and X are the quantities shown in each question below.

Example 8.1

100 cm^3 of water, at room temperature, was placed in a beaker and then heated with a burner supplying heat at a constant rate. The temperature of the water was recorded at regular intervals until 10 cm^3 of it had boiled away.

Y = Temperature of water $\qquad$ X = Time. $\hspace{4cm}$ (L)

The answer is **B**.

The temperature rises steadily until the liquid boils and then remains constant.

Example 8.2

A series of experiments was carried out to measure the heat given out when each of the following hydrocarbons was burned.
$CH_4, C_2H_6, C_3H_8, C_4H_{10}, C_5H_{12}$

Y = Heat given out on the   X = Relative molecular mass
   combustion of 1 mole   of hydrocarbon
   of hydrocarbon   (L)
The answer is **E**.

Each hydrocarbon differs from the next by the group $-CH_2-$, so the relative molecular mass increases steadily. As 1 mole of each successive member burns, more energy must be *supplied* to break an extra 1 mole of C–C bonds and 2 moles of C–H bonds. However, energy will be *evolved* on making the bonds in an extra 1 mole of carbon dioxide and 1 mole of water. The difference between the total energy absorbed and the total energy evolved will thus change by the same amount on going from one hydrocarbon to the next, giving graph **E**.

Example 8.3

The enthalpy changes of combustion of a number of cycloalkanes are as follows:
cyclopentane C_5H_{10} $\Delta H = -3317$ kJ mol^{-1}
cyclohexane C_6H_{12} $\Delta H = -3948$ kJ mol^{-1}
cycloheptane C_7H_{14} $\Delta H = -4632$ kJ mol^{-1}
When the enthalpy change of combustion of cyclononane, C_9H_{18}, is measured, the following data are obtained: the combustion of 0.21 g of cyclononane raises the temperature of water in a can (total heat capacity = 0.996 kJ K^{-1}) by 10 K.
(a) Calculate the enthalpy change of combustion of cyclononane.   **(4 marks)**

Heat evolved   = heat capacity × temperature rise
*   = 0.996 × 10 = 9.96 kJ*
Mol of C_9H_{18} = mass/molar mass (see Section 5.1)
Molar mass of C_9H_{18} = (9 × 12) + (18 × 1) = 126 g mol $^{-1}$
∴ Mol of C_9H_{18} = 0.21/126 = 1/600
If 1/600 mol of cyclononane produces 9.96 kJ
*   1 mol of cyclononane produces 9.96 × 600 = 5976 kJ*
∴ Enthalpy change of combustion of cyclononane is −5976 kJ mol^{-1}

Note the minus sign: heat is given out on burning.

(b) Plot a graph of enthalpy change of combustion of the cycloalkanes (on the *y* axis) (*see Fig. 8.6*) against number of carbon atoms in their molecules (on the *x* axis).
                                                                        (3 marks)
(c) An unknown cycloalkane has an enthalpy change of combustion of −5305 kJ mol^{-1}.
   Use the graph to find out how many carbon atoms this cycloalkane contains. **(2 marks)**
The cycloalkane contains 8 carbon atoms (Fig. 8.6).

(d) What is the formula of the unknown cycloalkane?   **(1 mark)**
The formula is C_8H_{16}.

The general formula of this series is C_nH_{2n}. In this case n = 8, so 2n = 16.

(e) Write an equation to represent its combustion to carbon dioxide and water.   **(2 marks)**
$C_8H_{16} + 12O_2 \rightarrow 8CO_2 + 8H_2O$

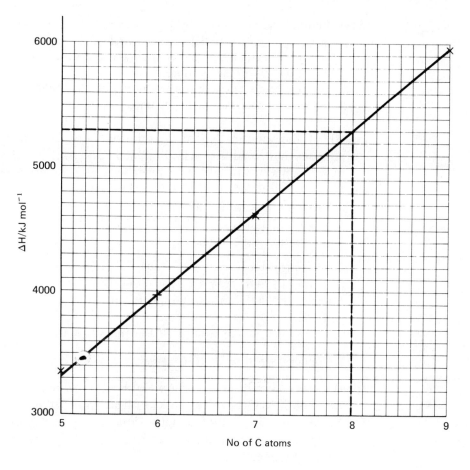

Fig. 8.6

Example 8.4

40 g of sodium hydroxide was dissolved in water so as to make 500 cm³ of solution. 50 cm³ portions of this solution were placed in insulated plastic cups and the temperature of each was noted. Various quantities of aqueous hydrochloric acid (at the same temperature) were added to each cup, and the temperature rise was observed; hence the heat change in kJ was calculated. The results are shown in Table 1.

Table 1

Volume of aqueous sodium hydroxide (cm³)	Volume of aqueous hydrochloric acid (cm³)	Heat energy evolved (kJ)
50	10	1.1
50	20	2.2
50	30	3.4
50	40	4.5
50	50	5.6
50	60	5.6
50	70	5.6

(a) Explain briefly why the heat change becomes constant after 50 cm³ has been added.
    (2 marks)

(b) How many moles of sodium hydroxide are contained in 50 cm³ of solution. **(2 marks)**

(c) Calculate the concentration of the aqueous hydrochloric acid in mol/dm⁻³. **(2 marks)**

(d) What quantity of heat energy would be evolved if a solution containing 1 mol of sodium hydroxide was neutralised by aqueous hydrochloric acid? **(2 marks)**

83

(e) Estimate the heat energy which would be evolved if a solution containing 1 mol of a metal hydroxide, $M(OH)_2$, was neutralised by aqueous hydrochloric acid. Explain briefly the reasoning behind your answer, and write both a molecular equation and an ionic equation for the reaction. **(4 marks)**

(f) Describe briefly how a reasonably pure crystalline sample of the hydrated salt formed in (e) could be isolated from its solution. **(4 marks)**

(AEB)

(a) All of the sodium hydroxide solution must be neutralised when 50 cm^3 of aqueous hydrochloric acid is added. The extra acid added in the last two experiments has no alkali to react with and therefore produces no extra heat.

(b) Molar mass of NaOH = (23 + 16 + 1) = 40 g mol^{-1}
∴ 500 cm^3 of solution contain 1 mol of NaOH
∴ 50 cm^3 of solution contain 0.1 mol of NaOH

(c) The equation for the reaction is

$NaOH(aq) + HCl(aq) \rightarrow NaCl(aq) + H_2O(l)$
∴ 1 mol of NaOH reacts with 1 mol of HCl
50 cm^3 of NaOH(aq) containing 0.1 mol of NaOH are neutralised by 50 cm^3 of HCl
∴ There must be 0.1 mol of HCl in the 50 cm^3 of HCl(aq)

∴ Concentration of HCl(aq) is $0.1 \times \dfrac{1000}{50} = 2$ mol dm^{-3} (or 2 mol/l)

(d) 0.1 mol of NaOH evolves 5.6 kJ of heat on neutralisation
∴ 1 mol of NaOH evolves 56 kJ of heat on neutralisation

(e) Since there are 2 mol of OH$^-$ ions to be neutralised, twice as much heat energy will be evolved, i.e. 112 kJ. The M^{2+} ions and Cl$^-$ ions do not take part in the reaction.

Equation $M(OH)_2(aq) + 2HCl(aq) \rightarrow MCl_2(aq) + 2H_2O(l)$
Ionic equation $(OH)^-(aq) + H^+(aq) \rightarrow H_2O(l)$

(f) See Section 1.4 (ii).

Example 8.5

One mole of magnesium atoms reacts with exactly one mole of copper(II) ions. In a series of experiments magnesium powder was added to copper(II) sulphate solution. In which of the following experiments would the temperature rise be the greatest? (Relative atomic mass: Mg = 24.)

A 9.6 g of Mg added to 1 dm^3 of 0.1 M aqueous CuSO$_4$
B 4.8 g of Mg added to 1 dm^3 of 0.2 M aqueous CuSO$_4$
C 2.4 g of Mg added to 1 dm^3 of 0.2 M aqueous CuSO$_4$
D 4.8 g of Mg added to 1 dm^3 of 0.1 M aqueous CuSO$_4$
E 2.4 g of Mg added to 1 dm^3 of 0.4 M aqueous CuSO$_4$ 　　　　　(AEB)

The answer is **B**.

The Mg atoms and Cu^{2+} ions react in the ratio 1 : 1 and in B there are 0.2 mol of Mg and 0.2 mol of Cu^{2+}. None of the other mixtures contains as much *reacting* material. For example, A contains 0.4 mol of Mg but only 0.1 mol of Cu^{2+}, so only 0.1 mol of Mg can react. The extra Mg makes no difference to the amount of heat produced.

Example 8.6

Using the apparatus shown in Fig. 1, 0.8 g of powdered copper is added to 100 cm^3 of 0.2 M silver nitrate solution and the mixture stirred gently with the thermometer. The temperature

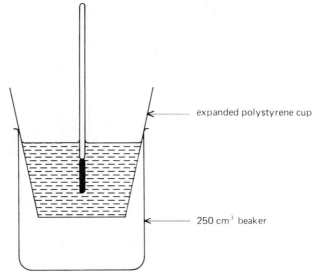

expanded polystyrene cup

250 cm³ beaker

Fig. 1

at the beginning of the experiment is 18.2°C and it rises to a maximum of 21.7°C. The equation for the reaction is

$$2AgNO_3(aq) + Cu(s) \rightarrow Cu(NO_3)_2(aq) + 2Ag(s).$$

(a) Why is a polystyrene cup used instead of a glass container and why is it placed in the beaker? **(2 marks)**

Expanded polystyrene is a good heat insulator and absorbs hardly any of the heat produced in the reaction. Placing the cup in the beaker improves the insulation by cutting out draughts and makes it less easy to knock over the cup, which is very light.

(b) How many moles of silver nitrate are present initially? **(2 marks)**

1 dm^3 of 0.2 M silver nitrate solution contains 0.2 mol of $AgNO_3$
∴ 100 cm^3 of the solution contains 0.02 mol of $AgNO_3$

(c) How many moles of copper atoms are needed to react with the silver nitrate? **(2 marks)**

From the equation, 2 mol $AgNO_3$ reacts with 1 mol Cu
∴ 0.02 mol $AgNO_3$ reacts with 0.01 mol Cu

(d) How many moles of copper atoms are present? Is this enough? **(2 marks)**

Moles of Cu = mass/molar mass = 0.8/63.5 = 0.0126
As only 0.01 mol is needed, this is enough.

(e) What is the temperature rise? **(1 mark)**

The temperature rise is (21.7 − 18.2) = 3.5°C

(f) Calculate the heat produced during the reaction, assuming that the density and specific heat capacity of the solution are the same as those of water. **(2 marks)**

Heat produced = mass × specific heat capacity × temperature rise
= 100 × 4.2 × 3.5 J
= 1470 J

The specific heat capacity of a substance is the amount of heat needed to raise the temperature of 1 g of it by 1 K (1°C).

(g) Calculate the enthalpy change of reaction in kJ per mole of copper atoms. **(2 marks)**

0.01 mol of Cu was used, producing 1470 J
∴ For 1 mole of Cu, heat produced would be 147000 J = 147 kJ
∴ enthalpy of reaction is −147 kJ mol⁻¹.

Note sign.

Fig. 2

(h) In a second experiment the cell shown in Fig. 2 is set up and its e.m.f. is found to be 0.46 V. The ionic equation for the reaction is

$$Cu(s) + 2Ag^+(aq) \rightarrow Cu^{2+}(aq) + 2Ag(s)$$

Write the ionic equation for the reaction taking place in the polystyrene cup in the first experiment. What can you say about the two reactions? **(2 marks)**

$Cu(s) + 2Ag^+(aq) \rightarrow Cu^{2+}(aq) + 2Ag(s)$
The reactions are the same — silver is being displaced from a solution containing its ions by a more reactive metal, copper (see page 128).

(i) How many moles of electrons must flow through the circuit for 1 mole of copper atoms to go into solution at the anode of the cell and for 2 moles of silver atoms to be deposited on the cathode? **(1 mark)**

Each Cu atom gives up 2 electrons when it becomes a Cu^{2+} ion, so 1 mole of Cu atoms gives up two moles of electrons.

(j) What is the charge carried by this amount of electrons? **(2 marks)**
Charge carried = number of mol of electrons × Faraday constant (see page 67)
= 2 × 96 500 = 193 000 coulombs

(k) When the cell is working,
number of joules released = potential difference × number of coulombs passed.
Calculate the maximum number of joules which could be released in this cell when 1 mole of copper atoms dissolves, assuming that the working voltage is the same as the e.m.f. **(1 mark)**
Number of joules released = 0.46 × 193 000 = 88 800, i.e. 88.8 kJ

The e.m.f. is the potential difference between the electrodes on open circuit, i.e. when no current is being drawn from the cell.

(l) Does the cell convert all of the energy available from the chemical reaction into electrical energy? **(1 mark)**

No, 147 kJ of energy are available, according to answer (g).

Example 8.7

In the cell shown in the diagram there is a flow of electrons from metal P to metal Q through the meter.

Which of the following produce this result?

	P	Q
A	silver	copper
B	zinc	copper
C	copper	zinc
D	silver	zinc

The answer is **B**. (SEB)

Atoms of the more reactive of the two metals give up electrons and go into solution as positive ions. The electrons flow to the less reactive metal (see Section 8.3).

8.6 Self-Test Questions

For questions 8.1–8.5 use grid 2 on page 2 to choose an answer **A–E**.

Question 8.1

The reaction between methane and chlorine occurs in the presence of ultra-violet light

BECAUSE

ultra-violet light is a source of energy which can initiate some chemical reactions.

(AEB)

Question 8.2

The products of an exothermic reaction contain more energy than the reactants at the same temperature and pressure

BECAUSE

energy is produced during an exothermic reaction.

(NISEC)

Question 8.3

Heat energy is liberated when a fuel is burned in air or oxygen

BECAUSE

energy is liberated when chemical bonds are broken.

(NISEC)

Question 8.4

The molar heat of vaporisation of sodium chloride is greater than the molar heat of vaporisation of water

BECAUSE

the forces of attraction between ions in sodium chloride are greater than the forces between water molecules.

(L)

Question 8.5

For the reaction

$H_2(g) + Cl_2(g) \rightarrow 2HCl(g)$

some energy changes are shown in the figure.

The heat of the reaction to form hydrogen chloride from hydrogen and chlorine molecules is:
A 437 + 244 + 866
B 437 + 244 + 165
C 681 − 437
D 244 − 165
E −866 + 681

(L)

8.7   Answers to Self-Test Questions

8.1 **A.**

8.2 **D.**

Since energy is *given out* in an exothermic reaction, the products must contain *less* energy than the reactants.

8.3 **C.**

8.4 **A.**

8.5 **E.**

Heat of reaction is the difference between the energy supplied to break the bonds in the reactants (437 kJ + 244 kJ) and that evolved by forming bonds in the products (866 kJ).

9 Rate of Reaction and Chemical Equilibrium

9.1 Rate of Reaction

If dilute hydrochloric acid is added to excess marble chips, carbon dioxide is given off and the mass of reactants decreases. A graph of decrease in mass against time is as shown in Fig. 9.1

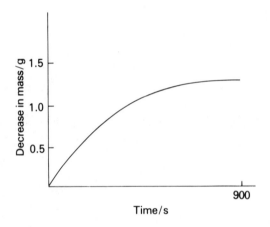

Fig. 9.1

The slope of the graph is steepest at the beginning, showing that the mass is decreasing at the greatest rate (i.e. the rate of evolution of carbon dioxide is greatest) when the acid is at its most concentrated. As the reaction proceeds the slope becomes less steep, indicating that the reaction is slowing down. This is because the acid is being used up and becoming more dilute. Where the graph becomes a horizontal straight line the reaction has ceased: no further change in mass occurs because all of the acid has been used up.

A **catalyst** is a substance which alters the rate of a chemical reaction but may be recovered unchanged in mass at the end. Positive catalysts speed up chemical reactions; negative catalysts (inhibitors) slow them down. Examples of positive catalysts include manganese(IV) oxide in the decomposition of hydrogen peroxide solution into water and oxygen (see Example 9.2), iron in the manufacture of ammonia by the Haber process (see Section 18.5), platinum in the manufacture of nitric acid by the Ostwald process (see Section 18.6) and vanadium(V) oxide in the manufacture of sulphuric acid by the contact process (see Section 18.4).

The rate of a chemical reaction may be increased by:

1. Making the reactants more finely divided.
2. Increasing the concentration of the reactants, or increasing the pressure if they are gases.
3. Increasing the temperature.
4. Adding a (positive) catalyst.
5. Increasing the light intensity (applies to a few reactions only) (see Example 8.1).

9.2 Reversible Reactions

A **reversible reaction** is one which can proceed in either direction depending on the conditions under which it is carried out.

For example, if blue copper(II) sulphate crystals are heated, water is given off and white anhydrous copper(II) sulphate remains. When water is added to this solid, blue hydrated copper(II) sulphate is formed once more.

$$CuSO_4 . 5H_2O(s) \rightleftharpoons CuSO_4(s) + 5H_2O(l)$$

(The $\rightleftharpoons$ sign shows that the reaction can proceed in both directions.)

9.3 Chemical Equilibrium

If a reversible reaction is carried out in a closed container so that the products cannot escape, the reaction will often appear to stop before all of the reactants are used up. This is because as soon as the products are formed they begin to react together to form the reactants again. At first the forward reaction is much faster than the backward one because the concentration of the reactants are much greater than the concentrations of the products. As the reaction goes on, the concentrations of the reactants fall, slowing the rate of the forward reaction. At the same time the concentrations of the products are building up, so the backward reaction increases in rate. A point is reached where the two rates are the same and the reaction appears to stop: the system is said to be **in equilibrium**.

If, when a system is in equilibrium, more reactants are added so that their concentrations are increased, the forward reaction goes at a faster rate. Only when more products have been formed, speeding up the backward reaction, is equilibrium re-established. Since more products have been formed, the equilibrium is said to have moved to the right. Similarly, adding *products* to a system in equilibrium moves the equilibrium to the *left* (see Example 9.5).

In a gaseous equilibrium in which there are more molecules on one side of the equation than the other, the equilibrium will be disturbed if the pressure changes. If the pressure is increased, the equilibrium moves towards the side with fewer molecules, which occupy a smaller volume (Avogadro's principle, Section 6.1). Decrease in pressure reverses the change (see Example 9.4).

Raising the temperature of a system in equilibrium moves the equilibrium in the direction of the endothermic change: lowering the temperature moves it in the direction of the exothermic change (see Example 9.4).

Addition of a catalyst enables equilibrium to be reached *more quickly* but has no effect on the *position* of equilibrium.

9.4 Worked Examples

Example 9.1

This question is about measuring the rate of the reaction between solutions of potassium peroxodisulphate, $K_2S_2O_8$, and potassium iodide, KI. It was studied by the following method: 20 cm^3 of potassium peroxodisulphate solution was mixed with 20 cm^3 of potassium iodide solution (an excess), 5 cm^3 of sodium thiosulphate solution and 1 cm^3 of starch solution.

The potassium peroxodisulphate reacts with the potassium iodide at a measurable rate forming iodine. As soon as the iodine is formed it reacts rapidly with the sodium thiosulphate until all the sodium thiosulphate is used up. The iodine formed after the sodium thiosulphate is used up gives a blue colour with the starch. The time taken for the blue colour to appear was recorded.

The experiment was repeated using potassium peroxodisulphate solutions of different concentrations and the results are shown in the table.

Peroxodisulphate concentration /mol dm^{-3}	Time (t) for blue colour to appear/sec	$\frac{1}{t}$ /sec^{-1}
0.3	20	0.05
0.2	30	0.033
0.15	40	0.025
0.05	120	0.0083

(a) If we wish to investigate the rate of a reaction why do we calculate $1/t$?   **(1 mark)**

In each experiment the same mass of iodine is needed to use up the 5 cm^3 of sodium thiosulphate solution and then produce the blue colour with the starch. If this constant mass, m, is produced in time t, then the average rate of production from the beginning to time t is m/t. Since m is the same each time we can write:

Average rate $\propto 1/t$

(e.g. if the rate doubles, the time is halved.)

(b) On the axes provided, plot a graph showing how $1/t$ varies with the concentration of the potassium peroxodisulphate solution.   **(2 marks)**

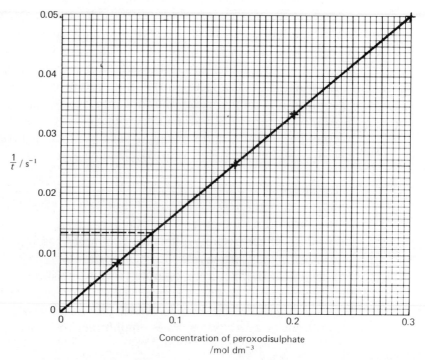

Concentration of peroxodisulphate
/mol dm^{-3}

(c) Explain why this graph shows that the rate of the reaction is proportional to the concentration of the potassium peroxodisulphate solution. **(1 mark)**

The straight-line graph indicates direct proportionality between concentration and 1/t, e.g. when the concentration doubles, trebles, etc., the value of 1/t changes by the same factor. Since 1/t is proportional to the rate (answer(a)) the rate must change to the same extent as 1/t and therefore rate is proportional to concentration.

(d) Use your graph to determine the time that would have been taken for the blue colour to appear if the potassium peroxodisulphate solution had been 0.08 M. **(1 mark)**

When the concentration is 0.08 M, i.e. 0.08 mol dm^{-3}, 1/t = 0.0135 s^{-1}
∴ t = 74 s

(e) In all the above experiments the solution of sodium thiosulphate used was 0.01 M. What would have been the time taken for the blue colour to appear if the experiment was repeated using 0.2 M potassium peroxodisulphate solution and 0.02 M sodium thiosulphate solution in the same volume as before? **(1 mark)**

(L)

The iodine will be produced at the same rate as before but twice as much will be needed to react with the sodium thiosulphate solution before the blue colour appears. Therefore the time taken will be more than 60 seconds.

The reaction slows down as it proceeds, so the time taken to produce twice as much iodine is *more than* 2 × 30 seconds.

Example 9.2

The table of observations shown below is taken from a laboratory investigation into the rate of decomposition of hydrogen peroxide using a manganese(IV) oxide catalyst. For each set of initial conditions, the time taken to collect a fixed volume of gas was noted. In each experiment 50 cm^3 of aqueous hydrogen peroxide and 1 g of catalyst were used.

Experiment	Concentration of aqueous hydrogen peroxide in mol/dm^3	Initial temperature in °C	Form of the catalyst	Time, in seconds, to collect a fixed volume of gas
A	0.1	20	powder	200
B	0.1	30	powder	115
C	0.1	40	powder	60
D	0.2	20	powder	100
E	0.3	20	powder	65
F	0.4	20	pellets	130
G	0.4	20	powder	50

(a) Draw a labelled diagram of an apparatus which could be used to perform this experiment. **(3 marks)**
(b) Write an equation for the reaction which takes place when hydrogen peroxide decomposes, and describe one simple test to identify the gas evolved. **(3 marks)**
(c) Which experimental results should be used to draw a graph to show the relationship between concentration of reactant and rate of reaction? Explain briefly the reasons for the choice. (**DO NOT DRAW A GRAPH**). **(4 marks)**
(d) (i) State and explain what happens to the rate of decomposition of the hydrogen peroxide when the concentration of its solution is increased.

(ii) Explain why the use of catalyst pellets instead of powder alters the rate of reaction. (See experiments **F** and **G**.)

(iii) State how one other factor investigated in this experiment affects the rate of reaction.   **(7 marks)**

(e) Define the term *catalyst* and describe briefly the essential steps of an experiment to prove that manganese(IV) oxide acts as a catalyst in this reaction.   **(7 marks)**

(AEB)

(a)

gas syringe

cold water

manganese (IV) oxide

hydrogen peroxide solution

Fig. 9.2

(b) $2H_2O_2(aq) \rightarrow 2H_2O(l) + O_2(g)$

The gas is oxygen and it relights a glowing splint.

(c) Results A, D, E and G should be used because the initial temperature and the form of the catalyst remain the same and only the concentration of the aqueous hydrogen peroxide and the rate of reaction vary.

(d) (i) As the concentration of the solution increases, the time taken to collect a fixed volume of gas decreases: this means that the rate of reaction is increasing. The rate is faster because there are more hydrogen peroxide molecules per unit volume to collide with the catalyst and decompose.

(ii) If the 1 g of catalyst is in the form of pellets it will have less surface area on which reaction can take place than if it were ground up into powder. Therefore the reaction is slower when the catalyst is pelleted.

(iii) As the temperature rises the reaction speeds up. This is because the molecules travel faster and collide more frequently and more vigorously with one another. The number of collisions per second which are sufficiently energetic to cause reaction is thereby increased, so the reaction speeds up.

(e) The definition of a catalyst is given in Section 9.1.

To show that manganese(IV) oxide acts as a catalyst in this experiment, the reaction should first be tried without the manganese(IV) oxide. The rate will be found to be very slow indeed — in fact it will probably appear that there is no reaction at all. The experiment should then be tried again, using a known mass of manganese(IV) oxide. The reaction will be quicker and, if the manganese(IV) oxide is filtered off at the end, washed, dried and reweighed, it will be found that its mass has not changed. Thus it will have satisfied the definition of a catalyst.

Example 9.3

Use grid 1 on page 2 to choose an answer **A–E**.

The carbon dioxide produced by adding dilute hydrochloric acid to *excess* marble chips of uniform size was collected in a gas syringe and its volume read at regular intervals.

The experiment was repeated twice more at the same temperature and the results plotted as shown.

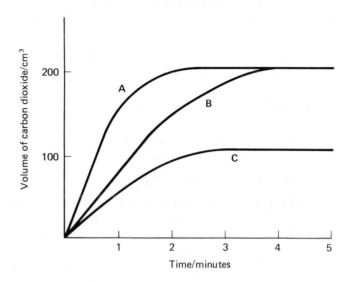

The graph shows that:
1. The number of moles of acid used in experiment **A** was greater than that used in **B**.
2. The acid used in experiment **A** was more concentrated than that in **B**.
3. The number of moles of acid used in **C** was less than that used in **A**.   (L)

The answer is **C**.

The marble chips are in excess, therefore all of the acid is used up in each experiment. 1 is incorrect – the same volume of carbon dioxide was given off in **A** and **B**, so the same number of moles of acid must have been used. 2 is correct – the reaction in **A** is faster, so the acid must be more concentrated than in **B**. 3 is correct – fewer moles of acid give less carbon dioxide.

Example 9.4

The formation of carbon monoxide and hydrogen from methane and steam at 750°C can be represented by the equation:

$$CH_4(g) + H_2O(g) \rightleftharpoons CO(g) + 3H_2(g); \quad \Delta H = -206 \text{ kJ}$$

(a) What mass of methane would have to react in order to produce 206 kJ of energy?

(1 mark)

1 mole of methane is needed, i.e. (12 + 4) = 16 g.

(b) Predict what will happen to the equilibrium concentration of hydrogen if
    (i) the temperature is raised   **(1 mark)**

Raising the temperature moves the equilibrium in a direction which results in heat being absorbed, i.e. to the left. This produces a lower concentration of hydrogen in the equilibrium mixture.

Lowering the temperature would do the opposite.

(ii) the pressure of the equilibrium mixture is increased **(1 mark)**
Increasing the pressure moves the equilibrium in a direction which results in a decrease in volume i.e. to the left (Section 9.3). This produces a lower concentration of hydrogen in the equilibrium mixture.

Lowering the pressure would do the opposite.

(iii) a catalyst is added **(1 mark)**
(AEB)
Adding a catalyst has no effect on the position of equilibrium and therefore does not change the equilibrium concentration of hydrogen.

Example 9.5

Use grid 1 on page 2 to choose an answer **A–E**.
Consider the following equilibrium

$$CO(g) + 2H_2(g) \rightleftharpoons CH_3OH(g)$$

The position of equilibrium may be moved to the right by:
1 adding more hydrogen
2 adding more carbon monoxide
3 removing methanol.
The answer is **A**.

Decreasing the concentration of a substance on one side of an equation has the same effect on the position of equilibrium as increasing the concentration of a substance on the other side.

9.5 Self-Test Questions

Question 9.1

The reaction between 10 g of calcium carbonate and 10 cm^3 of hydrochloric acid was studied at 10°C. The experiment was then repeated at 15°C and 20°C. The results were plotted graphically and are represented by the figure. **(AEB)**

C

D

E

Question 9.2

The rate of production of hydrogen by the reaction of magnesium with 0.5 M hydrochloric acid (containing 0.5 mole of HCl per dm^3) was investigated using the apparatus shown.

The following results were obtained with a laboratory temperature of 15°C and 1 atmosphere pressure, using 0.0669 g of magnesium ribbon.

Time in minutes	0	$\frac{1}{2}$	1	$1\frac{1}{2}$	2	$2\frac{1}{2}$	3	$3\frac{1}{2}$	4	$4\frac{1}{2}$	5	$5\frac{1}{2}$
Total volume of H_2 in cm^3 (at 15°C and 1 atm.)	0	9.5	18.0	26.5	33.5	41.4	48.0	54.0	59.0	62.0	63.0	63.0

(a) (i) On squared paper, plot a graph of volume of hydrogen (vertical axis) against time (horizontal axis). **(5 marks)**

   (ii) On the same graph paper, sketch and label the curve you would have expected if the hydrochloric acid had been heated to 25°C before the experiment. **(2 marks)**

(iii) What is the total volume of hydrogen obtained from 0.0669 g of magnesium at 15°C according to this experiment? **(2 marks)**

(iv) Calculate the volume that would have been obtained at this temperature from 1 mole of magnesium. **(4 marks)**

(v) What would this value have been at s.t.p.? How does your answer compare with the 22.4 dm³ normally accepted for the molar volume of a gas? Give one possible reason for the discrepancy you have found. **(6 marks)**

(b) When a similar experiment was conducted with pieces of calcium carbonate instead of magnesium, a value of 16.8 dm³ for the molar volume of carbon dioxide was found.

(i) Why do you think the value was so low? **(2 marks)**

(ii) State and explain two ways in which the rate of reaction of calcium carbonate with hydrochloric acid could be increased, other than by heating. **(4 marks)**

(OLE)

9.6   Answers to Self-Test Questions

9.1 The answer is **A**.

Increasing the temperature increases the rate of reaction. The number of moles of carbon dioxide is the same in each case but the volume is greater at higher temperatures.

9.2 (a) (i) and (ii), see Fig. 9.3.

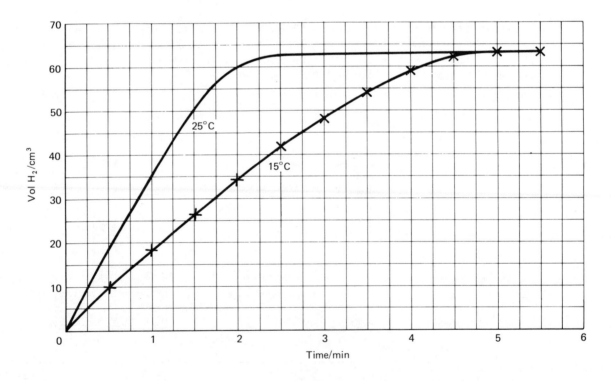

Fig. 9.3

The reaction would be faster at 25°C because the particles in the acid would be speeded up and would collide more frequently with the magnesium. However, the final volume of hydrogen would be the same as before because the same amounts of magnesium and hydrochloric acid are used and the hydrogen is collected at the same temperature.

(iii) 63.0 cm^3.

(iv) Moles of Mg used = mass/molar mass (see Section 5.1)

$$= 0.0669/24$$

0.0669/24 mol of Mg gives 63.0 cm^3 of H$_2$.

∴ 1 mol of Mg gives 63.0 ÷ 0.0669/24 = 22 600 cm^3 of H$_2$

(v) Volume at s.t.p. would be 22 600 × 273/288 = 21 400 cm^3

The value is lower than expected. Possibly the magnesium had an oxide coating.

(b) (i) Carbon dioxide is slightly soluble in water and could dissolve in both the dilute acid and the water in the trough.

(ii) The rate could be increased by using more concentrated acid so that more H$^+$(aq) ions would be colliding with the surface of the calcium carbonate.

If the calcium carbonate were broken up into smaller pieces there would be a greater surface area in contact with the acid and the reaction would be speeded up.

10 The Atmosphere and Combustion

10.1 Introduction

Air consists of a mixture of gases, the percentages being as shown in Fig. 10.1. Water vapour will also be present (cobalt(II) chloride paper turns pink in the air), the exact proportion depending on conditions.

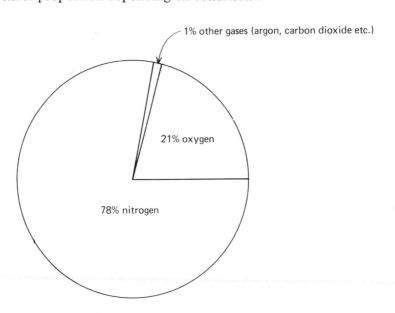

Fig. 10.1

Air in built-up areas will be polluted by fumes from cars, fires, factories, etc. Substances present may include dust, soot, lead compounds from car exhaust gases, carbon monoxide (see Section 14.6), nitrogen dioxide (see Section 15.2) and sulphur dioxide (see Section 16.8). Most of these are corrosive and/or poisonous. Finally, there are usually bacteria and viruses present which may or may not be harmful.

N.B. Hydrogen is not generally found in the atmosphere.

10.2 Separating the Gases in the Air

Since air is a mixture of gases, it can be separated into its components by physical means – fractional distillation of liquid air. The air is cooled from room temperature; ice is removed at 0°C and solid carbon dioxide at −78°C. The remaining gases are compressed, cooled and allowed to expand again. When the air expands, its temperature falls. The whole cycle is repeated until eventually liquefaction occurs. Fractional distillation then takes place to yield nitrogen (b.p. −196°C), argon (b.p. − 186°C) and finally oxygen (b.p. −183°C).

10.3 Processes which use up Oxygen

There are three main ways in which oxygen is used up − burning, corrosion and respiration. If a piece of iron is allowed to rust or a substance is allowed to burn in a closed container, then the percentage of oxygen in the air can be found, as Examples 10.2 and 10.6 show.

(a) Burning (Combustion)

When a substance burns in air it combines with oxygen (i.e. oxidation occurs). Conbustion continues until all of the substance or all of the oxygen is used up (see Example 10.5).

(b) Rusting

Iron will only rust if both air and water are present; dissolved salt is found to speed up the process (see Example 10.6). The gas in the air which is responsible for rusting is oxygen. Rusting, like combustion, is an example of oxidation, but in this case, the temperature is much lower and the reaction occurs much more slowly.

Many metals tarnish in air but the coating formed on the surface often prevents further corrosion, e.g. zinc, copper and aluminium (see Question 10.5). However, rust does not prevent air and water from reaching the iron underneath.

(c) Respiration

When we and other animals breathe, the air we breathe out is warmer and contains more water vapour and carbon dioxide than it did when we inhaled it. We are 'burning' food inside us to provide energy for movement and warmth (see Example 10.5). The overall change may be summed up as

sugar + oxygen → carbon dioxide + water + energy

10.4 Photosynthesis

Combustion, rusting and respiration remove oxygen from the atmosphere. Photosynthesis replaces the oxygen.

Photosynthesis is the process by which green plants synthesise carbohydrates from carbon dioxide and water, using sunlight as the source of energy and chlorophyll as a catalyst, oxygen being liberated into the air.

The overall change may be written:

carbon dioxide + water + energy → sugar + oxygen

which is the reverse of the equation summarising respiration.

101

10.5 Worked Examples

Example 10.1

If air is bubbled through pure water (pH 7), the pH gradually changes to 5.7. The gas in air which is responsible for this change is

A carbon dioxide

B nitrogen

C hydrogen

D argon

E oxygen.   (L)

The answer is **A**.

Air contains carbon dioxide and this is an acidic oxide, dissolving in water to give carbonic acid.

Example 10.2

In order to find the proportion by volume of one of the main constituents of air, a sample of air was passed through two wash bottles, the first containing aqueous sodium hydroxide and the second containing concentrated sulphuric acid, and was then collected in a gas syringe.

(a) Suggest a reason for passing the air through

  (i) aqueous sodium hydroxide

To remove carbon dioxide.

  (ii) concentrated sulphuric acid.   **(2 marks)**

To dry the gas.

(b) The volume of gas collected in the syringe was 80 cm^3. This was passed several times over hot copper powder until no further contraction of volume took place. After cooling to the original temperature the volume was found to be reduced to 63.2 cm^3.

  (i) How would the copper change in appearance?

It would turn black.

  (ii) Which gas had been removed by the copper?

Oxygen.

  (iii) Calculate the volume of this gas present in the sample of air.

$80 - 63.2\ cm^3 = 16.8\ cm^3$.

  (iv) Calculate the percentage of this gas present in the sample of air.   **(5 marks)**

$\% Oxygen = \dfrac{Volume\ of\ oxygen}{Original\ volume\ of\ air} \times 100$

$\% Oxygen = \dfrac{16.8}{80} \times 100 = 21$

(c) (i) What is the main gas remaining in the syringe?

Nitrogen.

  (ii) There will be small amounts of other gases remaining in the syringe. Name one of these gases.   **(2 marks)**

Argon.

In addition to nitrogen there are traces of the noble gases, e.g. argon, neon, helium.

(d) How would you treat the solid remaining to obtain copper for re-use? **(1 mark)**
(L)

The solid remaining is copper(II) oxide. It needs to be reduced to copper, e.g. by heating it in a stream of hydrogen.

Example 10.3

Explain why magnesium gains in mass but coal loses mass when each is burned in air.
(2 marks)

Both substances combine with oxygen when they burn but the magnesium forms a solid product which can be weighed. The coal forms gaseous products which go into the atmosphere and are not weighed.

Example 10.4

A small child has been playing with matches and his clothes have caught fire. Explain how you would put out the flames. **(2 marks)**

Air must be excluded as quickly as possible so that burning will cease. Therefore the child must be wrapped up in something like a rug or a blanket or turned over so that the flames are between his body and the floor.

Example 10.5

The equation for the complete oxidation of glucose is

$$C_6H_{12}O_6 + 6O_2 \rightarrow 6CO_2 + 6H_2O$$

This is an exothermic process.
(a) Use this process, or any other, to explain the difference between *combustion* and *respiration*. **(5 marks)**

When combustion takes place, the glucose burns in air and combines with oxygen. When we breathe, the same reaction occurs. The difference is that in respiration, the reaction occurs more slowly and at a lower temperature than in combustion.

(b) (i) What is meant by the term *exothermic*? **(2 marks)**
An exothermic reaction is one which gives out heat (see page 77).

(ii) State two other processes, physical or chemical, that are exothermic. **(2 marks)**
Exothermic processes include neutralisation of an acid by an alkali,
e.g. $HCl(aq) + NaOH(aq) \rightarrow NaCl(aq) + H_2O(l)$
and passing an electric current through a wire, e.g. in an electric fire.

(c) (i) Give the general name for the process by which glucose is converted into ethanol by yeast. **(1 mark)**
Fermentation (see Section 19.7).

(ii) Write an equation for this process. **(2 marks)**
(OLE)

$C_6H_{12}O_6(aq) \rightarrow 2C_2H_5OH(aq) + 2CO_2(g)$

Example 10.6

(a) Name the two substances which are essential if iron is to rust. **(2 marks)**
(i) *Water.* (ii) *Oxygen.*

103

(b) Name one other substance which will accelerate the rusting process. **(1 mark)**
Salt

(c) Why is the use of this substance of particular importance to motorists? **(1 mark)**
Salt is put on the roads in winter to melt the ice — an ice/salt mixture has a lower melting point than pure ice. The salt must be washed off to prevent rapid rusting of the car.

(d) Give three methods which can be used to prevent rusting. **(3 marks)**
(i) *Painting.*
(ii) *Coating with grease or oil.*
(iii) *Coating with metal, e.g. tin plating or galvanising.*

In order to prevent rusting, air and water must be kept away from the iron.

(e) Draw labelled diagrams to show three experiments you could do to show that the substances mentioned in (a) (i) and (ii) are needed for iron nails to rust and that if either of the substances is absent, no rusting occurs. **(3 marks)**
See Fig. 10.2.

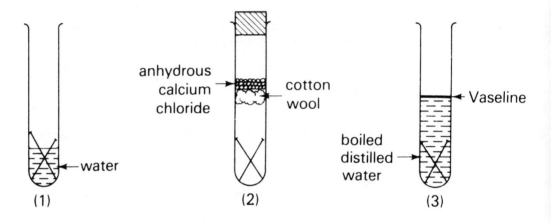

Fig. 10.2

Experiment 1	Experiment 2	Experiment 3
(a) (i) and (ii) present	*(a) (i) absent*	*(a) (ii) absent*
— rusting occurs	*— no rusting*	*— no rusting*

Some moist iron wool was placed in a test tube and the tube was inverted and placed in a beaker of water. The apparatus was inspected each day for one week. The iron rusted and the level of the water in the tube rose during the first few days. After this, no further change took place, even though some air remained and not all of the iron was rusty. The air left in the tube was found to put out a burning splint.

(f) What fraction of the air, approximately, has been used up? **(1 mark)**

The water has moved 2 cm up the tube.

$$\% \, Air \, used = \frac{2}{10} \times 100 = 20\%$$

(g) Does this experiment show that the air is made up of (i) one, (ii) two, (iii) at least two, gases? Explain your answer. **(2 marks)**

At least two gases. One gas has been used up but we have no means of knowing in this experiment how many gases remain in the tube.

(h) Which gas has been used up during rusting? How can you tell? **(2 marks)**

Oxygen. Oxygen is needed for a splint to burn; since the splint went out, the air must no longer contain oxygen.

(i) What would be the effect on the level of the water if a larger piece of iron wool were used? How did you reach your conclusion? **(2 marks)**

No effect. Not all the iron had rusted and so a larger piece of iron would make no further change.

10.6 Self-Test Questions

Questions 10.1 and 10.2 concern the following account.

A strip of copper metal 5 cm by 1 cm was folded over to make a square 1 cm by 1 cm and pressed down tightly. It was heated in a bunsen burner and the outside went black. It was allowed to cool down and then unfolded. The inside was still copper coloured.

Question 10.1

The outside was black and the inside copper coloured because:
A the inside was not hot enough
B air reached the inside but not the outside
C air reached the outside but not the inside
D oxygen reached the outside and nitrogen reached the inside
E the air removed something from the outside of the copper.

Question 10.2

This experiment tells you that the percentage of oxygen in the air is about:
A 20%
B 40%
C 60%
D 80%
E no conclusion can be drawn.

Question 10.3

Which one of the following terms describes the reaction represented by the equation

$$C_4H_8(g) + 6O_2(g) \rightarrow 4CO_2(g) + 4H_2O(g)?$$

A combustion
B cracking

C displacement
D dissociation
E photosynthesis. (AEB)

Question 10.4

Which one of the following would not produce carbon dioxide?
A heating carbon in air
B reacting limewater with air
C burning starch in air
D burning a candle in air
E breathing.

Question 10.5

Use grid 1 on page 2 to choose an answer A–E.
When exposed to moist air, aluminium corrodes less rapidly than does iron because aluminium
1 is less reactive than iron
2 has a very high melting point
3 develops a protective layer of aluminium oxide. (AEB)

10.7 Answers to Self-Test Questions

10.1 C.

10.2 E.

Do not be trapped into thinking that the answer is A. The percentage of oxygen in the air *is* approximately 20% but this experiment does not tell you this.

10.3 A.

10.4 B.

Limewater goes milky when carbon dioxide is passed through it – it absorbs carbon dioxide.

10.5 E.

11 Water and Hydrogen

11.1 Introduction

Pure water, formula H_2O, is a colourless, odourless, tasteless liquid which freezes at $0°C$ and boils at $100°C$ at 1 atm pressure (see Question 11.1). Water is unusual in that it expands on freezing whereas most liquids contract. Thus ice is less dense than water and forms on the surface rather than at the bottom of the liquid.

Water reacts with reactive metals, non-metals and various compounds (see Example 11.1), e.g.

$$2Na(s) + 2H_2O(l) \rightarrow 2NaOH(aq) + H_2(g) \qquad \text{(see Section 13.2)}$$
$$SO_2(aq) + H_2O(l) \rightleftharpoons H_2SO_3(aq) \qquad \text{(see Section 16.8)}$$

(a) Tests for Water

White anhydrous copper(II) sulphate turns blue and blue cobalt(II) chloride turns pink when water is added.

$$CuSO_4(s) + 5H_2O(l) \rightleftharpoons CuSO_4.5H_2O(s)$$
$$\text{white} \qquad\qquad\qquad \text{blue}$$
$$CoCl_2(s) + 6H_2O(l) \rightleftharpoons CoCl_2.6H_2O(s)$$
$$\text{blue} \qquad\qquad\qquad \text{pink}$$

These two reactions simply prove that a liquid *contains* water. To prove that a liquid is *pure* water, a boiling point determination must be carried out as well (see Question 11.1).

11.2 Water as a Solvent

A **solution** consists of a **solute** dissolved in a **solvent**; if the solvent is water then an aqueous solution is obtained.

A **saturated solution** is one that contains as much solute as can be dissolved at the temperature concerned, in the presence of undissolved solute (see Question 11.2).

The **solubility** of a solute in a solvent at a particular temperature is the mass of solute required to saturate 100 g of solvent at that temperature (see Example 11.2).

For most solids, the solubility in a given solvent increases as the temperature is raised but the reverse is true for gases: the solubility decreases with rise in temperature (see Question 11.3). The gases which are most soluble in water are those which react with it in some way, e.g. ammonia, hydrogen chloride.

A graph showing the variation of solubility with temperature is known as a solubility curve (see Example 11.3).

Fractional crystallisation is the process whereby substances are separated by repeated partial crystallisation of a solution (see Example 11.3).

Many crystals contain water chemically combined within them. This water is referred to as water of crystallisation and salts containing it are called hydrated salts. Water of crystallisation can often be driven off by gentle heating and when this is done it is found that there is a definite number of water molecules associated with every formula unit of the compound concerned.

Water of crystallisation is that definite quantity of water with which some substances are associated on crystallising from an aqueous solution.

Efflorescence is the giving up of water of crystallisation to the atmosphere (see Example 11.4).

Substances like calcium chloride-6-water and sodium hydroxide are **deliquescent**, i.e. they absorb water from the atmosphere and if left long enough, dissolve in it. On the other hand, substances like concentrated sulphuric acid and copper(II) oxide are **hygroscopic**, i.e. they absorb water vapour from the atmosphere but do not change state.

11.3   Water Supplies

Our water supplies come from rivers, lakes and underground sources. These are replenished by the rain by means of the water cycle.

When water evaporates from a sea or lake, the vapour rises and condenses to form many very small droplets (a cloud). If these droplets come together, they fall as rain which eventually returns to a sea or lake so that the cycle can begin again.

In recent years, water pollution has become a serious problem. Water contains dissolved oxygen which is used by fish and other aquatic creatures and also by bacteria which feed on animal and vegetable remains and keep our rivers healthy. Too much untreated sewage causes the bacteria to multiply and they may use up so much oxygen that there is insufficient left for fish to survive. Fertilisers, insecticides, detergents and industrial waste all help to upset the delicate balance of life in the water (see Example 11.5).

Our drinking water must contain none of the pollutants mentioned above. The water is filtered and chlorine added to kill bacteria. In some areas, a trace of sodium fluoride is added to reduce dental decay. Tap water contains other dissolved solids, particularly calcium and magnesium salts (see Section 13.3).

11.4   Hydrogen, H_2

Hydrogen is generally prepared in the laboratory by the action of dilute sulphuric acid on zinc in the apparatus shown in Example 11.6.

$$Zn(s) + H_2SO_4(aq) \rightarrow ZnSO_4(aq) + H_2(g)$$

(a) Test for Hydrogen

A mixture of hydrogen with air or oxygen explodes when a flame is applied.

$$2H_2(g) + O_2(g) \rightarrow 2H_2O(g)$$

(b) Properties of Hydrogen

1. Hydrogen is a colourless, odourless gas.
2. It is almost insoluble in water.
3. It is less dense than air.
4. Pure hydrogen burns quietly in air with a faint, blue flame to give water (see Question 11.1).
5. On heating, hydrogen reduces the oxides of metals low in the reactivity series (see Example 11.6), e.g.

   $$CuO(s) + H_2(g) \rightarrow Cu(s) + H_2O(g)$$

6. Hydrogen reacts with some metals and non-metals (see Example 11.7), e.g.

   $$N_2(g) + 3H_2(g) \rightleftharpoons 2NH_3(g) \qquad \text{(see Example 18.6)}$$

(c) Uses of Hydrogen (see Example 11.7)

1. In the large-scale syntheses of ammonia and hydrogen chloride (see Example 18.6 and Section 17.1).
2. In the hardening of oils to make margarine and cooking fats (see Example 18.4).

(d) Manufacture of Hydrogen

Hydrogen is produced on a large scale:

1. in the cracking of oils (see Section 19.5);
2. in the electrolysis of brine (see Example 18.4); and
3. by the action of steam on hydrocarbons such as methane (North Sea Gas).

11.5 Worked Examples

Example 11.1

(a) Sketch and label the apparatus you would use to purify water by distillation. **(5 marks)**
(b) Write equations for the reactions between cold water and (i) quicklime; (ii) ammonia; (iii) chlorine; (iv) nitrogen dioxide. **(5 marks)**
(c) Explain the terms: (i) solute; (ii) solubility; (iii) deliquescent. **(5 marks)**
(SUJB)

(a) See Fig. 1.3. The flask contains impure water; pure water will distil over.

(b) (i) $H_2O(l) + CaO(s) \rightarrow Ca(OH)_2(s)$ (see Section 13.3).

  (ii) water $+ NH_3(g) \rightleftharpoons NH_3(aq)$
   $H_2O(l) + NH_3(aq) \rightleftharpoons NH_4^+(aq) + OH^-(aq)$ (see Section 15.3).

  (iii) water $+ Cl_2(g) \rightleftharpoons Cl_2(aq)$
   $H_2O(l) + Cl_2(aq) \rightleftharpoons HCl(aq) + HOCl(aq)$ (see Section 17.3)

  (iv) $2NO_2(g) + H_2O(l) \rightarrow HNO_3(aq) + HNO_2(aq)$ (see Section 15.2)

(c) (i) A solute is a substance which dissolves in a solvent to give a solution.
(ii) The solubility of a solute in a solvent at a particular temperature is the mass of solute required to saturate 100 g of solvent at that temperature.
(iii) A substance is deliquescent if it absorbs water vapour from the atmosphere to such an extent that a solution results.

Example 11.2

(a) Describe how you would determine the solubility of sodium nitrate at room temperature.
(7 marks)

(b) What happens when sodium nitrate is
(i) heated alone,
(ii) heated with copper filings and concentrated sulphuric acid?
Write appropriate equations. **(8 marks)**
(SUJB)

(a) Place 100 cm^3 of water in a beaker and add sodium nitrate, with stirring, until no more will dissolve. Filter the solution. Place the filtrate in a weighed evaporating basin and evaporate to dryness over a steam bath. Reweigh the evaporating basin.

$$\text{Mass of evaporating basin} = w_1 \text{ g}$$
$$\text{Mass of evaporating basin + sodium nitrate} = w_2 \text{ g}$$
$$\text{Mass of sodium nitrate dissolved} = w_2 - w_1 \text{ g}$$
$$= w \text{ g}$$

If we assume that 1 cm^3 of water has a mass of 1 g, then 100 g of water dissolves w g of sodium nitrate
Solubility of sodium nitrate = w g (100 g water)$^{-1}$

(b) (i) Sodium nitrate melts and decomposes to give oxygen and sodium nitrite (see Section 15.6).

$$2NaNO_3 \text{ (l)} \rightarrow 2NaNO_2 \text{ (l)} + O_2 \text{ (g)}$$

(ii) Sodium nitrate reacts with concentrated sulphuric acid to give nitric acid. The nitric acid formed reacts with copper to evolve brown fumes of nitrogen dioxide

$$NaNO_3 \text{ (s)} + H_2SO_4 \text{ (l)} \rightarrow NaHSO_4 \text{ (s)} + HNO_3 \text{ (l)}$$
$$4HNO_3 \text{ (l)} + Cu \text{(s)} \rightarrow Cu(NO_3)_2 \text{ (aq)} + 2H_2O \text{(l)} + 2NO_2 \text{ (g)}$$

Example 11.3

Look at the graph shown in the figure then answer the following.
(a) Which compound is the more soluble in boiling water? **(1 mark)**
(b) At what temperature are sodium chloride and potassium chlorate(V) equally soluble in water? **(1 mark)**
(c) A mixture of 30 g sodium chloride, 30 g potassium chlorate(V), and 100 g of water, is stirred for a long time at 100°C. Will all the solid dissolve? If the mixture is now cooled to 20°C, what will happen? **(4 marks)**
(d) What is the mass of 6 moles of potassium chlorate(V) (KClO$_3$)? Is it possible to make a 6 M solution of potassium chlorate(V) at 20°C? (Use the graph to justify your answer.) **(4 marks)**

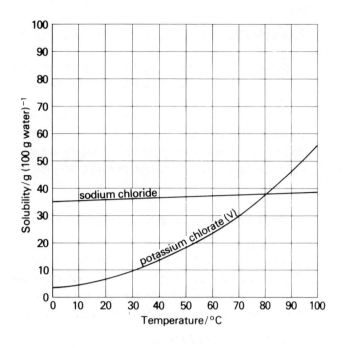

(a) Potassium chlorate(V).

(b) 81°C.

(c) Yes.

At 100°C, the solubilities of both potassium chlorate(V) and sodium chloride are above 30 g $(100 \text{ g water})^{-1}$ and therefore all the solid dissolves.

At 20°C, the solubility of sodium chloride is 36 g $(100 \text{ g water})^{-1}$ whilst that of potassium chlorate(V) is 7 g $(100 \text{ g water})^{-1}$. This means that all the sodium chloride will remain in solution but 23 g of potassium chlorate(V) will crystallise out.

(d)

See Section 20.3

Relative molecular mass of $KClO_3$ = 39 + 35.5 + 3 × 16
$$= 122.5$$
Mass of 6 moles of potassium chlorate(V) = 6 × 122.5 g
$$= 735 \text{ g}$$
A 6 M solution of potassium chlorate(V) contains 735 g dm^{-3}
$$= 73.5 \text{ g } (100 \text{ g water})^{-1}.$$
The solubility of potassium chlorate(V) is only 7 g $(100 \text{ g water})^{-1}$ at 20°C.
∴ it is not possible to make a 6 M solution at 20°C.

Example 11.4

Explain the following observation: Washing soda crystals become coated with a white powder when left in the air. **(3 marks)**
(SUJB)

The reason for this change is that washing soda crystals effloresce, i.e. give up some of their water of crystallisation to the atmosphere. The white powder which forms is sodium carbonate-1-water.

$$Na_2CO_3.10H_2O(s) \rightarrow Na_2CO_3.H_2O(s) + 9H_2O(g)$$

111

Example 11.5

Excess nitrates or excess heat in a river can be regarded as pollution. In each case, describe **one** possible source of this pollution and the effect on the river and its environment.

(a) Various nitrates.

Source: Fertilisers, e.g. ammonium nitrate or sodium nitrate. Fertilisers are added to soil but heavy rain has the effect of washing them into rivers. **(1 mark)**

Effect: The addition of fertilisers to a river has the effect of upsetting the ecological balance of the river by promoting the too rapid growth of lower plant life. For example, vast amounts of algae could grow on the surface of the river, thus reducing the amount of light to plants on the bottom of the river. These plants decay, no longer generate oxygen and thus the animals in the river die. **(2 marks)**

(b) Excess heat.

Source: Industrial effluent. Many industrial processes use water as a coolant. If this hot water is discharged into a river, then the temperature increases. **(1 mark)**

Effect: As long as the temperature increase is moderate, the effect is generally beneficial since the growth of all forms of aquatic life is promoted. **(2 marks)**

(c) Write the formula for calcium nitrate. **(1 mark)**

$Ca(NO_3)_2$ (AEB)

Example 11.6

(a) How would you prepare hydrogen in the laboratory by
    (i) electrolysis,
    (ii) some other method?
In each case write an equation for the reaction in which hydrogen is produced and give the reagents and necessary conditions. **(5 marks)**

(b) A current of dry hydrogen was passed over 4.78 g of heated lead oxide, the excess hydrogen being burnt in the air. 4.14 g of lead was obtained.
    (i) Calculate the empirical formula of the oxide.

        $A_r(O) = 16$; $A_r(Pb) = 207$

    (ii) Name one other oxide which can be reduced to the metal by hydrogen.
    (iii) Name one other oxide which cannot be reduced to the metal by hydrogen.
                                         (5 marks)

(c) (i) Write an equation for the reaction between hydrogen and ethene. Name the product and give the necessary conditions.
    (ii) In the margarine industry, this type of reaction is used to convert animal and vegetable oils into solid fats. What does this tell you about the bonding in natural oil molecules? **(3 marks)**

(d) There are vast reserves of hydrogen in sea water and its use as a fuel carries no pollution risk. Suggest one reason in each case why
    (i) we have not obtained hydrogen on a large scale from water,
    (ii) its use as a fuel carries no pollution risk. **(2 marks)**

(a) (i) Hydrogen may be obtained by the electrolysis of dilute sulphuric acid using platinum or carbon electrodes (see Section 7.2).

$$\text{At cathode } 4e^- + 4H^+(aq) \rightarrow 4H(g)$$
$$\downarrow$$
$$2H_2(g)$$

(ii)

Hydrogen is generally prepared by the action of dilute sulphuric acid on zinc in the apparatus shown in Fig. 11.1. The addition of a little copper(II) sulphate solution will speed the reaction up.

dilute sulphuric acid → dropping funnel

gas jar → hydrogen

bee-hive shelf

trough

granulated zinc and copper(II) sulphate

Fig. 11.1

$$Zn(s) + H_2SO_4(aq) \rightarrow ZnSO_4(aq) + H_2(g)$$

(b)　(i)　Mass of oxygen combined with 4.14 g of lead = 4.78 − 4.14 = 0.64 g

$$
\begin{array}{llll}
& & Pb & : O \\
\text{ratio of g} & & 4.14 & : 0.64 \\
\text{ratio of mol} & & \dfrac{4.14}{207} & : \dfrac{0.64}{16} \\
& = & 0.02 & : 0.04 \\
& = & 1 & : 2
\end{array}
$$

Empirical formula is PbO_2 (see Section 5.1)

(ii)　Copper (II) oxide

(iii)　Sodium oxide.

Hydrogen will reduce only the oxides of those metals which are low in the reactivity series (see Section 13.1).

(c)　(i)　$H_2(g) + C_2H_4(g) \rightarrow C_2H_6(g)$

ethane

Hydrogen adds on to ethene in the presence of a finely divided nickel catalyst at about 200°C.

(ii) This tells us that natural oil molecules must contain C=C bonds, i.e. they are unsaturated.

(d)　(i) Hydrogen can be obtained from sea water by electrolysis but the cost of electricity makes this method too expensive.

(ii) When hydrogen is burnt, the only product is water, which is not a pollutant.

$$2H_2(g) + O_2(g) \rightarrow 2H_2O(g)$$

Example 11.7

(a) Describe, with the aid of a balanced equation, a reduction reaction which does not involve the use of hydrogen gas. Explain why the reaction which you have described can be classified as a reduction process.　**(8 marks)**

(b)　(i) Write an equation for the reaction between hydrogen and chlorine.　**(2 marks)**

(ii) What volume of product would be obtained by complete reaction of 11.2 dm³ of hydrogen, all gaseous volumes being measured at s.t.p.?　**(3 marks)**

(iii) What **mass** of chlorine would be reduced by this volume of hydrogen?　**(3 marks)**

(c) Write brief notes on **two** large-scale uses of hydrogen.　**(4 marks)**

(OLE)

(a) If carbon monoxide is passed over heated black copper(II) oxide, red/brown copper is obtained, the excess carbon monoxide being burnt.

$$CuO(s) + CO(g) \rightarrow Cu(s) + CO_2(g)$$

The copper(II) oxide has lost oxygen and has therefore been reduced.

(b) (i) $$H_2(g) + Cl_2(g) \rightarrow 2HCl(g)$$

   (ii) $$H_2(g) + Cl_2(g) \rightarrow 2HCl(g)$$

	1 molecule	1 molecule	2 molecules
By Avogadro's principle	1 volume	1 volume	2 volumes
i.e.	11.2 dm³	11.2 dm³	22.4 dm³

22.4 dm³ of hydrogen chloride are obtained.

(iii)   dm³ $Cl_2(g) = 11.2$

     mol $Cl_2(g) = \dfrac{11.2}{22.4} = \dfrac{1}{2}$

     at s.t.p.

     g $Cl_2(g) = \dfrac{1}{2} \times 71$ ($M_r(Cl_2(g)) = 71$

              $= 35.5$

Mass of chlorine reduced by 11.2 dm³ of hydrogen = 35.5 g.

(c) Ammonia is made industrially by combining hydrogen with nitrogen at a temperature of 500°C and a pressure of 250 atm in the presence of an iron catalyst (see Section 18.5).

$$N_2(g) + 3H_2(g) \rightleftharpoons 2NH_3(g)$$

Hydrogen is also used to convert animal and vegetable oils (which contain carbon to carbon double bonds) into solid fats (see Example 11.6).

Example 11.8

(a) The figure shows the apparatus used to determine the composition of water by mass.

(i) Name the gas evolved in A.

(ii) Write the equation for the reaction in A.

(iii) What is the purpose of B?

(iv) Write the equation for the reaction in C.

(v) What is the purpose of D?

(vi) Why is it necessary to allow the reaction in A to continue for some considerable time before the excess gas is ignited at jet E and the copper oxide is heated?

(vii) At the end of the experiment it was found that the increase in mass of D was 0.9 g, and the decrease of the copper(II) oxide was 0.8 g. What do these figures give for the composition of water by mass? **(10 marks)**

(b) Draw a labelled diagram of the apparatus you would use to determine the composition of water by volume. **(5 marks)**

(a) (i) Hydrogen.
   (ii) $Zn(s) + H_2SO_4(aq) \rightarrow ZnSO_4(aq) + H_2(g)$
   (iii) The anhydrous calcium chloride in B is used to dry the hydrogen. This ensures that the water absorbed in D has been produced in the reaction in C and was not present in the hydrogen initially.
   (iv) $CuO(s) + H_2(g) \rightarrow Cu(s) + H_2O(g)$
   (v) To absorb the water produced in C.
   (vi) Initially the apparatus is filled with air; air/hydrogen mixtures are explosive. Therefore air must be expelled from the apparatus before the hydrogen is ignited.
   (vii) Mass of water produced $\quad= 0.9$ g
   Mass of oxygen lost $\quad=$ mass of oxygen in water $= 0.8$ g
   by copper(II) oxide
   Mass of hydrogen in water $=$ mass of water $-$ mass of oxygen
   $\qquad\qquad\qquad\qquad\qquad = 0.9 - 0.8$ g
   $\qquad\qquad\qquad\qquad\qquad = 0.1$ g
   Composition of water by mass $= 0.1$ g hydrogen : 0.8 g oxygen
   $\qquad\qquad\qquad\qquad\qquad\qquad = 1 : 8$

(b) See Fig. 7.2 and Section 7.2.

Either of these sets of apparatus illustrated in Fig. 7.2 is suitable. The electrolyte is sodium fluoride solution and graduated test tubes are used to collect the gases. Pure water is a very poor conductor of electricity but its conductivity is improved by dissolving a substance such as sodium fluoride in it. The sodium and fluoride ions are not discharged and so do not affect the overall result. When this experiment is carried out, it is found that

volume of hydrogen : volume of oxygen $= 2 : 1$.

11.6 Self-Test Questions

Question 11.1

A pupil set up the apparatus shown in the figure.
(a) Name the substance labelled A in the figure, and state **one** physical test which would help to identify it. **(3 marks)**
(b) Explain the significance of the tube filled with anhydrous calcium chloride granules. **(2 marks)**
(c) For each of the following substances, name an alternative reagent which could be used successfully in its place:
   (i) impure zinc; **(1 mark)**
   (ii) dilute sulphuric acid; **(1 mark)**
   (iii) anhydrous calcium chloride granules. **(1 mark)**
(d) Write down a balanced equation to represent the reaction between the substances named in your answers to (c) (i) and (c) (ii) above. **(1 mark)**
(e) Write down an aspect of chemistry which the pupil could demonstrate with this equipment. **(2 marks)**

anhydrous calcium
chloride granules

gentle suction

cold water

A

impure zinc +
dilute sulphuric
acid

(OLE)

Question 11.2

Use grid 1 on page 2 to choose an answer **A–E**.

The table shows the solubility of potassium nitrate at various temperatures, expressed as grams of potassium nitrate per hundred grams of water.

Temperature in °C	20	30	40	50	60
Solubility	32	45	62	84	106

Which of the following mixtures gives a saturated solution?
1 40 g potassium nitrate in 50 g water at 50°C
2 30 g potassium nitrate in 75 g water at 30°C
3 90 g potassium nitrate in 200 g water at 30°C

(AEB)

Question 11.3

The solubility of nitrogen monoxide in water at room temperature is one volume to one volume. Given that 1 mole of nitrogen monoxide occupies 24.0 dm³ at room temperature and pressure, how many moles of the gas will dissolve in 1 dm³ of water under these conditions? How would an increase in temperature affect the solubility? **(3 marks)**

(SUJB)

116

Question 11.4

A desert survival kit contains a plastic sheet and cup. A hole is dug in the ground and the sheet is stretched over the hole whilst a stone in the middle forms the sheet into a cone. In the heat of the sun, moisture from the ground collects on the underside of the sheet, runs down to the point of the cone and drips into the cup. The overall process that takes place is an example of

A distillation
B evaporation
C filtration
D solution
E solvent extraction.

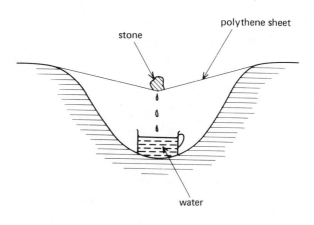

(AEB)

11.7   Answers to Self-Test Questions

11.1 (a) Water. The boiling point of the liquid could be found — water boils at 100°C at 1 atm pressure.
   (b) Anhydrous calcium chloride is used to dry the hydrogen. It is no use trying to prove that water is produced if water is present already.
   (c) (i) iron;
       (ii) dilute hydrochloric acid;
       (iii) potassium hydroxide pellets or calcium oxide.
   (d) $Fe(s) + 2HCl(aq) \rightarrow FeCl_2(aq) + H_2(g)$
   (e) Water is obtained by burning hydrogen in air.

11.2 E.

---

1 Mass of potassium nitrate dissolved = $40 \times \dfrac{100}{50}$ = 80 g (100 g water)$^{-1}$.

This is less than 84 g (100 g water)$^{-1}$ (the solubility at 50°C). The solution is unsaturated.

2 Mass of potassium nitrate dissolved = $30 \times \dfrac{100}{75}$ = 40 g (100 g water)$^{-1}$.

The solution is unsaturated.

3 Mass of potassium nitrate dissolved = $90 \times \dfrac{100}{200}$ = 45 g (100 g water)$^{-1}$.

This is equal to the solubility at 30°C and so the solution is saturated.

11.3 Nitrogen monoxide : Water
    1 volume : 1 volume
    1 dm^3 : 1 dm^3
Vol nitrogen monoxide   = 1 dm^3
Moles nitrogen monoxide = $\dfrac{1}{24}$

$\dfrac{1}{24}$ mol nitrogen monoxide will dissolve in 1 dm^3 water.

Generally, an increase in temperature decreases the solubility of gases.

11.4 **A.**

12 Acids, Bases and Salts

12.1 Introduction

Acidity is measured on the **pH scale**, a scale of numbers normally ranging from 0 to 14. A pH value of 7 is neutral, less than 7 is acidic and more than 7 is alkaline. A *universal indicator* gives different colours corresponding to different pH values, typical results being red for pH = 1, purple for pH = 14.

12.2 Acids

An **acid** is a substance giving hydrated hydrogen ions, H^+(aq), in aqueous solution (see also Section 12.5). Sometimes hydrated hydrogen ions are considered as H^+ ions joined to individual water molecules, in which case they are referred to as *oxonium ions*, H_3O^+. Acids show their normal properties only if water is present because these properties are due to H^+(aq) ions, not to the molecules of the acids.

(a) Properties of Acids

1. Acids taste sour.
2. Acids have pH values less than 7 and turn blue litmus red.
3. With reactive metals (e.g. magnesium, zinc, iron) they give hydrogen.

   acid   + metal $\rightarrow$ salt   + hydrogen
   $2HCl(aq) + Mg(s) \rightarrow MgCl_2(aq) + H_2(g)$
   or $2H^+(aq) + Mg(s) \rightarrow Mg^{2+}(aq) + H_2(g)$

N.B. (i) Metals below iron in the reactivity series (see Section 13.1) do not give hydrogen with dilute acids.
   (ii) Dilute nitric acid gives one or more of the oxides of nitrogen, not hydrogen, when reacted with metals.

4. With bases, neutralisation occurs to give a salt and water *only* (see Section 12.6).

   acid   + base $\rightarrow$ salt   + water
   $2HNO_3(aq) + CuO(s) \rightarrow Cu(NO_3)_2(aq) + H_2O(l)$
   or $2H^+(aq) \quad + O^{2-}(s) \rightarrow \qquad\qquad H_2O(l)$

5. With carbonates (and hydrogencarbonates) effervescence occurs:

   acid   + carbonate $\rightarrow$ salt   + water   + carbon dioxide
   $H_2SO_4(aq) + ZnCO_3(s) \rightarrow ZnSO_4(aq) + H_2O(l) + CO_2(g)$
   or $2H^+(aq) \quad + CO_3^{2-}(s) \rightarrow \qquad\qquad H_2O(l) + CO_2(g)$

12.3 Bases and Alkalis

Bases are substances containing oxide ions, O^{2-}, or hydroxide ions, OH^-. They are usually oxides or hydroxides of metals.

Alkalis are soluble bases: they give hydrated hydroxide ions on dissolving in water. The common alkalis are potassium hydroxide, sodium hydroxide, calcium hydroxide and ammonia solution (often called ammonium hydroxide).

(a) Properties of Bases

1. Bases evolve ammonia (choking alkaline gas) from ammonium salts, especially on warming.

$$CaO(s) + (NH_4)_2SO_4(s) \rightarrow CaSO_4(s) + H_2O(l) + 2NH_3(g)$$
$$\text{or } O^{2-}(s) + 2NH_4^+(s) \rightarrow H_2O(l) + 2NH_3(g)$$

2. With acids, bases give a salt and water *only* (see properties of acids).

(b) Properties of Alkalis

Since alkalis are bases, they have the two properties given above. Their solutions have the following additional properties.

1. They feel soapy.
2. They have pH values greater than 7 and turn red litmus blue.
3. With aluminium and zinc they give hydrogen and an aluminate or a zincate.

12.4 Strengths of Acids and Bases

Acids with low pH values, such as hydrochloric, nitric and sulphuric acids are called *strong acids*. Similarly, alkalis with high pH values, such as solutions of potassium hydroxide and sodium hydroxide, are called *strong alkalis*. These substances are strong electrolytes (see Section 7.1) and are completely ionised in aqueous solution. *Weak* acids and alkalis have pH values nearer to 7: they are incompletely ionised in aqueous solution and are weak electrolytes. Examples include ethanoic acid and ammonia solution (see Section 7.1).

12.5 The Brønsted − Lowry Theory of Acids and Bases

According to this theory, an acid is a proton donor and a base is a proton acceptor.

These definitions include all of the familiar acids and bases but extend the range to other substances.

e.g. $HCl(aq) + H_2O(l) \rightleftharpoons H_3O^+(aq) + Cl^-(aq)$ . . . . (i)

In the forward reaction the water molecule accepts a proton from the hydrogen chloride molecule − therefore the hydrogen chloride molecule is an acid and the water molecule is a base. In the back reaction the oxonium ion is the acid and the chloride ion the base.

When ammonia reacts with water the equation is:

$NH_3(aq) + H_2O(l) \rightleftharpoons NH_4^+(aq) + OH^-(aq)$ . . . .(ii)
base   acid   acid   base

Notice that the water acts as a *base* in (i) and as an *acid* in (ii). Substances which show both acidic and basic properties are said to be **amphoteric**.

12.6 Salts

A **normal salt** is the product formed when all of the hydrogen ions of an acid are replaced by metal or ammonium ions, e.g. zinc chloride, $ZnCl_2$, is a salt of hydrochloric acid and sodium sulphate, Na_2SO_4, is a salt of sulphuric acid.

An **acid salt** is one in which only some of the hydrogen ions of an acid have been replaced by metal or ammonium ions. For example, in sodium hydrogen sulphate, $NaHSO_4$, only half of the hydrogen ions in sulphuric acid have been replaced by sodium ions (see Example 12.5).

The number of hydrated hydrogen ions obtained from one molecule of an acid is called the **basicity** of the acid. Thus hydrochloric acid, HCl, has a basicity of one and is *monobasic*, sulphuric acid, H_2SO_4, has a basicity of two and is *dibasic*.

Neutralisation is the reaction between the hydrated hydrogen ions of an acid and the oxide or hydroxide ions of a base to form water, a salt being formed at the same time.

(a) Methods of Preparing Salts

There are three main methods of making salts and it is necessary to know whether a salt is soluble in water before the correct method can be chosen. Table 12.1 shows the solubilities of common salts and should be memorized.

Table 12.1

Salts	Carbonates	All *insoluble* except potassium, sodium and ammonium carbonates.
	Chlorides	All *soluble* except silver and lead chlorides. Lead chloride is soluble in hot water.
	Nitrates	All *soluble*.
	Sulphates	All *soluble* except barium and lead sulphates. Calcium sulphate is only slightly soluble.

Note: all common potassium, sodium and ammonium salts are soluble.

1. Insoluble salts are prepared by the *precipitation method*.
2. Potassium, sodium and ammonium salts are prepared by the *titration method*.
3. All other soluble salts are made by the *insoluble base method*.
4. In addition to the above methods, *direct synthesis* from the elements is sometimes used, especially for anhydrous chlorides.

Details of these methods are given in Example 12.3.

12.7 Worked Examples

Example 12.1

Hydrogen is produced from:
A Copper and aqueous sulphuric acid.

B Lead and aqueous nitric acid.
C Magnesium and aqueous sulphuric acid.
D Silver and aqueous hydrochloric acid.
E Zinc and aqueous nitric acid.

The answer is **C**.

See Section 12.2 and 13.1.

Example 12.2

On warming with aqueous sodium hydroxide, compound X produced a gas which turned moist red litmus paper blue. The compound X could be
A aluminium nitrate
B ammonium nitrate
C calcium nitrate
D potassium nitrate
E zinc nitrate.   (AEB)

The answer is **B**.

See Properties of bases, Section 12.3.

Example 12.3

(a) Some of the ways in which *salts* may be prepared are (i) by synthesis, (ii) by reaction of acids with alkalis, (iii) by reaction of insoluble bases with acids and (iv) by precipitation.
    Give **one** example of **each** of these four reactions, and for each name the reagents you would use, write an equation and state briefly how you would isolate a reasonably pure dry sample of the salt. **(4 × 5 marks)**
(b) Write an ionic equation for each of the reactions in (a) (ii) and (a) (iv), and explain the reaction in (a) (i) in terms of electron transfer. **(5 marks)**
                                                                                              (OLE)

(a)   (i) Anhydrous iron(III) chloride is made by synthesis, starting with iron filings and a supply of dry chlorine gas.

$$2Fe(s) + 3Cl_2(g) \rightarrow 2FeCl_3(s)$$

The iron filings are heated in a combustion tube in a stream of dry chlorine. Brown fumes of iron(III) chloride sublime off and condense as dark brown crystals in a cool receiver (see Example 17.2).

  (ii) Sodium sulphate may be prepared by the reaction of an alkali with an acid (titration), starting with sodium hydroxide solution and dilute sulphuric acid.

$$2NaOH(aq) + H_2SO_4(aq) \rightarrow Na_2SO_4(aq) + 2H_2O(l)$$

A known volume of sodium hydroxide solution is placed in a conical flask and a few drops of indicator such as litmus added. Dilute sulphuric acid is added carefully from a burette, with stirring, until the indicator shows that the solution is neutral. The volume of acid added is noted. The solution is thrown away, the flask rinsed with distilled water and the

122

experiment repeated using the same volumes of acid and alkali but this time without the indicator (which would contaminate the product). The solution is evaporated until crystals form in a cooled drop and then the flask is left to cool. The resulting crystals of sodium sulphate are filtered off, washed with a little cold distilled water and dried between filter papers.

This method works for all potassium, sodium and ammonium salts *except* for the carbonates. For acid salts see Example 20.6 (c).

(iii) Zinc nitrate may be prepared by the reaction of an insoluble base with an acid, starting with zinc oxide and dilute nitric acid.

$$ZnO(s) + 2HNO_3(aq) \rightarrow Zn(NO_3)_2(aq) + H_2O(l)$$

Dilute nitric acid is warmed in a beaker and zinc oxide is added in small portions, with stirring, until excess remains undissolved in the bottom of the beaker. This shows that all of the acid has been neutralised. The excess solid is filtered off and dry crystals of zinc nitrate obtained from the filtrate as described in the previous section.

This method will work using an insoluble metal carbonate, or even in some cases the metal itself, in place of the insoluble base. Substituting the zinc carbonate or zinc powder for the zinc oxide would still give crystals of zinc nitrate.

(iv) Silver chloride could be made by precipitation, starting with solutions of silver nitrate and sodium chloride.

$$AgNO_3(aq) + NaCl(aq) \rightarrow AgCl(s) + NaNO_3(aq)$$

Equal volumes of solutions of the same concentration in $mol\ dm^{-3}$ are mixed so that the mole ratio of the two solutes is the same as in the equation. The resulting white precipitate of silver chloride is filtered off, washed with a little distilled water and dried between filter papers.

This method can be used for *all insoluble salts or insoluble hydroxides*. The two starting materials are chosen so that each contains one of the ions which will join to form the precipitate. Both starting materials *must* be soluble. The other ions present *must not* combine to form a second precipitate as this would be impossible to separate from the required product, e.g. if silver sulphate and barium chloride solutions had been chosen in the above example a mixture of silver chloride and barium sulphate would have been given.

$$Ag_2SO_4(aq) + BaCl_2(aq) \rightarrow 2AgCl(s) + BaSO_4(s)$$

If the *positive ion* which will go into the precipitate is always paired with *nitrate ions* and the *negative ion* from the precipitate with *sodium ions*, as in the original example, then soluble sodium nitrate will always be the second product and no complication will occur.

(b) $H^+(aq) + OH^-(aq) \rightarrow H_2O(l)$
or $H_3O^+(aq) + OH^-(aq) \rightarrow 2H_2O(l)$
     $Ag^+(aq) + Cl^-(aq) \rightarrow AgCl(s)$

In (a) (i) three electrons are transferred from each iron atom to three chlorine atoms. The iron atoms are oxidised to Fe^{3+} ions and the chlorine atoms reduced to Cl^- ions.

Example 12.4

(a) A solution of a compound **R** in water (concentration 0.1 mol/dm^3) had a pH of 4 and reacted **slowly** with sodium carbonate to evolve a gas **T**.

A solution of a compound **W** in water (concentration 0.1 mol/dm^3) had a pH of 1 and reacted **rapidly** with sodium carbonate to produce the same gas **T**.

(i) Give the name of one substance in each case which would fit the description of **R**, **T** and **W**.

(ii) Name the particle common to the solutions of **R** and **W** which is also responsible for the reactions of these solutions with sodium carbonate. Write an ionic equation for the reaction of this particle with a carbonate ion.

(iii) Explain briefly why there is a difference in the rate of evolution of gas **T**. (Assume that the temperature was constant during the experiments.) **(8 marks)**

(b) A solution containing 2.84 g of sodium sulphate was mixed with a solution containing 6.62 g of lead(II) nitrate and a white precipitate **P** was formed; this precipitate was filtered, washed and dried. The filtrate was carefully concentrated and colourless crystals **Q** were obtained on cooling.

(i) Name the precipitate **P** and write a molecular equation for its formation.

(ii) Calculate the maximum mass of **P** which could have been obtained.

(iii) Identify **Q** and calculate the maximum theoretical mass of **Q** which could have been obtained. Give **one** reason why the mass obtained in practice would have been less than the theoretical mass. **(8 marks)**

(AEB)

(a) (i) R could be ethanoic acid, T is carbon dioxide and W could be dilute hydrogen chloride.

(ii) The particle is a hydrated hydrogen ion, $H^+(aq)$ (or oxonium ion, $H_3O^+(aq)$)

$$2H^+(aq) + CO_3^{2-}(s) \rightarrow H_2O(l) + CO_2(g)$$
$$\text{or } 2H_3O^+(aq) + CO_3^{2-}(s) \rightarrow 3H_2O(l) + CO_2(g)$$

(iii) Ethanoic acid is a weak acid and is not completely ionised in aqueous solution. Dilute hydrochloric acid is a strong acid and *is* completely ionised in aqueous solution. Thus the concentration of $H^+(aq)$ ions is greater in dilute hydrochloric acid than in dilute ethanoic acid and the reaction is faster.

(b) (i) **P** is lead(II) sulphate.
$$Pb(NO_3)_2(aq) + Na_2SO_4(aq) \rightarrow PbSO_4(s) + 2NaNO_3(aq)$$

(ii) mol $Pb(NO_3)_2$: mol Na_2SO_4 : mol $PbSO_4 = 1 : 1 : 1 \ldots \ldots \ldots$ (A)

$$\text{mol } Pb(NO_3)_2 \text{ used} \quad = \frac{6.62}{331} = 0.02$$

$$\text{mol } Na_2SO_4 \text{ used} \quad = \frac{2.84}{142} = 0.02$$

$$\therefore \text{ mol } PbSO_4 \text{ formed} \quad = 0.02 \quad \text{(from A)}$$
$$\therefore \text{ g } \quad PbSO_4 \text{ formed} \quad = 0.02 \times 303$$
$$= 6.06$$

(iii) **Q** is sodium nitrate.

Maximum amount of **Q** obtainable from 0.02 mol of $Pb(NO_3)_2$ and 0.02 mol of Na_2SO_4 is 0.04 mol (from equation).

$$\therefore \text{ Maximum mass} \quad = 0.04 \times 85 \text{ g}$$
$$= 3.4 \text{ g}$$

In practice some sodium nitrate would be lost in the filtrate when the crystals are filtered off from the saturated solution in which they have grown.

Example 12.5

Sodium hydrogensulphate, $NaHSO_4$, is an acid salt. Its solution turns universal indicator paper red.

(a) What is meant by an 'acid salt'? **(1 mark)**

See definition in Section 12.6.

(b) What, roughly, is the pH of sodium hydrogensulphate solution? **(1 mark)**

1

Sodium hydrogencarbonate solution turns universal indicator paper green.

(c) What is the approximate pH of sodium hydrogencarbonate solution? **(1 mark)**

8

(d) Is sodium hydrogencarbonate an acid salt? Explain your answer. **(2 marks)**

Even though it is alkaline in solution, sodium hydrogencarbonate, $NaHCO_3$, is an acid salt because only half of the hydrogen ions in carbonic acid (carbon dioxide solution) have been replaced by sodium ions.

(e) What would you expect to see if solutions of sodium hydrogensulphate and sodium hydrogencarbonate were mixed? **(1 mark)**

The mixture would fizz.

Because acid + hydrogencarbonate gives carbon dioxide.

(f) Write an equation for the reaction. **(2 marks)**

$NaHSO_4(aq) + NaHCO_3(aq) \rightarrow Na_2SO_4(aq) + H_2O(l) + CO_2(g)$

Ionic equations for the reactions which occur when the two salts dissolve in water are

$HSO_4^-(aq) + H_2O(l) \rightleftharpoons H_3O^+(aq) + SO_4^{2-}(aq)$ (i)

$HCO_3^-(aq) + H_2O(l) \rightleftharpoons H_2CO_3(aq) + OH^-(aq)$ (ii)

(g) Define the terms 'acid' and 'base' according to the Brønsted-Lowry theory.

See definitions in Section 12.5. **(2 marks)**

(h) Which particles are acids and which are bases in equation (i)? **(2 marks)**

HSO_4^- and H_3O^+ are acids; H_2O and SO_4^{2-} are bases.

(i) Which particles are acids and which are bases in equation (ii)? **(2 marks)**

H_2O and H_2CO_3 are acids; HCO_3^- and OH^- are bases.

(j) Which word describes the behaviour of water in these two reactions? **(1 mark)**

Amphoteric.

12.8 Self-Test Questions

Question 12.1

Hydrogen chloride dissolves in water and in dry methylbenzene (toluene).

(a) Use the following table to describe what will happen (if anything) when the reagents shown are added to each solution. **(6 marks)**

Reagent	Solution of hydrogen chloride in water	Solution of dry hydrogen chloride in dry methylbenzene
Dry neutral litmus paper		
Magnesium		
Anhydrous sodium carbonate		

(b) Explain why these two solutions behave differently. **(4 marks)**

(AEB)

Question 12.2

Which of the following compounds is a salt?
A Calcium oxide
B Lead(II) carbonate
C Sodium hydroxide
D Hydrogen chloride

(SEB)

Question 12.3

This question is about different methods of making nickel(II) nitrate, $Ni(NO_3)_2$.
Method I 25 cm^3 of 2M nitric acid, HNO_3, was placed in a beaker and green nickel(II) carbonate, $NiCO_3$, was added until it was in excess. After filtration green nickel(II) nitrate solution was obtained.
(a) Why was *excess* nickel(II) carbonate used?   **(1 mark)**
(b) Why must the beaker be much larger than the volume of acid used?   **(1 mark)**
(c) Write a balanced equation for the reaction, including state symbols.   **(2 marks)**
Method II Nickel(II) oxide was dissolved in nitric acid according to the equation

$$NiO(s) + 2HNO_3(aq) \rightarrow Ni(NO_3)_2(aq) + H_2O(l)$$

(d) What volume of 2M nitric acid would be required to neutralise 7.5 g of nickel(II) oxide?
     (Relative atomic masses: O = 16, Ni = 59)   **(3 marks)**
Method III Nickel(II) chloride solution was added to lead(II) nitrate solution

$$NiCl_2(aq) + Pb(NO_3)_2(aq) \rightarrow PbCl_2(s) + Ni(NO_3)_2(aq)$$

(e) Outline the main operation required to obtain nickel(II) nitrate crystals from 1.0 M
     nickel(II) chloride solution and 1.0 M lead(II) nitrate solution.   **(2 marks)**

(L)

Question 12.4

Use grid 1 on page 2 to choose an answer **A–E**.
Which of the following pairs of reagents will react to form a precipitate?
1 Aqueous barium nitrate and aqueous sulphuric acid
2 Aqueous sodium hydroxide and aqueous nitric acid
3 Copper(II) carbonate and aqueous hydrochloric acid

(AEB)

12.9   Answers to Self-Test Questions

12.1 (a)

Reagent	Solution of hydrogen chloride in water	Solution of dry hydrogen chloride in dry methylbenzene
Dry neutral litmus paper	Turns red	No change
Magnesium	Effervescence of hydrogen	No change
Anhydrous sodium carbonate	Effervescence of carbon dioxide	No change

(b) Hydrogen chloride consists of covalent molecules. When it dissolves in water
    it reacts to form $H^+(aq)$ (or $H_3O^+(aq)$) ions and $Cl^-(aq)$ ions and the resulting
    solution is therefore acidic. It dissolves in methylbenzene without reacting
    and, as the resulting solution does not contain $H^+(aq)$ ions, it is not acidic.

The reactions in the middle column of the table are typical reactions of an acid.

$$2H^+(aq) + Mg(s) \rightarrow Mg^{2+}(aq) + H_2(g)$$
$$2H^+(aq) + CO_3^{2-}(aq) \rightarrow H_2O(l) + CO_2(g)$$

12.2 B.

D is an acid, the others are bases.

12.3 (a) To make sure that all of the dilute nitric acid had been used up.
   (b) The mixture will fizz and froth up, owing to the evolution of carbon dioxide.
   (c) $NiCO_3(s) + 2HNO_3(aq) \rightarrow Ni(NO_3)_2(aq) + H_2O(l) + CO_2(g)$
   (d) From the equation, mol NiO : mol HNO_3 = 1 : 2 .... (A)

$$g\ NiO = 7.5$$
$$mol\ NiO = \frac{7.5}{75}$$
$$mol\ HNO_3 = \frac{7.5}{75} \times 2 \quad (from\ A)$$
$$= 0.2$$

2 mol of HNO_3 are contained in 1 dm^3 of 2M solution

See Section 20.3.
$\therefore$ 0.2 mol of HNO_3 is contained in 0.1 dm^3 of 2M solution
$\therefore$ Volume of acid required = 0.1 dm^3 = 100 cm^3
   (e) Mix equal volumes of the two solutions, filter off the precipitate of lead(II) chloride and obtain crystals of nickel(II) nitrate from the filtrate as described in part (a) (ii) of Example 12.3.

12.4 D.

The products are (1) barium sulphate (insoluble) and nitric acid (2) sodium nitrate and water (3) copper(II) chloride, carbon dioxide and water.

13 The Metals

13.1   Introduction

When metals are arranged in order of decreasing chemical reactivity, the *reactivity series* is obtained. The chemical properties of a metal and its compounds are related to the position of the metal in the reactivity series as shown in Table 13.1.

Table 13.1

	Action of cold air	*Action of water*	*Action of dilute hydrochloric and sulphuric acids*	*Reduction of oxides*	*Nature of hydroxides*	*Effect of heat on carbonates*	*Effect of heat on nitrates*	
K Na	rapidly attacked	violent in cold	explode	not reduced by carbon or hydrogen	strongly basic: stable to heat	stable	give nitrite and oxygen	K Na
Ca	attacked	attacked in cold			weakly basic or amphoteric:	give oxide and carbon dioxide with increasing ease as series is descended	give oxide, nitrogen dioxide and oxygen with increasing ease as series is descended	Ca
Mg Al Zn	little action: protective oxide coating formed	react with steam	give hydrogen with decreasing vigour as series is descended	reduced by hot carbon	on heating give oxide and water with increasing ease as series is descended			Mg Al Zn
Fe	rusts in moist air			reduced by hot carbon or hydrogen				Fe
Pb Cu	little action	no reaction	no reaction					Pb Cu

(a) Displacement Reactions

Any metal will displace one lower in the reactivity series from aqueous solutions containing its ions. For example, if a piece of iron is placed in copper(II) sulphate solution, a reddish brown deposit of copper forms on the iron and the blue colour of the solution fades. This is a redox reaction (see Section 4.5) in which the iron atoms are oxidised by each losing two electrons and going into solution as Fe^{2+} ions: Cu^{2+} ions are reduced by each gaining two electrons and forming a solid deposit of copper atoms (see Example 13.1 and Questions 13.1 and 13.2).

$$Fe(s) + Cu^{2+}(aq) \rightarrow Fe^{2+}(aq) + Cu(s)$$

A metal cannot displace another one above it in the reactivity series. Thus if a piece of copper were placed in iron(II) sulphate solution, no reaction would occur.

Hydrogen fits into the series between lead and copper. Magnesium ribbon will therefore displace hydrogen from aqueous solutions containing its ions (i.e. acids).

e.g. $Mg(s) + 2H^+(aq) \rightarrow Mg^{2+}(aq) + H_2(g)$

Since copper is below hydrogen in the series, it does not liberate the gas from dilute acids. In practice, lead does not do so either.

(b) Reduction of Metallic Oxides

A metallic oxide can be reduced to the metal by heating it with another metal which is higher in the reactivity series (see Example 13.2(d)).

e.g. $Zn(s) + PbO(s) \rightarrow ZnO(s) + Pb(s)$

Carbon fits into the series between aluminium and zinc. On heating, it will reduce the oxide of zinc and those metals below it, being itself oxidised to carbon monoxide or carbon dioxide.

Metals above zinc can reduce carbon dioxide on heating. For example, magnesium burns with a bright white light in carbon dioxide, being oxidised to a white ash of magnesium oxide. The carbon dioxide is reduced to black specks of carbon.

$2Mg(s) + CO_2(g) \rightarrow 2MgO(s) + C(s)$

Hydrogen behaves in this type of reaction as if it were *level* with iron. (Note that this is higher than its position for displacement reactions.) It will reduce the oxides of iron and metals below it, being itself oxidised to water. Iron and the metals above it reduce water to hydrogen and are themselves oxidised (see Table 13.1 and Example 13.4).

(c) Thermal Stability of Metallic Compounds

In general, the higher a metal is in the reactivity series, the less likely are its compounds to decompose on heating (see Table 13.1 and Question 13.2).

13.2 Potassium, Sodium and Lithium — The Alkali Metals

These are soft, silvery metals which are stored under oil because they rapidly tarnish in air. Lithium comes between sodium and calcium in the reactivity series.

In water, potassium melts and rushes around the surface as a silvery ball. Hydrogen is formed, and burns with a lilac flame owing to the presence of the potassium. The other product is potassium hydroxide solution.

$2K(s) + 2H_2O(l) \rightarrow 2KOH(aq) + H_2(g)$

Sodium reacts slightly less vigorously (the hydrogen does not inflame) and lithium less vigorously still.

The hydroxides of these metals are all strong alkalis.

Potassium nitrate and potassium sulphate are important fertilisers. Sodium hydroxide is an important industrial alkali, sodium carbonate is a water softener (see Section 13.3) and sodium hydrogencarbonate is an ingredient of baking powder and health salts. Sodium chloride is used in preparing food and in the manufacture of chlorine and sodium hydroxide in the mercury cathode cell (see Section 18.2).

13.3 Calcium and Magnesium — The Alkaline Earth Metals

These are fairly reactive metals. Calcium reacts quite vigorously with cold water, producing hydrogen and a milky suspension of slightly soluble calcium hydroxide (see Example 13.4(b) and Question 13.3(f)).

$$Ca(s) + 2H_2O(l) \rightarrow Ca(OH)_2(aq) + H_2(g)$$

Magnesium reacts *very* slowly with cold water but burns when heated in steam to give magnesium oxide and hydrogen.

$$Mg(s) + H_2O(g) \rightarrow MgO(s) + H_2(g)$$

Calcium oxide (quicklime) is an important industrial base, made by heating calcium carbonate (chalk or limestone). It reacts violently with water to form calcium hydroxide, which is a cheap industrial alkali and can be used to neutralise soil acidity (see Example 13.5).

Magnesium metal is used in lightweight alloys, while magnesium hydroxide (Milk of Magnesia) reduces stomach acidity.

(a) Hardness of Water (see Example 13.6 and Question 13.4)

Hard water is water which does not readily form a lather with soap. Hardness is mostly caused by dissolved calcium or magnesium ions which react with soap to form an insoluble precipitate (scum) — see page 203. Soapless detergents do not have insoluble calcium and magnesium salts and therefore do not form scum.

Hardness which can be removed simply by boiling is called **temporary hardness**, It is due to dissolved magnesium hydrogencarbonate or calcium hydrogencarbonate, which decompose on heating to give a precipitate of the corresponding carbonate. How water becomes temporarily hard is described in Example 13.6(b).

Hardness which cannot be removed by boiling is called permanent hardness and is often due to dissolved sulphates of calcium and magnesium.

Methods of removing hardness ('softening' water) include:

1. Boiling — temporary hardness only.
2. Distillation — effective but expensive.
3. Adding sodium carbonate (washing soda) to precipitate insoluble magnesium carbonate or calcium carbonate.
4. Ion exchange. Some substances, called ion exchange resins, remove dissolved ions from hard water and replace them with ions of their own. If the cations (positive ions) are replaced with $H^+(aq)$ ions and the anions (negative ions) with $OH^-(aq)$ ions, these combine to form water molecules and the resulting product is very pure *deionised water*.

13.4 Aluminium

Aluminium is a silvery metal which, in spite of its high position in the reactivity series, is stable in air and water. This is because it is coated with a thin layer of oxide, which protects it from further attack. It dissolves in dilute hydrochloric acid and in sodium hydroxide solution, liberating hydrogen in both cases.

Aluminium oxide and aluminium hydroxide are amphoteric (see Section 12.5).

The metal is used to make milk-bottle tops and food containers; it is also used in overhead electric cables and in light alloys. Its manufacture is described in Example 18.2.

13.5 Zinc

Zinc resembles aluminium to some extent, though its oxide coating is less protective. It gives hydrogen with dilute hydrochloric acid and with sodium hydroxide solution, and its oxide and hydroxide are amphoteric. Zinc oxide has the characteristic property of turning yellow on heating and back to white on cooling.

The metal is used to protect steel from rusting: the zinc coating (galvanising) corrodes instead of the steel. It is also used in roofing, to make the cases for dry batteries and to make alloys such as brass.

13.6 Iron

Iron is a member of the centre block of the periodic table (the transition metals). These metals have more than one oxidation number (valency), form coloured ions in solution and can act as catalysts. The rusting of iron is dealt with in Section 10.3 and Example 10.6.

When heated in air, iron forms magnetic iron oxide, Fe_3O_4. Heating in steam gives the same oxide, together with hydrogen. The other stable oxide is iron(III) oxide, Fe_2O_3. Iron(II) hydroxide (dirty green) and iron(III) hydroxide (reddish brown) are formed by precipitation when sodium hydroxide solution is added to a solution of an iron(II) salt or an iron(III) salt.

Iron(II) salts are generally pale green and less stable than the corresponding iron(III) salts, which are yellow or brown. Conversion of iron(II) compounds to iron(III) compounds involves loss of electrons and therefore is an example of oxidation. The reverse process is reduction.

$$Fe^{2+} \underset{\text{reduction}}{\overset{\text{oxidation}}{\rightleftharpoons}} Fe^{3+} + e^-$$

Cast iron is cheap but impure, hard and brittle; *wrought iron* is almost pure iron and is softer and more flexible. *Steels* are alloys of iron with carbon and other elements such as chromium and manganese.

The manufacture of iron and steel is described in Section 18.1 and Example 18.3.

13.7 Lead

Lead is a soft metal, affected only very slowly by air and water. Dilute hydrochloric and sulphuric acids have little action on it because it becomes coated with insoluble lead(II) chloride or lead(II) sulphate. Dilute nitric acid rapidly dissolves it, giving a solution of lead(II) nitrate and a mixture of the oxides of nitrogen.

There are three oxides of lead. Lead(II) oxide is an amphoteric orange solid, dissolving in dilute acids which have soluble lead(II) salts and in sodium hydroxide solution to give sodium plumbate(II).

e.g. $PbO(s) + 2HNO_3(aq) \rightarrow Pb(NO_3)_2(aq) + H_2O(l)$

Lead(IV) oxide is a brown powder which is a powerful oxidising agent. On heating it gives off oxygen and leaves a residue of orange lead(II) oxide.

$2PbO_2(s) \rightarrow 2PbO(s) + O_2(g)$

The third oxide of lead is red lead oxide, Pb_3O_4, which behaves as if it were a mixture of lead(II) oxide and lead(IV) oxide, i.e. $(2PbO + PbO_2)(s)$. The correct name for this compound is therefore dilead(II) lead(IV) oxide.

Lead(II) hydroxide is a white amphoteric solid, dissolving, like lead(II) oxide, in those dilute acids which have soluble lead(II) salts and in sodium hydroxide solution.

Apart from lead(II) nitrate and lead(II) ethanoate, the common lead(II) salts are insoluble in water. Lead(II) chloride is soluble in hot water but is deposited as crystals when the solution cools again.

Lead is used in roofing, in car batteries, for shielding against X-rays and radioactive material, and in alloys such as solder. Tetraethyl-lead(IV) (TEL) is added to petrol as an anti-knock compound and consequently causes lead pollution of the air.

13.8 Copper

Copper, like iron, is a transition metal. It slowly tarnishes on exposure to air but is unaffected by water or steam. It is below hydrogen in the reactivity series and cannot displace the gas from dilute acids. Like lead, it dissolves in dilute nitric acid, giving a solution of blue copper(II) nitrate, together with nitrogen monoxide. If *concentrated* nitric acid is used, brown fumes of nitrogen dioxide are evolved.

Copper(I) oxide is a red solid, formed when Fehling's solution, which contains copper(II) ions, is reduced by heating with glucose. Copper(II) oxide is a black basic solid.

Pale blue copper(II) hydroxide is insoluble in water but dissolves in ammonia solution to give a royal blue solution containing complex tetraaminecopper(II) ions, $[Cu(NH_3)_4]_{2+}^m$ (aq).

Copper is used in roofing, as an electrical conductor and to make water pipes. It is alloyed with zinc to make brass and with tin to make bronze.

13.9 Differences Between Metals and Non-Metals

See Example 13.4 and Table 4.1.

13.10 Worked Examples

Example 13.1

The following facts are known about four metals, P, Q, R and S.
 (i) R displaces P and S from solutions of their ions;
 (ii) Q reacts with water, R does not;
(iii) if plates of P and S are dipped into an electrolyte and joined by wires through a meter, electrons flow from P to S through the meter.

The order of activity, the most active being placed first, is

A R, Q, S, P
B Q, S, P, R
C P, S, Q, R
D Q, R, P, S   (SEB)

The answer is **D**.

(i) tells us that R is above P and S in the reactivity series; (ii) tells us that Q is above R; (iii) tells us that P is forming positive ions, leaving behind electrons which flow to S. If P forms ions more readily than S it must be more reactive than S.

Example 13.2

Refer to the following metals in answering this question:

aluminium   iron   potassium

copper   magnesium   zinc

(a) Name two metals which you would **not** use in the laboratory to prepare hydrogen from an appropriate aqueous acid. Give a reason in each case.   **(4 marks)**

Metal: *copper*. Reason: *because it is below hydrogen in the reactivity series.*

Metal: *potassium*. Reason: *because the reaction is too violent.*

(b) (i) Name two metals which, though high in the 'reactivity series', do not tarnish or corrode noticeably in air.   **(2 marks)**

Aluminium, zinc.

(ii) Explain why this is the case for one of the metals you have chosen.   **(2 marks)**

Aluminium is coated with a thin layer of aluminium oxide, which protects it from further reaction with the air.

(c) Name one metal which forms common compounds in which the metal can exist in one of two oxidation (valency) states. Give the formulae of two of its compounds, one illustrating each state.   **(3 marks)**

Name of metal: *iron.*

Formulae of compounds: $FeCl_2$ and $FeCl_3$.

(d) You are informed that a finely divided metal, when heated with the oxide of a metal lower in the 'reactivity series', will usually react highly exothermically.

(i) Write the equation for such a reaction. Both metals concerned should be selected from the list given.   **(2 marks)**

$Mg(s) + CuO(s) \rightarrow MgO(s) + Cu(s)$

(ii) Suggest two practical safety measures which should be employed in demonstrating this reaction.   **(2 marks)**

Use a small quantity of the mixture and use a safety screen or, better, a fume cupboard.

(e) 'Yellow metal' is an alloy containing 60% copper and 40% zinc by weight. Calculate the number of moles of zinc atoms in 260 g of the alloy. (Zn = 65)   **(3 marks)**

(NISEC)

g *of zinc in 260 g of alloy* $= 260 \times \dfrac{40}{100} = 104$

Moles of atoms in 104 g of zinc $= \dfrac{104}{65}$

$= 1.6$

Example 13.3

The following experiment was carried out on a metal M. Sufficient warm, concentrated nitric acid was added **just** to dissolve the metal. Brown fumes were given off and a colourless solution remained. A small piece of cleaned copper was then added to this solution. A precipitate formed and the copper dissolved.

(a) What were the brown fumes?   **(1 mark)**

(b) Which of the following could have been the metal M?

Zinc, silver, magnesium, iron.   **(1 mark)**

(c) What would have happened to the metal M if it had been warmed with hydrochloric acid instead of nitric acid? Explain your answer.   **(2 marks)**

(SEB)

(a) Nitrogen dioxide.

See Section 15.2.

(b) Silver.

M must be below copper in the reactivity series since copper displaces it from solution.

(c) Nothing would have happened because M is below hydrogen in the reactivity series and therefore cannot displace it from dilute acids.

Example 13.4

(a) Draw a table to illustrate the differences between the following properties of metals and non-metals:
  (i) physical appearance
  (ii) electrical properties
  (iii) chemical properties of their oxides
  (iv) type of bonding present in their chlorides. **(8 marks)**
(b) Compare the reactions, if any, of the metals calcium, copper and iron with (i) water or steam, (ii) dilute hydrochloric acid and place the metals in order of decreasing reactivity. Write equations for any reactions that you describe. **(7 marks)**

(a)

Properties	*Metals*	*Non-metals*
Appearance	Shiny solids	Gases, liquids or dull solids
Electrical properties	Conduct electricity well when solid or molten	Do not conduct electricity
Chemical properties of oxides	Usually ionic, basic or amphoteric solids	Usually covalent acidic gases
Type of bonding in chlorides	Ionic	Covalent

(b) (i) Calcium reacts fairly vigorously with cold water.

See Section 13.3 for details and equation.

Iron reacts on heating in steam to give magnetic iron oxide and hydrogen.

$$3Fe(s) + 4H_2O(g) \rightleftharpoons Fe_3O_4(s) + 4H_2(g)$$

Copper does not react with water or with steam, even on heating.

(ii) Calcium reacts very vigorously with cold dilute hydrochloric acid, forming calcium chloride solution and hydrogen.

$$Ca(s) + 2HCl(aq) \rightarrow CaCl_2(aq) + H_2(g)$$

Iron reacts fairly slowly with cold dilute hydrochloric acid, forming iron(II) chloride solution and hydrogen.

$$Fe(s) + 2HCl(aq) \rightarrow FeCl_2(aq) + H_2(g)$$

Copper does not react with dilute hydrochloric acid.
The order of reactivity of the three metals is thus calcium, iron, copper.

Example 13.5

(a) Name **three** naturally occurring forms of calcium carbonate. **(3 marks)**
(b) How is calcium carbonate converted into
  (i) calcium oxide **(3 marks)**

      (ii) calcium hydroxide?   **(4 marks)**
      Give the equations for the reactions involved.
   (c) Discuss the part that calcium compounds play in
        (i) the extraction of iron,   **(7 marks)**
        (ii) agriculture,   **(4 marks)**
        (iii) the building industry.   **(3 marks)**
                                               (AEB)

(a) Chalk, limestone, marble.

(b) (i) By heating strongly to drive off carbon dioxide.

$$CaCO_3(s) \rightarrow CaO(s) + CO_2(g)$$

    (ii) By adding water carefully to the calcium oxide formed in (i). Much heat is produced and the solid swells up to form a fine powder.

$$CaO(s) + H_2O(l) \rightarrow Ca(OH)_2(s)$$

(c) (i) See Example 18.3.
    (ii) Calcium carbonate and calcium hydroxide can be used to neutralise soil acidity. Calcium phosphate is used to make superphosphate fertiliser.
    (iii) When limestone and clay are heated strongly together, cement is formed. Calcium sulphate is used in making plaster.

Example 13.6

(a) Some fresh calcium oxide is exposed to the air and weighed at regular intervals. At first there is a fairly rapid increase in mass and this is followed by a much slower increase which eventually ceases.

Explain these observations.

                                            (8 marks)

(b) Explain why
    (i) calcium carbonate is an essential ingredient of the material which goes into the blast furnace in the extraction of iron;
    (ii) calcium carbonate is insoluble in water, yet caves or potholes are common in limestone districts;
    (iii) calcium carbonate is insoluble in water, yet some hot-water pipes become blocked up by layers of this carbonate.   **(3 × 4 marks)**
                                              (OLE)

(a) The rapid increase in mass is caused by reaction between the calcium oxide and the moisture in the air to form calcium hydroxide.

$$CaO(s) + H_2O(g) \rightarrow Ca(OH)_2(s)$$

    The much slower increase in mass which follows is due to reaction between the calcium hydroxide (alkaline) and carbon dioxide (acidic) in the air to form calcium carbonate. When this reaction is complete, no further change in mass occurs.

$$Ca(OH)_2(s) + CO_2(g) \rightarrow CaCO_3(s) + H_2O(g)$$

All alkaline hydroxides react in a similar way with carbon dioxide.

(b) (i) See Example 18.3.
    (ii) Rain water dissolves a little carbon dioxide as it falls through the air and much more as it soaks through the soil, where the gas is produced by living organisms. The resulting carbonic acid dissolves limestone (calcium carbonate) to form calcium hydrogencarbonate solution, giving rise to caves and potholes, and making the water temporarily hard.

$$CaCO_3(s) + H_2O(l) + CO_2(g) \rightleftharpoons Ca(HCO_3)_2(aq)$$

(iii) The reaction shown by the above equation is reversible. When water containing temporary hardness is heated the reaction goes backwards, causing layers of insoluble calcium carbonate to be built up in hot-water pipes and boilers.

Example 13.7

Use grid 1 on page 2 to choose an answer **A–E**.
A metal X forms a green chloride of formula XCl_2. It is likely that X
1 is a transition metal
2 forms a carbonate with the formula XCO_3
3 is in the same group of the Periodic Table as magnesium.   (L)
The answer is **B**.

Transition metals have coloured ions (see Section 13.6).

Example 13.8

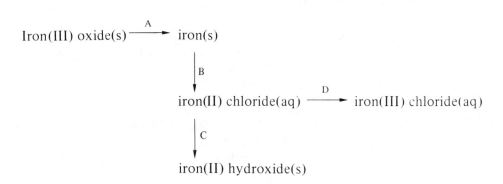

(a) State the reagents and conditions needed for each of the above one-stage conversions, writing an equation for each reaction.   **(9 marks)**
(b) Why can reaction D be described as an electron transfer reaction? Illustrate your answer with an ionic equation.   **(3 marks)**

(a) **A** Heat strongly with carbon.
$$Fe_2O_3(s) + 3C(s) \rightarrow 2Fe(s) + 3CO(g)$$
B Dissolve in cold dilute hydrochloric acid.
$$Fe(s) + 2HCl(aq) \rightarrow FeCl_2(aq) + H_2(g)$$

Heating iron in chlorine would give iron(III) chloride.

C Add cold dilute sodium hydroxide solution.
$$FeCl_2(aq) + 2NaOH(aq) \rightarrow Fe(OH)_2(s) + 2NaCl(aq)$$
D Bubble chlorine gas into the solution in the cold.
$$2FeCl_2(aq) + Cl_2(g) \rightarrow 2FeCl_3(aq)$$
(b) Each Fe^{2+} ion loses an electron and is oxidised to an Fe^{3+} ion.
Each chlorine atom gains an electron and is reduced to a Cl^- ion.
Thus electrons are transferred from Fe^{2+} ions to chlorine atoms.
$$2Fe^{2+}(aq) + Cl_2(g) \rightarrow 2Fe^{3+}(aq) + 2Cl^-(aq)$$

Example 13.9

(a) Describe, giving essential practical details and an equation, how a sample of pure, dry lead(II) sulphate could be prepared, starting from lead(II) nitrate crystals.   **(9 marks)**

(b) When dilead(II) lead(IV) oxide is heated, it decomposes according to the equation

$$2Pb_3O_4 \rightarrow 6PbO + O_2$$

   (i) Calculate the mass of lead(II) oxide which could be obtained from 6.85 g of dilead(II) lead(IV) oxide, showing clearly how you arrive at the answer.

   (ii) Describe briefly one test to confirm that oxygen is evolved in this reaction.

   (iii) If lead(II) oxide is heated in a stream of dry hydrogen gas, what products will result? Write an equation for the reaction and explain why this can be considered to be an example of redox.   **(11 marks)**

(c) Describe what is observed when aqueous hydrogen sulphide is mixed with aqueous lead(II) nitrate, and write an equation for the reaction.   **(4 marks)**

(AEB)

(a) The method is precipitation. The lead(II) nitrate crystals are dissolved in water and added to sodium sulphate solution. Details are given in Example 12.3 (a).

$$Pb(NO_3)_2(aq) + Na_2SO_4(aq) \rightarrow PbSO_4(s) + 2NaNO_3(aq)$$

(b) (i)
$$2Pb_3O_4(s) \rightarrow 6PbO(s) + O_2(g)$$
$$\text{mol } Pb_3O_4 : \text{mol } PbO = 2:6 = 1:3 \dots\dots\dots\dots\dots\dots A$$
$$\text{g } Pb_3O_4 = 6.85$$
$$\text{mol } Pb_3O_4 = \frac{6.85}{685} \qquad \boxed{M_r(Pb_3O_4) = 685}$$
$$\therefore \text{mol } PbO = \frac{6.85}{685} \times 3 \qquad \text{(from A)}$$
$$\text{g } PbO = \frac{6.85}{685} \times 3 \times 223 \qquad \boxed{M_r(PbO) = 223}$$
$$= 6.69$$

   (ii) If a glowing splint is held over the heated mixture it will relight, confirming that oxygen is being evolved.

   (iii) Lead and water will be formed.

$$PbO(s) + H_2(g) \rightarrow Pb(s) + H_2O(g)$$

   The lead(II) oxide has been reduced (it has lost oxygen) and the hydrogen has been oxidised (it has gained oxygen). Therefore this reaction is an example of redox.

(c) A black precipitate of lead(II) sulphide is produced.

$$Pb(NO_3)_2(aq) + H_2S(aq) \rightarrow PbS(s) + 2HNO_3(aq)$$

13.11 Self-Test Questions

Use grid 2 on page 2 to choose an answer **A–E** for Questions 13.1 and 13.2.

Question 13.1

Magnesium reacts with aqueous hydrochloric acid, whereas metal X does not. From this, it would be expected that
1. magnesium would displace X from a solution containing ions of X
2. magnesium would react more readily with oxygen than X
3. magnesium oxide would be more difficult to reduce than the oxide of X.   (AEB)

Question 13.2

Metal X is higher in the activity series than hydrogen and metal Y is lower. It is probable that
1. the nitrate of X is the more stable
2. X is the more reactive to water
3. X displaces Y from a solution of one of its salts   (AEB)

Question 13.3

Use the following list of metals to answer the questions below: aluminium, calcium, copper, iron, lead, magnesium, potassium. Each metal may be used once, more than once or not at all. Select **one** metal in each case which
(a) forms an amphoteric oxide.   **(1 mark)**
(b) would **NOT** displace lead from aqueous lead(II) ions.   **(1 mark)**
(c) reacts on heating with dry chlorine to form a black solid.   **(1 mark)**
(d) will form compounds which impart a lilac (pink) colour to a bunsen flame.   **(1 mark)**
(e) forms a chloride which is insoluble in cold water, but is soluble in hot water.   **(1 mark)**
(f) will sink to the bottom of a beaker of cold water and react vigorously liberating a colourless gas.   **(1 mark)**
                                                                                                         (AEB)

Question 13.4

The extent of temporary hardness of water may be estimated by titration of the hydrogen-carbonate ions in solution with hydrochloric acid according to the equation

$$Ca(HCO_3)_2 + 2HCl \rightarrow CaCl_2 + 2H_2O + 2CO_2$$

(a) In an experiment a 100 cm^3 sample of tap water required 12.0 cm^3 of 0.05 M hydrochloric acid to give an end point using methyl orange indicator.
  (i) How many moles of HCl were added?   **(3 marks)**
  (ii) How many moles of Ca(HCO$_3$)$_2$ were present in 100 cm^3 of tap water, assuming
       that no other carbonates or hydrogencarbonates were present?   **(2 marks)**
  (iii) How many moles of Ca(HCO$_3$)$_2$ were there per dm^3 of tap water?   **(3 marks)**
  (iv) What is the concentration of Ca(HCO$_3$)$_2$ in grams per dm^3?   **(2 marks)**
  (v) Why is an indicator used to find the end point of this titration?   **(3 marks)**
(b) (i) Describe how you could investigate whether a sample of tap water contained both
        temporary and permanent hardness.   **(3 marks)**
    (ii) Explain, with ionic equations, how sodium carbonate removes both forms of hard-
         ness.   **(3 marks)**
(c) Describe experiments you could carry out to prove that the scale in a kettle was mostly
    calcium carbonate.   **(6 marks)**
                                                                                                         (OLE)

13.12 Answers to Self-Test Questions

13.1 **A.**

See Section 13.1.

13.2 **A.**

See Section 13.1.

13.3 (a) aluminium.

Or lead.

  (b) copper.

The metal must be *below* lead in the reactivity series.

(c) iron.

Iron(III) chloride is black, or dark brown.

(d) potassium.

See Section 20.2.

(e) lead.

See Section 13.7.

(f) calcium.

See Section 13.3.

13.4 (a) (i) 1 000 cm^3 of 0.05 M hydrochloric acid contains 0.05 mol of HCl (see Section 20.3).

$$\therefore 12.0 \text{ cm}^3 \text{ of acid contains } 0.05 \times \frac{12}{1000} \text{ mol of HCl}$$

$$= 0.0006 \text{ mol of HCl}$$

(ii) From the equation, mol HCl : mol Ca(HCO$_3$)$_2$ = 2 : 1 = 1 : $\frac{1}{2}$

$$\therefore \text{mol Ca(HCO}_3)_2 = 0.0003$$

(iii) If 100 cm^3 of tap water contains 0.0003 mol of Ca(HCO$_3$)$_2$

$$\therefore 1 \text{ dm}^3 (1\,000 \text{ cm}^3) \text{ contains } 0.003 \text{ mol of Ca(HCO}_3)_2$$

(iv) Molar mass of Ca(HCO$_3$)$_2$ = 40 + 2(1 + 12 + 48) = 162 g mol^{-1}

$$\therefore 1 \text{ dm}^3 \text{ of tap water contains } 0.003 \times 162 = 0.486 \text{ g Ca(HCO}_3)_2$$

i.e. Concentration of Ca(HCO$_3$)$_2$ = 0.486 g per dm^3

(v) An indicator is needed because there is no colour change, no precipitate and no obvious evolution of gas during the titration and therefore no other way of telling where the end point occurs.

(b) (i) Place 50 cm^3 of distilled water in a conical flask, and 0.5 cm^3 of soap solution, stopper the flask and shake it vigorously. If a lather does not remain unbroken on the surface of the water for two minutes, add further 0.5 cm^3 portions of soap solution, shaking after each addition, until it does.

Repeat with 50 cm^3 of tap water in place of the distilled water. If the tap water requires more soap solution than the distilled water did, it is hard.

Boil another 50 cm^3 portion of tap water for a few minutes and then allow it to cool. Replace any water that has evaporated with distilled water so that the volume is again 50 cm^3 and test this with soap solution as before.

If the third sample needs the same volume of soap solution as the first, the hardness was all temporary and has disappeared on boiling. If it needs the same volume as the second sample, the hardness is all permanent and none has disappeared. If the result is somewhere between those of the first and second samples, some, but not all of the hardness has disappeared, so both types must have been present.

(ii) Sodium carbonate removes both forms of hardness by precipitating calcium and magnesium ions as insoluble carbonates.

$$Mg^{2+}(aq) + CO_3^{2-}(aq) \rightarrow MgCO_3(s)$$
$$Ca^{2+}(aq) + CO_3^{2-}(aq) \rightarrow CaCO_3(s)$$

(c) Test for calcium ions and carbonate ions as described in Chapter 20.

14 Carbon

14.1 Carbon

Carbon is an element which exhibits allotropy.

Allotropy is the existence of an element in more than one form in the same state.

The final condition is important in distinguishing allotropy from straightforward melting and boiling.

Carbon has two allotropes, diamond and graphite. Both consist of pure carbon which may be proved by burning equal masses of the two substances in excess oxygen when the same mass of carbon dioxide is obtained from each but no other product is formed (see Question 14.1). Diamond and graphite have widely differing physical properties, these differences being due to variations in the way the atoms are packed together (see Example 14.1).

(a) Reactions and Uses of Carbon

1. Diamond — used in gemstones, cutting tools, rock borers.
2. Graphite — used as a lubricant, moderator in atomic reactors, electrical conductor and in pencil 'leads' (mixed with clay).
3. Carbon is a reducing agent — when carbon is heated with the oxides of the less reactive metals, it reduces them to the metal and is itself oxidised to carbon dioxide

   $$2CuO(s) + C(s) \rightarrow 2Cu(s) + CO_2(g) \qquad \text{(see Section 13.1)}$$

   In industry, coke is used to extract a number of metals such as zinc and iron from their oxide ores.
4. Animal charcoal (made by heating bones in the absence of air) — purifies substances by adsorbing coloured material on its surface.
5. Wood charcoal (made by heating wood in the absence of air) — used to adsorb gases.
6. Carbon fibre — used to strengthen plastics.

14.2 Carbon Dioxide, CO_2

Carbon dioxide may be prepared by the action of almost any acid on any carbonate but the reaction most commonly employed is that between dilute hydrochloric acid and marble chips (calcium carbonate) (see Example 14.3). The gas is passed through water to remove hydrogen chloride and is collected by downward delivery as shown in Example 14.5.

$$CaCO_3(s) + 2HCl(aq) \rightarrow CaCl_2(aq) + H_2O(l) + CO_2(g)$$

(a) Test for Carbon Dioxide

Carbon dioxide turns lime water milky.

$$Ca(OH)_2(aq) + CO_2(g) \rightarrow CaCO_3(s) + H_2O(l)$$

(b) Properties of Carbon Dioxide

1. Carbon dioxide is a colourless, odourless gas.
2. It is denser than air.
3. It dissolves slightly in water to give an acidic solution.

$$CO_2(g) + water \rightleftharpoons CO_2(aq)$$
$$CO_2(aq) + H_2O(l) \rightleftharpoons 2H^+(aq) + CO_3^{2-}(aq)$$

4. Since carbon dioxide is an acidic oxide, it is more soluble in alkalis than in water.

$$CO_2(g) + 2NaOH(aq) \rightarrow Na_2CO_3(aq) + H_2O(l)$$

With excess carbon dioxide, the sodium carbonate formed reacts further to give sodium hydrogencarbonate.

$$Na_2CO_3(aq) + H_2O(l) + CO_2(g) \rightleftharpoons 2NaHCO_3(aq)$$

5. Carbon dioxide does not burn and will only support the combustion of substances which are hot enough to decompose it into its elements (see Example 14.2).

(c) Uses of Carbon Dioxide

1. In fizzy drinks (see Example 14.2).
2. In fire extinguishers (see Example 14.2).
3. As a refrigerant.
4. In the manufacture of sodium carbonate (see Section 18.3).
5. Health salts and baking powder contain sodium hydrogencarbonate and a solid acid such as tartaric acid which react together when water is added to produce carbon dioxide.

(d) Manufacture of Carbon Dioxide

Carbon dioxide is manufactured by heating limestone (calcium carbonate). It is stored under pressure in cylinders.

$$CaCO_3(s) \rightarrow CaO(s) + CO_2(g)$$

14.3 Carbonates

Potassium, sodium and ammonium carbonates are soluble in water, all others being insoluble. The insoluble carbonates can be obtained as precipitates by mixing together solutions containing the required metal ions and carbonate ions.

$$ZnSO_4(aq) + Na_2CO_3(aq) \rightarrow ZnCO_3(s) + Na_2SO_4(aq)$$

Soluble carbonates are prepared from carbon dioxide and the corresponding alkali.

$$CO_2(g) + 2KOH(aq) \rightarrow K_2CO_3(aq) + H_2O(l)$$

All carbonates react with acids to give a salt, water and carbon dioxide (see Example 14.5).

$$CuCO_3(s) + H_2SO_4(aq) \rightarrow CuSO_4(aq) + H_2O(l) + CO_2(g)$$

Carbonates of metals low down in the reactivity series split up on heating to give the metal oxide and carbon dioxide (see Question 14.4).

$$PbCO_3(s) \rightarrow PbO(s) + CO_2(g)$$

14.4 Hydrogencarbonates

The only common solid hydrogencarbonates are those of potassium and sodium; calcium and magnesium hydrogencarbonates are found only in solution. All are prepared by passing excess carbon dioxide through a solution or a suspension of the corresponding hydroxide or carbonate.

$$K_2CO_3(aq) + H_2O(l) + CO_2(g) \rightleftharpoons 2KHCO_3(aq)$$

Hydrogencarbonates give carbon dioxide with acids and when heated.

$$NaHCO_3(s) + HCl(aq) \rightarrow NaCl(aq) + H_2O(l) + CO_2(g)$$
$$2NaHCO_3(s) \rightarrow Na_2CO_3(s) + H_2O(l) + CO_2(g)$$

14.5 The Carbon Cycle

The percentage of carbon dioxide in the atmosphere remains fairly constant. The ways in which carbon atoms circulate in nature are shown in the carbon cycle (see Example 14.6).

14.6 Carbon Monoxide, CO

Carbon monoxide is prepared by passing dry carbon dioxide over strongly heated carbon in the apparatus shown in Example 14.4.

(a) Properties of Carbon Monoxide

1. Carbon monoxide is a colourless, odourless gas.
2. It is slightly less dense than air.
3. It is almost insoluble in water.
4. Carbon monoxide burns in air with a blue flame to form carbon dioxide.

$$2CO(g) + O_2(g) \rightarrow 2CO_2(g)$$

5. It reduces the oxides of the less active metals on heating (see Example 14.5).

$$PbO(s) + CO(g) \longrightarrow Pb(s) + CO_2(g)$$

6. It is extremely poisonous (see Example 14.4).

14.7 Worked Examples

Example 14.1

Carbon is an element which exhibits allotropy. The structures of the two allotropes, diamond and graphite, are shown in the figure.

(a) Explain what is meant by the term 'allotropy'. **(2 marks)**
Allotropy is the existence of an element in more than one form in the same state.

(b) By considering the structures of the allotropes, explain why
　　(i) graphite conducts electricity but diamond does not. **(2 marks)**
In diamond, each carbon atom is using its four bonding electrons to form covalent bonds to four other atoms. In graphite, each carbon atom is bonded to only three others, even though four electrons are available for bonding. The extra electrons are free to move from one hexagon to the next within a layer and thus conduct an electric current.

　　(ii) graphite is soft but diamond is hard. **(2 marks)**
Graphite is made up of layers of hexagons of carbon atoms. The bonding in each layer is strong but the layers are only held together by weak van der Waals' forces. The layers of carbon atoms can thus slide easily over one another. However, in diamond all the bonds are very strong.

　　(iii) graphite has a much lower density than diamond. **(2 marks)**
Although both allotropes consist entirely of carbon atoms, graphite has a more open structure than that of diamond and hence has a lower density.

　　(iv) both substances have high melting points. **(2 marks)**
This is because they both consist of giant structures of atoms (see Section 4.3).

Example 14.2

(a) (i) Give an equation for a reaction in which carbon dioxide is behaving as an oxidising agent. **(1 mark)**

(ii) Mention, and briefly explain, two uses of carbon dioxide in everyday life. **(4 marks)**

(b) (i) Carbon monoxide reacts with iron to give iron carbonyl, $Fe(CO)_5$. How many grams of iron carbonyl could be obtained from 1 dm^3 of carbon monoxide, measured at room temperature and pressure? **(5 marks)**

(a) (i) $2Mg(s) + CO_2(g) \rightarrow 2MgO(s) + C(s)$

Carbon dioxide oxidises the magnesium to white magnesium oxide, itself being reduced to black carbon.

(ii) Carbon dioxide is used in fire extinguishers. Carbon dioxide does not burn and will only support the combustion of substances which are hot enough to decompose it into its elements, e.g. magnesium. The compressed gas may itself be directed on to the fire to blanket the flames (carbon dioxide is more dense than air) or it may be used to eject water, foam or powder from the extinguisher.

Carbon dioxide is used to make fizzy drinks. The carbon dioxide is dissolved under pressure; removing the top from the bottle releases this pressure and bubbles of gas come out of solution.

(b) (i) $Fe(s) + 5CO(g) \rightarrow Fe(CO)_5(l)$

$\text{mol } CO(g) : \text{mol } Fe(CO)_5(l) = 5 : 1 = 1 : 1/5 \ldots\ldots\ldots\ldots\ldots\ldots A$

$dm^3 \, CO(g) = 1$

$\text{mol } CO(g) = 1/24$ (molar volume = 24 $dm^3 \, mol^{-1}$ at room temperature and pressure)

$\text{mol } Fe(CO)_5(l) \qquad = \dfrac{1}{24} \times \dfrac{1}{5} \quad \text{(from A)}$

$\text{g } Fe(CO)_5(l) \qquad = \dfrac{1}{24} \times \dfrac{1}{5} \times 196 \quad (M_r \, (Fe(CO)_5) = 196)$

$\qquad\qquad = 1.63$

Example 14.3

Carbon dioxide is not produced:

A during photosynthesis
B when copper(II) carbonate is heated
C when dilute hydrochloric acid is added to marble chips
D during the fermentation of glucose solution
E when oxygen is passed over heated diamonds.

The answer is **A**.

Carbon dioxide is used up during photosynthesis, not produced.

Example 14.4

Carbon monoxide may be prepared in the apparatus shown in the figure.

(a) Give a physical property of carbon monoxide that is indicated by this method of collection. **(1 mark)** carbon dioxide → / fire-brick / carbon monoxide

carbon   HEAT

concentrated sulphuric acid   concentrated potassium hydroxide solution   water

Carbon monoxide is insoluble in water.

(b) Why is the gas bubbled through potassium hydroxide solution?　**(1 mark)**
This is done to remove unchanged carbon dioxide.

Carbon dioxide reacts with potassium hydroxide solution to form potassium carbonate.

$CO_2(g) + 2KOH(aq) \rightarrow K_2CO_3(aq) + H_2O(l)$

(c) Write a symbol equation to show how carbon dioxide reacts with carbon.　**(2 marks)**
$C(s) + CO_2(g) \rightarrow 2CO(g)$

(d) What would happen if
　(i) a lighted taper were applied to a gas jar of carbon monoxide,　**(2 marks)**
Carbon monoxide burns with a blue flame to form carbon dioxide.
$2CO(g) + O_2(g) \rightarrow 2CO_2(g)$

　(ii) the product were shaken with limewater?　**(2 marks)**
The resulting carbon dioxide will turn the limewater milky.
$Ca(OH)_2(aq) + CO_2(g) \rightarrow CaCO_3(s) + H_2O(l)$
*　　　　　white precipitate*

(e) Explain how breathing in carbon monoxide interferes with the ability of the haemoglobin in the blood to act as an oxygen carrier.　**(2 marks)**

Oxygen combines with haemoglobin and is carried round the blood stream as bright red oxyhaemoglobin, which is unstable and readily gives up its oxygen where required. Carbon monoxide combines with haemoglobin to form cherry-red carboxyhaemoglobin. This is much more stable than oxyhaemoglobin and thus the blood can no longer act as an oxygen carrier.

Example 14.5

(a) (i) Draw a labelled diagram of the apparatus you would use to prepare and collect carbon dioxide, starting with marble chips. Give the equation for the reaction.
　　(ii) State two ways in which the rate of reaction could be increased.　**(6 marks)**
(b) In many places calcium hydrogencarbonate is present in tap water. Explain why this happens. Explain the formation of stalactites and stalagmites in caves through which such water drips.　**(6 marks)**
(c) How could carbon monoxide be prepared from carbon dioxide? Give details of an experiment to prove that carbon monoxide is a reducing agent.　**(8 marks)**
(a) (i) Fig. 14.1.
　　$CaCO_3(s) + 2HCl(aq) \rightarrow CaCl_2(aq) + H_2O(l) + CO_2(g)$
　(ii) The rate could be increased by using more concentrated acid or smaller pieces of marble (see Section 9.1).

Fig. 14.1

(b) Rain water contains dissolved carbon dioxide (see Example 13.6). If this water passes through chalk or limestone regions, then it will dissolve the calcium carbonate to form calcium hydrogencarbonate.

$$CaCO_3(s) + H_2O(l) + CO_2(g) \rightleftharpoons Ca(HCO_3)_2(aq)$$

The slow evaporation of drops of dilute calcium hydrogencarbonate solution hanging from cave roofs causes the above process to reverse and this leaves minute deposits of calcium carbonate behind. As a result of this, stalactites form. Where drops of solution fall to the floor and evaporate, stalagmites grow upwards.

(c) See Example 14.4.

Oxides of the less active metals, e.g. copper(II) oxide, are readily reduced by passing carbon monoxide over the heated metal oxide in the apparatus shown in Fig. 14.2.

Fig. 14.2

The gas collected in the gas jar is shown to be carbon dioxide by testing it with limewater which goes milky. The black copper(II) oxide turns to reddish-brown copper and thus reduction of the copper(II) oxide must have occurred.

$$CuO(s) + CO(g) \rightarrow Cu(s) + CO_2(g)$$

Example 14.6

(a) Explain why the percentage of carbon dioxide in the air stays approximately constant. Give AT LEAST TWO ways in which carbon dioxide is added and TWO ways in which it is removed from the air to illustrate your answer. **(4 marks)**

(b) A white precipitate is formed when
   (i) carbon dioxide is blown into limewater;
   (ii) temporarily hard water is boiled;
   (iii) washing soda is added to water containing dissolved magnesium chloride.
   In each case name the precipitate and write an equation.   **(6 marks)**
(c) Carbon monoxide can be formed according to the equation

$$CO_2 + C \rightarrow 2CO.$$

   (i) Under what conditions does the reaction take place?
   (ii) How would you make sure the carbon monoxide collected was free from unchanged carbon dioxide?
   (iii) Give TWO reasons why carbon monoxide is always collected over water and not by air displacement.
   (iv) Assuming complete conversion, what volume of carbon monoxide can be obtained from 1 dm^3 of carbon dioxide? (All volumes are measured at s.t.p.)   **(5 marks)**
                                                                   (SUJB)

(a) The percentage of carbon dioxide in the air stays approximately constant owing to the delicate balance between the processes evolving the gas and those absorbing it. Carbon dioxide is added through combustion of substances such as coal and petroleum and through respiration. Photosynthesis and the dissolving of carbon dioxide in water remove the gas from the atmosphere.

The ways in which carbon atoms circulate in nature are shown in the carbon cycle (Fig. 14.3).

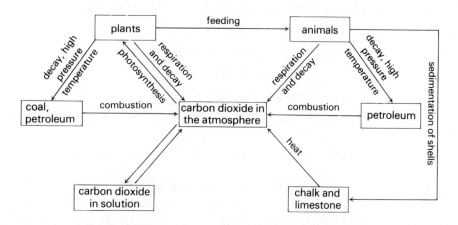

Fig. 14.3

(b) (i) Calcium carbonate is formed.

$$Ca(OH)_2\,(aq) + CO_2\,(g) \rightarrow CaCO_3\,(s) + H_2O\,(l)$$

   (ii) Again, calcium carbonate (or magnesium carbonate) is formed (see Section 13.3).

$$Ca(HCO_3)_2\,(aq) \rightarrow CaCO_3\,(s) + H_2O\,(g) + CO_2\,(g)$$

   (iii) Magnesium carbonate is the precipitate.

$$MgCl_2\,(aq) + Na_2CO_3\,(aq) \rightarrow MgCO_3\,(s) + 2NaCl\,(aq)$$

(c) (i) Carbon dioxide is passed over strongly heated carbon (see Example 14.4).
   (ii) I would pass the product through potassium hydroxide solution.
   (iii) Carbon monoxide is poisonous – this method of collection minimises the risk of carbon monoxide escaping into the air. The density of carbon monoxide is similar to that of air; therefore, collecting the gas by air displacement would be difficult.

147

(iv) 2 dm³ of carbon monoxide is produced.

$CO_2 + C \rightarrow 2CO$
1 mole of carbon dioxide produces 2 moles of carbon monoxide.
1 volume of carbon dioxide produces 2 volumes of carbon monoxide.
1 dm³ of carbon dioxide produces 2 dm³ of carbon monoxide.

Example 14.7

Carbon is able to form a large number of compounds because it:
A is the most abundant element in the earth's crust
B can join onto other carbon atoms to form chains
C exists in two allotropic forms
D forms carbon dioxide which is present in the atmosphere
E occurs in living things.

The answer is **B**.

Example 14.8

Petrol is a mixture of hydrocarbons of the type C_nH_{2n+2}.
(a) Explain the presence of the following gases in the exhaust fumes of a car (equations are **not** expected as part of your answer):
   (i) carbon dioxide;   (2 marks)

Complete combustion of a hydrocarbon produces carbon dioxide and water vapour (see Section 19.2).

   (ii) carbon monoxide.   (2 marks)

If insufficient oxygen is present, then incomplete combustion occurs and carbon monoxide is formed.

(b) Explain the origins of the following substances which are also present in the exhaust fumes:
   (i) lead(II) oxide and lead(II) bromide;   (2 marks)

Tetraethyl-lead(IV) is added to petrol to prevent premature ignition of the mixture of petrol and air in the cylinder of an engine. When burned, this compound produces lead(II) oxide.

To prevent a build-up of lead in the engine, 1,2-dibromoethane is added to the petrol. From this, lead(II) bromide is formed.

   (ii) oxides of nitrogen such as NO and NO_2.   (2 marks)
                                                                           (OLE)

Oxides of nitrogen are produced when the oxygen and nitrogen in the air combine at the high temperatures produced in the engine.

14.8 Self-Test Questions

Question 14.1

Use grid 1 on page 2 to choose an answer **A–E**.
Diamond and graphite resemble each other chemically because they:
1 are both allotropes of carbon

2 both contain atoms of the same kind

3 have atoms arranged in the same way.

Question 14.2

A correct statement about charcoal, graphite, diamond and ethanol is that they all:

A are allotropes of carbon

B have high melting points

C are insoluble in water

D form carbon dioxide on combustion

E decompose on heating to form carbon. (L)

For Questions 14.3 and 14.4 use grid 2 on page 2 to choose an answer **A–E**.

Question 14.3

When carbon dioxide is bubbled into limewater (aqueous calcium hydroxide) a white precipitate is obtained but this redissolves with excess carbon dioxide

BECAUSE

calcium hydroxide is amphoteric.

Question 14.4

When copper(II) carbonate is heated, it turns black

BECAUSE

carbon is one of the constituent elements of copper(II) carbonate.

(L)

14.9 Answers to Self-Test Questions

14.1 B.

14.2 D.

The equations are

$C(s) + O_2(g) \rightarrow CO_2(g)$
$C_2H_5OH(l) + 3O_2(g) \rightarrow 2CO_2(g) + 3H_2O(l)$

14.3 C.

The white precipitate is calcium carbonate but this reacts further to give calcium hydrogencarbonate which is soluble.

$CaCO_3(s) + CO_2(g) + H_2O(l) \rightleftharpoons Ca(HCO_3)_2(aq)$

14.4 B.

When copper(II) carbonate is heated, black copper(II) oxide is formed.

$CuCO_3(s) \rightarrow CuO(s) + CO_2(g)$

15 Nitrogen and Phosphorus

15.1 Nitrogen, N_2

Nitrogen forms about 78% of the air and can be prepared from it by removing oxygen and carbon dioxide. Industrially, nitrogen is obtained by the fractional distillation of liquid air (see Section 10.2).

(a) Properties of Nitrogen

1. Nitrogen is a colourless, odourless gas.
2. It is a little less dense than air.
3. It is almost insoluble in water.
4. Nitrogen is generally unreactive. However, it forms nitrogen monoxide when sparked with oxygen and reacts with hydrogen to give ammonia (see Section 18.5).

$$N_2(g) + O_2(g) \rightleftharpoons 2NO(g)$$
$$N_2(g) + 3H_2(g) \rightleftharpoons 2NH_3(g)$$

(b) Uses of Nitrogen

1. In the manufacture of ammonia.
2. To provide an inert atmosphere.
3. As a refrigerant.

15.2 The Oxides of Nitrogen

Nitrogen dioxide, NO_2, is a dark brown gas with a pungent choking smell. It is extremely poisonous and is one of the pollutants emitted in car exhaust fumes. In the laboratory, nitrogen dioxide may be prepared by the action of concentrated nitric acid on copper or by heating lead(II) nitrate (Example 15.1).

$$Cu(s) + 4HNO_3(aq) \rightarrow Cu(NO_3)_2(aq) + 2H_2O(l) + 2NO_2(g)$$
$$2Pb(NO_3)_2(s) \rightarrow 2PbO(s) + 4NO_2(g) + O_2(g)$$

Nitrogen dioxide may be separated from oxygen by passing the mixture of gases through a U-tube immersed in an ice-salt bath. At room temperature, 'nitrogen dioxide' really consists of nitrogen dioxide and dinitrogen tetraoxide is equilib-rium with one another. Cooling this mixture produces liquid dinitrogen tetraoxide.

$$2NO_2(g) \rightleftharpoons N_2O_4(l)$$

On heating, nitrogen dioxide dissociates into nitrogen monoxide and oxygen and will support the combustion of both a splint and magnesium. It is an acidic oxide, dissolving readily in water to give a mixture of nitric and nitrous acids.

$$2NO_2(g) + H_2O(l) \rightarrow HNO_3(aq) + HNO_2(aq)$$

Nitrogen monoxide, NO, is a colourless gas which is prepared by the action of dilute nitric acid on copper. It is collected over water (see Example 15.1).

On contact with oxygen at room temperature, nitrogen monoxide is immediately oxidised to nitrogen dioxide. Nitrogen monoxide only supports combustion if the flame of the burning substance is hot enough to decompose it into its elements, the oxygen so produced permitting combustion to continue. A burning splint is extinguished but magnesium continues to burn.

Dinitrogen oxide, N_2O, is a colourless gas with a faint, sweetish smell. It is prepared by heating ammonium nitrate and is collected over water.

$$NH_4NO_3(l) \rightarrow N_2O(g) + 2H_2O(g)$$

It is the least thermally stable of the common nitrogen oxides and will even relight a glowing splint.

15.3 Ammonia, NH$_3$

Ammonia is prepared by warming any ammonium salt with any base (see Question 15.1).

$$2NH_4Cl(s) + Ca(OH)_2(s) \rightarrow CaCl_2(s) + 2H_2O(g) + 2NH_3(g)$$

The gas is dried by passing it over calcium oxide and is collected by upward delivery (Example 15.2). Ammonia is manufactured by the Haber process (see Section 18.5).

(a) Tests for Ammonia

Ammonia has a characteristic choking smell and will turn universal indicator paper purple. It gives white fumes of ammonium chloride when mixed with hydrogen chloride (see Example 15.3).

$$NH_3(g) + HCl(g) \rightleftharpoons NH_4Cl(s)$$

(b) Properties of Ammonia

1. Ammonia is a colourless gas with a pungent choking smell.
2. It is about half as dense as air.
3. Ammonia is very soluble in water, giving an alkaline solution.

$$NH_3(g) + \text{water} \rightleftharpoons NH_3(aq)$$
$$NH_3(aq) + H_2O(l) \rightleftharpoons NH_4^+(aq) + OH^-(aq)$$

Since it contains hydroxide ions, ammonia solution neutralises acids (giving ammonium salts) and will also precipitate insoluble metallic hydroxides from solutions containing the metal ions.

4. Ammonia does not burn in air but will burn in oxygen, forming nitrogen and steam (see Example 15.4). Air will oxidise ammonia if a platinum catalyst is present (see Section 18.6).

$$4NH_3(g) + 5O_2(g) \longrightarrow 4NO(g) + 6H_2O(g)$$

oxygen

$$4NO_2(g)$$

5. Ammonia is a reducing agent (see Examples 15.2 and 15.4), e.g. it will reduce the oxides of metals low in the reactivity series.

$$3CuO(s) + 2NH_3(g) \rightarrow 3Cu(s) + N_2(g) + 3H_2O(g)$$

(c) Uses of Ammonia

1. To make nitrogenous fertilisers, e.g. ammonium sulphate.
2. To make nitric acid by the Ostwald process (see Section 18.6).
3. Ammonia solution is used in cleaning.

15.4 Ammonium Salts

Ammonium salts are soluble in water and are prepared by the titration method (see Section 12.6). They decompose on heating and some, such as ammonium chloride, sublime (see Question 15.1). They react with sodium hydroxide solution on warming to give ammonia, this reaction being used to test for their presence.

$$NH_4Cl(aq) + NaOH(aq) \rightarrow NaCl(aq) + NH_3(g) + H_2O(l)$$

15.5 Nitric Acid, HNO$_3$

Nitric acid is prepared in the laboratory by heating sodium or potassium nitrate with concentrated sulphuric acid in the apparatus shown in Question 15.2. The use of all-glass apparatus is necessary because cork and rubber are rapidly attacked by nitric acid vapour.

$$KNO_3(s) + H_2SO_4(l) \rightarrow KHSO_4(s) + HNO_3(l)$$

Nitric acid is manufactured by the Ostwald process (see Section 18.6).

(a) Properties of Nitric Acid

1. Pure nitric acid is a colourless liquid with a fairly low boiling point.
2. On heating, it decomposes into water, nitrogen dioxide and oxygen. The reaction is catalysed by glass (see Example 15.5).

$$4HNO_3(aq) \rightarrow 2H_2O(l) + 4NO_2(g) + O_2(g)$$

3. Dilute nitric acid shows the usual properties of a strong acid (see Section 12.2 and Question 15.4) but it is reduced by metals to one or more of the oxides of nitrogen and does not generally give off hydrogen (see Example 15.5).

4. Concentrated nitric acid is a powerful oxidising agent, converting non-metals such as carbon and sulphur to their oxides and metals to the corresponding nitrates.

(b) Uses of Nitric Acid

1. To make fertilisers, e.g. ammonium nitrate.
2. To make explosives, e.g. TNT.

15.6 Nitrates

All nitrates are soluble in water and are prepared by the titration method (sodium, potassium and ammonium) or by the insoluble base method (see Section 12.6).

$$KOH(aq) + HNO_3(aq) \rightarrow KNO_3(aq) + H_2O(l)$$
$$PbO(s) + 2HNO_3(aq) \rightarrow Pb(NO_3)_2(aq) + H_2O(l)$$

All nitrates decompose on heating. Nitrates of metals at the top of the reactivity series (potassium, sodium) melt and split up to give the nitrite and oxygen.

$$2NaNO_3(l) \rightarrow 2NaNO_2(l) + O_2(g)$$

All other nitrates decompose to give the metal oxide, nitrogen dioxide and oxygen.

$$2Cu(NO_3)_2(s) \rightarrow 2CuO(s) + 4NO_2(g) + O_2(g)$$

(a) Tests for Nitrates

1. Nitrates react with concentrated sulphuric acid to give nitric acid; in the presence of copper powder, brown fumes of nitrogen dioxide are seen.
2. If concentrated sulphuric acid is carefully added to a mixture of a nitrate and iron(II) sulphate in aqueous solution, a brown ring will be seen at the junction of the two layers.

15.7 The Nitrogen Cycle

Nitrogen is essential to plants and animals for the production of protein. This element is recirculated in nature as shown in Example 15.7.

15.8 Proteins

Proteins are produced by living cells to build up animal and plant tissue. They are made from aminoacids, molecules of which contain an amino group ($-NH_2$) and a carboxylic acid group ($-COOH$). All of them evolve ammonia when heated with soda lime (see Example 15.6).

15.9 Phosphorus

Like nitrogen, phosphorus is found in group V of the periodic table. However, it is more reactive than nitrogen, e.g. it will burn with a brilliant yellow flame in a limited air supply to produce phosphorus(III) oxide, P_4O_6, or phosphorus(V) oxide, P_4O_{10}, if the oxygen is in excess. White phosphorus is spontaneously inflammable in chlorine giving phosphorus trichloride or phosphorus pentachloride if the chlorine is in excess. Red phosphorus is much less reactive.

Phosphates are needed for healthy plant and animal life.

15.10 Worked Examples

Example 15.1

(a) Outline the essential features of the manufacture of nitric acid from ammonia. (Details of the plant are **not** required.) **(9 marks)**

(b) Describe, with equations, how dinitrogen tetraoxide (nitrogen dioxide) and nitrogen monoxide may be obtained from nitric acid. (Details of purification or collection of the gases are **not** required.) How could you distinguish between these compounds?

(8 marks)

(c) (i) Calculate the percentage by mass of nitrogen in ammonium sulphate. **(4 marks)**

(ii) Both ammonium sulphate and sodium nitrate are used as fertilisers. Which is the faster acting? Explain your answer. **(4 marks)**

(a) See Example 18.7. (OLE)

(b) Dinitrogen tetraoxide (nitrogen dioxide) is obtained by the action of concentrated nitric acid on copper.

$$Cu(s) + 4HNO_3(aq) \rightarrow Cu(NO_3)_2(aq) + 2H_2O(l) + 2NO_2(g)$$

The 'nitrogen dioxide' produced is really an equilibrium mixture of nitrogen dioxide and dinitrogen tetraoxide (see Section 15.2).

Nitrogen monoxide is prepared by the action of dilute nitric acid (1 volume concentrated acid : 1 volume water) on copper.

$$3Cu(s) + 8HNO_3(aq) \rightarrow 3Cu(NO_3)_2(aq) + 4H_2O(l) + 2NO(g)$$

Nitrogen dioxide is a brown gas which is readily liquefied whereas nitrogen monoxide is a colourless gas which is immediately oxidised to brown fumes of nitrogen dioxide on contact with oxygen at room temperature.

$$2NO(g) + O_2(g) \rightarrow 2NO_2(g)$$

(c) (i) $(NH_4)_2SO_4$

Relative molecular mass $= (14 + 4) \times 2 + 32 + (4 \times 16)$

$= 132$

Percentage of nitrogen $= \dfrac{28}{132} \times 100$

$= 21.2$

(ii) Sodium nitrate. Most plants can take in nitrogen only in the form of nitrates. However, ammonium sulphate can be oxidised to a nitrate by bacteria and so can be used as a fertiliser.

Example 15.2

(a) A student was asked to show her classmates how to prepare a solution of ammonia gas in water, and she set up the apparatus shown in the figure.

State briefly **three** mistakes which she has made in her experiment. **(3 marks)**

Ammonia is produced by warming ammonium chloride with a base such as calcium hydroxide, not from ammonium chloride on its own.

$$2NH_4Cl(s) + Ca(OH)_2(s) \rightarrow CaCl_2(s) + 2H_2O(g) + 2NH_3(g)$$

The tube containing the two solids must be horizontal or sloping downwards. In the figure the tube slopes upwards: this means that the water produced would run back into the hot tube and crack it.

Ammonia is very soluble in water: 'sucking back' would result if it were dissolved by the method shown. The funnel arrangement must be used instead (see Example 18.6).

(b) Write down a balanced equation to show how ammonia gas will reduce copper(II) oxide to the free metal, nitrogen and water. **(1 mark)**

$$3CuO(s) + 2NH_3(g) \rightarrow 3Cu(s) + N_2(g) + 3H_2O(g)$$

(c) Calculate the maximum mass of copper(II) oxide which could be reduced by 68 g of ammonia gas. **(4 marks)**

(OLE)

$$mol\ NH_3(g) : mol\ CuO(s) = 2 : 3 = 1 : 3/2 \ldots\ldots\ldots\ldots\ldots\ldots\ldots\ldots\ A$$

$$g\ NH_3 = 68$$

$$mol\ NH_3 = \frac{68}{17} \qquad (M_r(NH_3) = 17)$$

$$= 4$$

$$mol\ CuO = 4 \times 3/2 \quad (from\ A)$$

$$g\ CuO = 4 \times 3/2 \times 80 \qquad (M_r(CuO) = 80)$$

$$= 480$$

Example 15.3

The gases methylamine (CH_5N) and ammonia are closely related compounds and have very similar properties. Each can be represented by the formula $R-NH_2$.
(i) State what R will be in the case of (1) ammonia, and (2) methylamine. **(4 marks)**
(ii) Predict the effect of methylamine on (1) water coloured purple with litmus solution, and (2) hydrogen chloride gas. **(6 marks)**

(OLE)

(i) (1) R = H
    (2) Methylamine has the formula CH_3NH_2.
        R = CH_3
(ii) (1) The litmus solution will turn blue since methylamine is an alkaline gas.

(2) Methylamine will react with hydrogen chloride to give white fumes, similar to ammonium chloride.

$$CH_3 NH_2 (g) + HCl(g) \rightleftharpoons CH_3 NH_3^+ Cl^- (s)$$
$$c.f. \ NH_3 (g) + HCl(g) \rightleftharpoons NH_4^+ Cl^- (s)$$

Example 15.4

(a) (i) What is the electron arrangement in a nitrogen atom?　　　　**(1 mark)**
2.5

(ii) By means of a drawing, show the electron arrangement in a nitrogen molecule.
　　　　(1 mark)

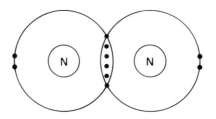

Fig. 15.1

(b) Ammonia burns in oxygen, forming nitrogen and water, according to the equation

$$4NH_3(g) + 3O_2(g) \rightarrow 2N_2(g) + 6H_2O(l)$$

If 80 cm^3 of ammonia are burnt in 100 cm^3 of oxygen, what will be the total volume of gas after combustion and what will be its composition?
(Assume that all volumes are measured at room temperature and pressure.)　　**(4 marks)**

$4NH_3(g)$	$+$	$3O_2(g)$	$\rightarrow$	$2N_2(g)$	$+6H_2O(l)$
4 molecules		3 molecules		2 molecules	6 molecules

By Avogadro's principle:

	4 volumes	3 volumes	2 volumes	–
i.e.	*80 cm^3*	*60 cm^3*	*40 cm^3*	–

Volume of gas after combustion = 40 cm^3 N$_2$ + (100 – 60) cm^3 O$_2$
= 40 cm^3 N$_2$ + 40 cm^3 O$_2$
= 80 cm^3

At room temperature, the water is present as a liquid and so its volume is negligible.

(c) (i) A jet of ammonia is spontaneously inflammable in chlorine producing nitrogen and hydrogen chloride. Write an equation for this reaction.　　**(2 marks)**

$2NH_3(g) + 3Cl_2(g) \rightarrow N_2(g) + 6HCl(g)$

(ii) What will be observed if excess ammonia is used?　　**(2 marks)**

White fumes of ammonium chloride are seen since the hydrogen chloride produced will react with excess ammonia, i.e.
$6NH_3(g) + 6HCl(g) \rightarrow 6NH_4 Cl(s)$
Adding the two equations together gives:
$8NH_3(g) + 3Cl_2(g) \rightarrow N_2(g) + 6NH_4 Cl(s)$

Example 15.5

(a) Describe the industrial preparation of nitric acid from ammonia.   **(5 marks)**
(b) Describe an experiment to show that nitric acid contains oxygen. Give an equation for the reaction which you use.   **(7 marks)**
(c) Explain why hydrogen is evolved when very dilute nitric acid is added to magnesium, but when concentrated acid is used nitrogen dioxide is evolved.   **(3 marks)**

(SUJB)

(a) See Example 18.7.
(b) The apparatus is set up as shown in Fig. 15.2 and the glass wool heated strongly. The first few bubbles of gas are allowed to escape into the atmosphere

Fig. 15.2

and then a test-tube full of the resulting gas is collected. This is tested with a glowing splint which relights, showing the gas to be oxygen.

$$4HNO_3(aq) \rightarrow 2H_2O(l) + 4NO_2(g) + O_2(g)$$

(c) When very dilute nitric acid is added to magnesium the nitric acid acts as a normal acid and hence reacts to give hydrogen.

$$Mg(s) + 2HNO_3(aq) \rightarrow Mg(NO_3)_2(aq) + H_2(g)$$

However, concentrated nitric acid acts as an oxidising agent and is itself reduced to nitrogen dioxide.

$$Mg(s) + 4HNO_3(aq) \rightarrow Mg(NO_3)_2(aq) + 2NO_2(g) + 2H_2O(l)$$

Example 15.6

A substance was heated with soda lime. An alkaline gas was given off. The substance could have been
A A protein.
B A sugar.
C Cellulose.
D A vegetable oil.   (SEB)

The answer is **A**.

Proteins are nitrogen containing compounds which react with soda lime to give ammonia.

Example 15.7

(i) What atmospheric conditions are needed for atmospheric nitrogen to be converted into nitrogen compounds in the soil (reaction 1)? **(1 mark)**

A lightning flash.

The energy in a lightning flash can cause atmospheric nitrogen and oxygen to combine to produce nitrogen monoxide. This combines with more oxygen to produce nitrogen dioxide which dissolves in water to enter the soil as nitric acid.

(ii) Some plants have bacteria in their roots and can absorb nitrogen directly from the atmosphere (reaction 2). Name one such plant. **(1 mark)**

Any leguminous plant, such as peas, beans or lupins, is a suitable answer.

(iii) What class of soluble nitrogen compound found in soil is absorbed through the roots of plants (reaction 3)? **(1 mark)**

Nitrates.

(iv) Name a type of nitrogen compound which is found in all plants and animals. **(1 mark)**

Proteins.

(v) How is reaction 4 brought about? **(1 mark)**

Plants are eaten by animals.

(vi) Suggest one way by which soluble nitrogen compounds in the soil are converted to atmospheric nitrogen (reaction 5). **(1 mark)**

Bacteria in the soil bring about this reaction.

(vii) Explain why it is necessary to add artificial fertilisers to the soil. **(2 marks)**

Man's removal of plants and animals from the land for use as food, together with modern methods of sewage disposal, result in insufficient nitrogen being returned to the soil by decay and excretion. It is essential to restore the balance using artificial fertilisers.

(viii) Name one nitrogen containing compound used as a fertiliser. **(1 mark)**

Any one of ammonium nitrate, sodium nitrate or ammonium sulphate is a suitable answer.

(ix) Name two other elements which are required for healthy plant life. **(1 mark)**

Potassium and phosphorus.

15.11 Self-Test Questions

Question 15.1

(a) The apparatus shown below was assembled and the ammonium chloride was gently heated. It was noticed that litmus paper A started to turn red and litmus paper B became blue; a white solid was seen to form near the cool, open end of the test-tube.

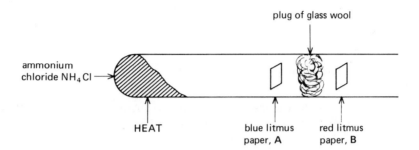

plug of glass wool

ammonium chloride NH_4Cl

HEAT

blue litmus paper, A

red litmus paper, B

  (i) Explain what happened to the ammonium chloride when it was heated and name the white solid formed near the open end of the test-tube. Write an appropriate equation.

  (ii) Explain briefly why the atmosphere in the vicinity of A became acidic while in the vicinity of B it became alkaline. **(12 marks)**

(b) (i) Name a chemical which reacts with ammonium chloride to form ammonia gas, and write an equation for the reaction. Give the name of a suitable drying agent for ammonia and state how the gas might be collected after drying.

  (ii) Calculate the volume of ammonia which could be obtained at room temperature and pressure from 10.7 g of ammonium chloride. **(8 marks)**

(c) Describe briefly **one** simple chemical test which would distinguish between aqueous ammonium chloride and aqueous ammonium sulphate. Write an equation for the reaction. **(4 marks)**

(AEB)

Questions 15.2–15.6

Directions. This group of questions deals with laboratory situations. Each situation is followed by a set of questions. Select the best answer for each question.

Questions 15.2–15.6 concern the preparation of nitric acid, using the simple distillation apparatus below. When sodium nitrate is mixed with concentrated sulphuric acid, an equilibrium is established:

$$NaNO_3(s) + H_2SO_4(l) \rightleftharpoons HNO_3(l) + NaHSO_4(s).$$

mixture of sodium nitrate and concentrated sulphuric acid

water-cooled condenser

HEAT

nitric acid

Nitric acid distils over when the mixture is heated. It is a fuming liquid with a boiling point of $83°C$ and a density of 1.5 g cm^{-3}. Sulphuric acid has a boiling point of $330°C$ and a density of 1.8 g cm^{-3}.

The 'nitric acid' obtained by this experiment is only 70% nitric acid by mass. Pure nitric acid is obtained by vacuum distillation. 63 g (1 mole) of pure nitric acid was added to water and then made up to 1000 cm^3 of solution and a rise in temperature of $4.8°C$ was observed. The dilute acid is a good conductor of electricity.
[4.2 kJ of heat energy raises the temperature of 1000 g of water by $1°C$.]

Question 15.2

Nitric acid distils off from the equilibrium mixture in the flask when it is heated because
A nitric acid is the only substance in the mixture which is capable of being vaporized
B nitric acid has a lower density than sulphuric acid
C nitric acid has a lower boiling point than sulphuric acid
D sulphuric acid must remain behind to form NaHSO$_4$
E sulphuric acid is stronger than nitric acid   (L)

Question 15.3

The distillation of the nitric acid affects the chemical equilibrium in the flask by making
A the reaction go more to the right
B the reaction go more to the left
C both forward and backward reactions slow down
D the temperature of the equilibrium mixture lower
E the nitric acid concentration greater   (L)

Question 15.4

Which of the following is a possible product of the reaction of dilute nitric acid with marble chips?
A Calcium
B Calcium oxide
C Calcium hydroxide
D Carbon dioxide
E Hydrogen   (L)

Question 15.5

The likely cause of the rise in temperature when the pure nitric acid is added to water is that
A the water is broken up into H$^+$ and OH$^-$ ions
B the acid is broken up into H$^+$ ions and nitrate ions
C the acid combines with the water to form H$_3$NO$_4$ molecules
D the water takes protons from the acid to form H$_3$O$^+$(aq) ions
E the acid is broken up by the water to give H$_2$(g)   (L)

Question 15.6

From the experimental observations, an approximate value of ΔH for the dilution of 1 mole of nitric acid is

A -4.2×4.8 kJ mol^{-1}

B $-\dfrac{4.2}{4.8}$ kJ mol^{-1}

C $-\dfrac{4.2}{63} \times 4.8$ kJ mol^{-1}

D $\dfrac{4.2}{63} \times 4.8$ kJ mol^{-1}

E $4.2 \times 4.8 \times 63$ kJ mol^{-1} (L)

15.12 Answers to Self-Test Questions

15.1 (a) (i) The ammonium chloride sublimed (see Section 1.4). On heating, ammonium chloride dissociates to give ammonia and hydrogen chloride but these gases recombine on cooling. The white solid is thus ammonium chloride.

$$NH_4Cl(s) \rightleftharpoons NH_3(g) + HCl(g)$$

(ii) Ammonia, being less dense than hydrogen chloride, diffuses more quickly through the glass wool plug so that it will reach litmus paper B before hydrogen chloride does.

(b) (i) Copper(II) oxide.

In fact, any base will do.

$$2NH_4Cl(s) + CuO(s) \rightarrow CuCl_2(s) + 2NH_3(g) + H_2O(g)$$

The gas may be dried using potassium hydroxide pellets or calcium oxide and collected by upward delivery of air.

(ii) From the above equation,

mol NH_4Cl : mol NH_3 = 2 : 2 = 1 : 1 . . . . A

g NH_4Cl = 10.7

mol NH_4Cl = $\dfrac{10.7}{53.5}$ $(M_r(NH_4Cl) = 53.5)$

mol NH_3 = $\dfrac{10.7}{53.5} \times 1$ (from A)

dm^3 NH_3 = $\dfrac{10.7}{53.5} \times 24$ (molar volume at room temperature and pressure = 24 dm^3 mol^{-1})

= 4.8

(c) If barium chloride solution is added, aqueous ammonium sulphate gives a white precipitate of barium sulphate.

$$(NH_4)_2SO_4(aq) + BaCl_2(aq) \rightarrow BaSO_4(s) + 2NH_4Cl(aq)$$

15.2 C.

15.3 A.

15.4 D.

Marble chips (calcium carbonate) react with nitric acid to give carbon dioxide.

$CaCO_3(s) + 2HNO_3(aq) \rightarrow Ca(NO_3)_2(aq) + H_2O(l) + CO_2(g)$

15.5 D.

Do not make the mistake of thinking that the answer is **B**. The nitric acid will break up into H^+ and nitrate ions but this is an endothermic process (bonds broken). The exothermic reaction that occurs is the hydration of the protons (bonds made), i.e.

$H_2O(l) + HNO_3(aq) \rightarrow H_3O^+(aq) + NO_3^-(aq)$

15.6 A (see Chapter 8).

16 Oxygen and Sulphur

16.1 Oxygen, O_2

Oxygen is prepared in the laboratory by adding 20 volumes hydrogen peroxide solution to manganese(IV) oxide as shown in Example 16.1 (see also Example 16.3).

$$2H_2O_2(aq) \rightarrow 2H_2O(l) + O_2(g)$$

Oxygen is manufactured by the fractional distillation of liquid air (see Section 10.2).

(a) Test for Oxygen

Oxygen relights a glowing splint.

(b) Properties of Oxygen

1. Oxygen is a colourless, odourless gas.
2. It is a little more dense than air.
3. It is slightly soluble in water.
4. Oxygen reacts with most elements to give their oxides (see Example 16.1), e.g. sodium burns with a yellow flame to give sodium oxide.

$$4Na(s) + O_2(g) \rightarrow 2Na_2O(s).$$

Sulphur burns with a bright blue flame to give mainly sulphur dioxide.

$$S(s) + O_2(g) \rightarrow SO_2(g)$$

(c) Uses of Oxygen

1. In steel making to remove impurities from cast iron (see Section 18.1).
2. In oxy-acetylene blowpipes which are used for cutting and welding steel.
3. As an aid to breathing, e.g. in hospitals and climbing.
4. In rocket fuels.

16.2 Oxides

Oxides are compounds of oxygen with one other element, e.g. sodium oxide, Na_2O. There are several different types of oxide and these are discussed in Example 16.2.

16.3　Metal Hydroxides

A **metal hydroxide** is made up of metal ions and hydroxide ions (OH^-). Most metal hydroxides are insoluble in water and may be prepared by precipitation (see Section 12.6), e.g.

$$FeCl_3(aq) + 3NaOH(aq) \rightarrow Fe(OH)_3(s) + 3NaCl(aq)$$

Soluble hydroxides can be formed by the addition of the metal oxide to water (see Example 16.1).

All metal hydroxides dissolve in acids to give a salt and water only but the amphoteric hydroxides (e.g. aluminium, zinc and lead hydroxides) dissolve in alkalis as well (see Question 16.1).

$$Cu(OH)_2(s) + H_2SO_4(aq) \rightarrow CuSO_4(aq) + 2H_2O(l)$$

The hydroxides of potassium and sodium are stable to heat but those of metals below sodium in the reactivity series decompose into the corresponding oxide and water on heating, e.g.

$$Cu(OH)_2(s) \rightarrow CuO(s) + H_2O(l)$$

16.4　Hydrogen Peroxide, H_2O_2

Hydrogen peroxide solution decomposes slowly at room temperature as shown in Section 16.1. It is an oxidising agent (see Example 16.3) but when mixed with oxidising agents more powerful than itself, hydrogen peroxide solution acts as a reducing agent, e.g. it will decolorise an acidified solution of potassium manganate(VII).

(a)　Uses of Hydrogen Peroxide

1. As a rocket fuel.
2. To bleach hair and clothing.
3. In toothpaste and antiseptics.

16.5　Sulphur

Sulphur is extracted from underground deposits by the Frasch process (see Example 16.6). There are two allotropes of sulphur: rhombic sulphur (stable below $96°C$) and monoclinic sulphur (stable above $96°C$) (see Example 16.4). If monoclinic sulphur is kept at room temperature for a few days it gradually changes to the rhombic form. Similarly rhombic sulphur changes to monoclinic sulphur at temperatures greater than $96°C$.

The temperature at which one allotrope of an element changes to another is called the *transition temperature*.

Both allotropes of sulphur consist of S_8 molecules in which the atoms are arranged in puckered rings but these molecules are packed together in different ways in the two types of crystal. If liquid sulphur (see Example 16.5) is rapidly cooled, a black pliable solid called plastic sulphur is obtained. This contains long chains of atoms which have not had time to reform S_8 rings.

164

(a) Properties of Sulphur

1. Sulphur is a yellow, non-metallic solid.
2. It is insoluble in water.
3. Sulphur is soluble in organic solvents, e.g. methylbenzene.
4. When heated, sulphur combines with most metals to form sulphides and with non-metals such as oxygen, chlorine and hydrogen, e.g.

$$Zn(s) + S(s) \rightarrow ZnS(s)$$
$$H_2(g) + S(s) \rightarrow H_2S(g)$$

(b) Uses of Sulphur

1. To make sulphuric acid.
2. To vulcanise (harden) rubber.
3. As a fungicide.
4. To make ointments and drugs.

16.6 Hydrogen Sulphide, H_2S

Hydrogen sulphide is prepared in the laboratory by the action of a dilute acid on a metal sulphide, e.g.

$$FeS(s) + 2HCl(aq) \rightarrow FeCl_2(aq) + H_2S(g)$$

The gas is bubbled through distilled water to remove hydrogen chloride and is then collected by downward delivery.

(a) Test for Hydrogen Sulphide

Hydrogen sulphide smells of bad eggs and turns a moist lead(II) ethanoate paper black (see Question 16.3).

$$(CH_3COO)_2Pb(aq) + H_2S(g) \rightarrow PbS(s) + 2CH_3COOH(aq)$$

(b) Properties of Hydrogen Sulphide

1. Hydrogen sulphide is a colourless, very poisonous gas.
2. It has a characteristic smell.
3. It is slightly more dense than air.
4. It is slightly soluble in water.
5. Hydrogen sulphide burns in air with a blue flame to give steam and sulphur dioxide but if the air supply is limited, sulphur is formed.
6. It is a powerful reducing agent.

16.7 Sulphides

A sulphide is a compound made up of sulphur and one other element, e.g. lead(II) sulphide, PbS.

Most sulphides are insoluble in water. They can be prepared by direct combination of the metal and sulphur:

$$Zn(s) + S(s) \rightarrow ZnS(s)$$

or by bubbling hydrogen sulphide through a solution of the appropriate metal salt (see Example 16.4 and Question 16.2).

$$CuSO_4(aq) + H_2S(g) \rightarrow CuS(s) + H_2SO_4(aq)$$

Because hydrogen sulphide so readily forms metal sulphides, it darkens lead paints and tarnishes clean metal surfaces.

Metal sulphides react with dilute acids to give hydrogen sulphide.

16.8 Sulphur Dioxide, SO_2

Sulphur dioxide is prepared by warming a dilute acid with a sulphite. The gas is dried by passing it through concentrated sulphuric acid and is collected by downward delivery.

$$Na_2SO_3(s) + 2HCl(aq) \rightarrow 2NaCl(aq) + H_2O(l) + SO_2(g)$$

(a) Tests for Sulphur Dioxide

Sulphur dioxide has a characteristic choking smell and turns a moist potassium dichromate(VI) paper from orange to green owing to reduction.

(b) Properties of Sulphur Dioxide

1. Sulphur dioxide is a colourless, poisonous gas.
2. It has a characteristic smell.
3. It is about twice as dense as air.
4. Sulphur dioxide is very soluble in water. It reacts with water to give a solution of sulphurous acid, H_2SO_3.
5. It is a powerful reducing agent. An aqueous solution of sulphur dioxide is readily oxidised to sulphuric acid, H_2SO_4.
6. It is an oxidising agent. Sulphur dioxide can react as an oxidising agent with reducing agents more powerful than itself, e.g. burning magnesium continues to burn with a bright white flame, forming yellow sulphur and a white ash of magnesium oxide.

$$2Mg(s) + SO_2(g) \rightarrow 2MgO(s) + S(s)$$

(c) Uses of Sulphur Dioxide

1. As an intermediate in the production of sulphuric acid.
2. As a bleaching agent.
3. To preserve food.

16.9 Sulphur Trioxide, SO_3

Sulphur trioxide is prepared in the laboratory by the catalytic (platinised asbestos) oxidation of sulphur dioxide (see Example 16.7).

$$2SO_2(g) + O_2(g) \rightleftharpoons 2SO_3(g)$$

It reacts violently with water to form sulphuric acid.

16.10 Sulphuric Acid, H_2SO_4

Sulphuric acid is prepared by dissolving sulphur trioxide in concentrated sulphuric acid and then pouring the liquid into water (see Section 18.4).

(a) Properties of Concentrated Sulphuric Acid (see Example 16.10)

1. Sulphuric acid is a colourless, oily liquid.
2. It is **hygroscopic** (it absorbs water vapour from the atmosphere – see Section 11.2). This makes it useful for drying gases (see Example 16.9 and Question 16.4).
3. It is a **dehydrating agent** (it can remove chemically combined water or the elements of water from other compounds) (see Example 16.10).
4. Concentrated sulphuric acid is a powerful oxidising agent (see Example 16.11).
5. It will displace more volatile acids when heated with their salts.
6. Dilute sulphuric acid behaves as a typical strong acid (see Section 12.2 and Example 16.7).

(b) Uses of Sulphuric Acid

1. To manufacture fertilisers, such as ammonium sulphate and 'superphosphate'.
2. In the production of synthetic fibres and plastics.
3. To 'pickle' steel (i.e. clean the surface prior to plating with another metal).
4. To make soapless detergents.
5. In car batteries.

16.11 Sulphates and Hydrogensulphates

These are prepared as described in Section 12.6. Hydrogensulphates are examples of acid salts.

(a) Test for Sulphates

If dilute hydrochloric acid followed by a few drops of barium chloride solution is added to a sulphate solution, a white precipitate of barium sulphate is obtained, e.g.

$$Na_2SO_4(aq) + BaCl_2(aq) \rightarrow BaSO_4(s) + 2NaCl(aq).$$

16.12 Worked Examples

Example 16.1

Oxygen can be prepared by adding hydrogen peroxide solution to manganese(IV) oxide. The manganese(IV) oxide is recovered unchanged in mass at the end of the reaction.

(a) What is the function of the manganese(IV) oxide in this reaction? **(1 mark)**
(b) Draw a diagram of the apparatus which you could use to prepare and collect several gas jars of oxygen. **(3 marks)**

Sodium and sulphur both burn in oxygen and the product of each reaction is soluble in water.

(c) Name the product formed when each element burns in oxygen. **(2 marks)**
(d) Give the names and approximate pH values of the two aqueous solutions. **(3 marks)**

When zinc combines with oxygen the compound formed is insoluble in water but dissolves in both dilute hydrochloric acid and in sodium hydroxide solution.

(e) What is the word used to describe the behaviour of the zinc compound? **(1 mark)**
(f) Describe in outline the commercial preparation of oxygen from the air? **(3 marks)**
(g) Give two large-scale uses of oxygen. **(2 marks)**

(a) The manganese(IV) oxide acts as a catalyst.

(b)

Fig. 16.1

(c) Sodium oxide. Sulphur dioxide.

The equations for these reactions are

$4Na(s) + O_2(g) \rightarrow 2Na_2O(s)$
$S(s) + O_2(g) \rightarrow SO_2(g)$

(d) Sodium hydroxide pH 12. Sulphurous acid pH 4.

The equations for these reactions are
$Na_2O(s) + H_2O(l) \rightarrow 2NaOH(aq)$
$SO_2(g) + water \rightleftharpoons SO_2(aq)$
$SO_2(aq) + H_2O(l) \rightleftharpoons H_2SO_3(aq)$

(e) Amphoteric.
(f) Oxygen is manufactured by the fractional distillation of liquid air (see Section 10.2).
(g) Choose any two of the uses in Section 16.1 for your answer.

Example 16.2

Classify the following oxides as acidic, basic, neutral or amphoteric:
(i) ZnO;
(ii) NO_2;

(iii) MgO;

(iv) Al_2O_3;

(v) CO. (5 marks)

(i) Amphoteric;

(ii) acidic;

(iii) basic;

(iv) amphoteric;

(v) neutral.

There are several types of oxide:

(a) Acidic oxides are usually the oxides of non-metals. They react with bases to form salts and with alkalis to form salts and water only. Many of them combine with water to form acids.

(b) Basic oxides are the oxides of metals. They react with acids to form salts and water only. If they dissolve in water they form alkalis.

(c) Neutral oxides are oxides of a few non-metals. They react with neither acids nor bases.

(d) Amphoteric oxides are the oxides of certain metals in the middle groups of the periodic table, e.g. aluminium, zinc and lead. They have the properties of both acidic and basic oxides, i.e. they react with both alkalis and acids to form salts and water only.

Example 16.3

(a) Hydrogen peroxide is an *oxidising agent*. Explain this statement by reference to its reactions with

(i) lead(II) sulphide (black). (2 marks)

The reaction which takes place is

$PbS(s) + 4H_2O_2(aq) \rightarrow PbSO_4(s) + 4H_2O(l)$

Oxygen is added to black lead(II) sulphide, oxidising it to white lead(II) sulphate.

(ii) iron(II) sulphate solution. (3 marks)

The reaction is

$2FeSO_4(aq) + H_2O_2(aq) + H_2SO_4(aq) \rightarrow Fe_2(SO_4)_3(aq) + 2H_2O(l)$

Green $Fe^{2+}(aq)$ ions lose electrons and are oxidised to brown/yellow $Fe^{3+}(aq)$ ions.

(b) Hydrogen peroxide decomposes in the presence of a *catalyst*.

(i) Write an equation for the decomposition. (2 marks)

$2H_2O_2(aq) \rightarrow 2H_2O(l) + O_2(g)$

(ii) Name a suitable catalyst and explain the meaning of this term. (3 marks)

(OLE)

A suitable catalyst is manganese(IV) oxide.

A catalyst is a substance which alters the rate of a chemical reaction but may be recovered unchanged in mass at the end (see Section 9.1).

Example 16.4

(a) Starting from powdered roll sulphur, describe how you would prepare two allotropic forms. Make sketches to show the difference in crystal structure. (8 marks)

(b) Give TWO large-scale uses of sulphur. (2 marks)

(c) Hydrogen sulphide reacts with lead ions in solution according to the equation:

$$Pb^{2+}(aq) + H_2S(g) \rightarrow PbS(s) + 2H^+(aq).$$

What volume of hydrogen sulphide at s.t.p. will be needed to react with a solution containing 0.2 mole of lead(II) ions, and what mass of lead(II) sulphide will be precipitated?   **(5 marks)**
(SUJB)

(a) A boiling tube containing 20 cm³ methylbenzene is placed in a beaker of water at 80°C (no flames). A spatula measure of powdered roll sulphur is added, the mixture stirred for 5 minutes and then filtered. The filtrate is allowed to cool when it yields crystals of rhombic sulphur.

A spatula measure of powdered roll sulphur is added to the mixture obtained in the first part of the experiment and the apparatus set up as shown in Fig. 16.2.

20 cm length of glass tubing

HEAT

Fig. 16.2

The mixture is warmed gently over a small flame until the liquid boils. The tube is then wrapped in a cloth and allowed to cool down slowly to yield crystals of monoclinic sulphur (Fig. 16.3).

rhombic sulphur

monoclinic sulphur

Fig. 16.3

(b) Choose any two of the uses in Section 16.5 for your answer.
(c) $Pb^{2+}(aq) + H_2S(g) \rightarrow PbS(s) + 2H^+(aq)$

mol $Pb^{2+}(aq)$: mol $H_2S(g) = 1 : 1$

$$\text{mol Pb}^{2+}(\text{aq}) = 0.2$$
$$\text{mol H}_2\text{S}(\text{g}) = 0.2$$
$$\text{dm}^3 \text{ H}_2\text{S}(\text{g}) \text{ at s.t.p.} = 0.2 \times 22.4 \quad \text{(see Section 6.1)}$$
$$= 4.48$$
$$\text{mol Pb}^{2+}(\text{aq}) : \text{mol PbS}(\text{s}) = 1 : 1$$
$$\text{mol PbS}(\text{s}) = 0.2$$
$$\text{g PbS}(\text{s}) = 0.2 \times 239 \quad (M_r(\text{PbS}) = 207 + 32 = 239)$$
$$= 47.8$$

Example 16.5

(a) What changes would you observe when powdered roll sulphur is heated in a test tube to just below its boiling point? **(5 marks)**
(b) Given a finely powdered mixture of sulphur, salt and chalk, describe how you would recover a pure dry sample of each. **(7 marks)**
(c) Hydrogen sulphide can be prepared by treating iron(II) sulphide with dilute sulphuric acid. What volume of hydrogen sulphide, measured at s.t.p., can be obtained from 17.6 g of iron(II) sulphide? **(3 marks)**
(SUJB)

(a) Sulphur melts at 113°C to give a mobile (runny) amber liquid. As the temperature rises the liquid darkens and at about 180°C it becomes very viscous (thick). If the temperature is increased still further the liquid once more becomes mobile.

When the sulphur has just melted the S_8 rings are moving with random motion. Increasing the temperature increases the energy of the collisions between the S_8 rings and causes them to break open and join together to form long chains containing up to 10^6 atoms. These chains become entangled with one another, thus preventing the liquid from flowing, i.e. it becomes viscous. Further increase of temperature means that the vibration of the atoms within the chains causes them to break up into shorter lengths and the liquid becomes mobile again.

(b) Sulphur is soluble in methylbenzene. Methylbenzene is added to the mixture which is stirred well and then filtered. The filtrate (sulphur solution) is collected in an evaporating basin and the methylbenzene allowed to evaporate at room temperature.

Salt is soluble in water. The residue from the first part is added to warm water, stirred and filtered. The filtrate (salt solution) is evaporated to dryness (see Section 1.4).

The chalk is the residue on the filter paper. This can be washed with water and dried in a warm oven.

NB. You are asked to obtain a dry sample of each substance — it is not sufficient just to separate the solids.

(c) $\text{FeS}(\text{s}) + \text{H}_2\text{SO}_4(\text{aq}) \rightarrow \text{FeSO}_4(\text{aq}) + \text{H}_2\text{S}(\text{g})$
$$\text{mol FeS}(\text{s}) : \text{mol H}_2\text{S}(\text{g}) = 1 : 1$$

$$\text{g FeS}(\text{s}) = 17.6 \quad . \quad . \quad . \quad . \quad . \quad . \quad . \quad \text{A}$$

$$\text{mol FeS}(\text{s}) = \frac{17.6}{88} \quad M_r(\text{FeS}) = 56 + 32 = 88$$

$$\text{mol H}_2\text{S}(\text{g}) = \frac{17.6}{88} \times 1 \quad \text{(from A)}$$

171

$$\text{dm}^3 \ H_2S(g) \text{ at s.t.p.} = \frac{17.6}{88} \times 22.4 \qquad \text{(see Section 6.1)}$$

$$= 4.48$$

Example 16.6

Sulphur is extracted from underground deposits by the Frasch process. Three concentric pipes, A, B and C, are sunk down to the deposits as shown in the figure.

Water at 170°C is pumped down the outer pipe.

(i) Explain how it is possible to obtain water with a temperature of 170°C.　　(1 mark)
(ii) What is the water used for?　　(1 mark)
(iii) What is passed down tube C?　　(1 mark)
(iv) What happens in tube B?　　(1 mark)

(i) Water boils at 100°C at 1 atm pressure. If the pressure is increased, the boiling point of the water is raised.
(ii) The water is used to melt the sulphur.
(iii) Hot compressed air.
(iv) A froth of water, air and molten sulphur is forced up the middle pipe and is led off to settling tanks where the sulphur separates out.

Example 16.7

(a) Aqueous hydrochloric acid was reacted with sodium sulphite and a gas **A** was evolved. This gas was dried, mixed with oxygen and then passed over a catalyst, **B**, maintained at 400°C; an exothermic reaction occurred. The product was cooled by an ice-salt mixture and colourless crystals, **C**, were formed. When these crystals were dissolved in excess water, heat was evolved and a colourless solution, **D**, which had a very low pH value, resulted.

(i) Identify **A**, **B**, **C** and **D**, and write equations for the reactions which occurred.
(ii) Suggest a suitable drying agent for gas **A**.
(iii) Describe **one** chemical test which could be used to identify gas **A**.
(iv) State and explain what would happen if the temperature of the catalyst were raised to 500°C.
(v) Write an ionic equation for the reaction which would occur between solution **D** and zinc metal.

(vi) Name the product of the reaction of **D** with excess ammonia and state one use for
it. **(19 marks)**

(b) 1 dm³ of aqueous hydrochloric acid of concentration 1 mol/dm³ was exactly neutralised
by aqueous sodium hydroxide and the heat energy liberated was 57 kJ.

  (i) Write an ionic equation for the reaction which took place.

  (ii) How much heat energy would be evolved if 1 dm³ of the hydrochloric acid was
  neutralised by aqueous calcium hydroxide?

Explain clearly your reasoning. **(5 marks)**

(AEB)

(a)   (i) A is sulphur dioxide.

$$Na_2SO_3(s) + 2HCl(aq) \rightarrow 2NaCl(aq) + H_2O(l) + SO_2(g)$$

B is platinised asbestos.

In industry the catalyst is made from vanadium(V) oxide and alkali metal sulphates.

C is sulphur trioxide.

$$2SO_2(g) + O_2(g) \rightleftharpoons 2SO_3(g)$$

D is sulphuric acid.

$$SO_3(s) + H_2O(l) \rightarrow H_2SO_4(aq)$$

  (ii) Concentrated sulphuric acid.

  (iii) A moist potassium dichromate(VI) paper turns green in sulphur dioxide
  owing to reduction.

  (iv) An increase in temperature reduces the yield of sulphur trioxide. If the
  temperature is raised, the system will adjust itself in such a way as to
  tend to lower the temperature again. Since the forward reaction is
  exothermic, the reverse reaction must be endothermic and so a shift in
  the equilibrium to the left will tend to lower the temperature (see
  Section 9.3).

  (v) $Zn(s) + 2H^+(aq) \rightarrow Zn^{2+}(aq) + H_2(g)$

  (vi) The product is ammonium sulphate which is used as a fertiliser.
  $$2NH_3(aq) + H_2SO_4(aq) \rightarrow (NH_4)_2SO_4(aq)$$

(b)   (i) $H^+(aq) + OH^-(aq) \rightarrow H_2O(l)$

  (ii) 57 kJ. The ionic equation for this reaction is the same as in (i). Since
  the same volume of hydrochloric acid is used the same amount of heat
  energy is evolved (see Section 8.2).

Example 16.8

(a) Write down balanced equations to show how

  (i) sulphur dioxide may form sulphur trioxide; **(2 marks)**

$$2SO_2(g) + O_2(g) \rightleftharpoons 2SO_3(g)$$

  (ii) sulphur trioxide forms sulphuric acid. **(2 marks)**

$$SO_3(s) + H_2O(l) \rightarrow H_2SO_4(aq) \quad \text{(see Example 16.7)}$$

(b) Rain falling near some power stations is often slightly acidic. This 'acidic' rain may be
seen to affect some city statues and buildings but not others. Explain this observation.

(2 marks)

(OLE)

Coal-burning power stations generate sulphur dioxide which dissolves in water to form sulphurous acid and by oxidation sulphuric acid ('acidic' rain). The 'acidic' rain will attack those building materials which react with acids, e.g. marble.

Example 16.9

Explain the following observation: concentrated sulphuric acid left in an unstoppered bottle increases in volume. **(3 marks)**
(SUJB)

Concentrated sulphuric acid is hygroscopic, i.e. it absorbs moisture from the atmosphere, thereby increasing in volume and becoming more dilute.

Example 16.10

Describe how sulphuric acid reacts with each of the following. State whether concentrated or dilute acid is used and write an equation for the reaction.
  (i) sodium chloride,
 (ii) potassium nitrate,
(iii) copper(II) sulphate crystals,
(iv) sugar,
 (v) magnesium. **(2 marks each)**

 (i) Concentrated sulphuric acid can displace more volatile acids when reacted with their salts. The mixture effervesces (fizzes) and produces steamy fumes of hydrogen chloride even in the cold (see Section 17.1).

$$NaCl(s) + H_2SO_4(l) \rightarrow NaHSO_4(s) + HCl(g)$$

 (ii) A similar reaction occurs with potassium nitrate and concentrated sulphuric acid but this time heat is necessary (see Section 15.5). Nitric acid distils over as a yellow liquid.

$$KNO_3(s) + H_2SO_4(l) \rightarrow KHSO_4(s) + HNO_3(l)$$

(iii) Concentrated sulphuric acid converts blue crystals of copper(II) sulphate-5-water to the white anhydrous salt. It is behaving as a dehydrating agent.

$$CuSO_4.5H_2O(s) \rightarrow CuSO_4(s) + 5H_2O(l)$$

(iv) Concentrated sulphuric acid will remove the elements of water (i.e. hydrogen and oxygen atoms in the ratio of 2 : 1) from sugar? The mixture gets hot, swells up and leaves a black mass of carbon.

$$C_{12}H_{22}O_{11}(s) \rightarrow 12C(s) + 11H_2O(l)$$

The sulphuric acid is acting as a dehydrating agent here as well.

NB. Do not confuse dehydration with drying. A drying agent only removes water that is not chemically combined.

 (v) Dilute sulphuric acid is behaving here as a typical strong acid. Magnesium effervesces with dilute sulphuric acid to produce hydrogen.

$$Mg(s) + H_2SO_4(aq) \rightarrow MgSO_4(aq) + H_2(g)$$

Example 16.11

Use grid 2 on page 2 to choose an answer **A-E**.

If concentrated sulphuric acid is heated with copper, hydrogen is given off

BECAUSE

hydrogen is above copper in the reactivity series

The answer is **D**.

Concentrated sulphuric acid acts as an oxidising agent and is itself reduced to sulphur dioxide:

$$Cu(s) + 2H_2SO_4(l) \rightarrow CuSO_4(s) + 2H_2O(l) + SO_2(g).$$

16.13 Self-Test Questions

For Questions 16.1 and 16.2, use grid 1 on page 2 to choose an answer **A-E**.

Question 16.1

If aqueous sodium hydroxide is added to the aqueous solution of a metal salt S, a white precipitate is formed but this redissolves in excess aqueous sodium hydroxide. Salt S could be
1 aluminium sulphate
2 zinc chloride
3 lead(II) nitrate

Question 16.2

Hydrogen sulphide is passed into an aqueous solution of a metal salt and the precipitate formed is filtered off. The filtrate will be acidic if the metal salt was
1 iron(II) sulphate
2 copper(II) nitrate
3 zinc chloride.

Question 16.3

A solid compound was treated with dilute hydrochloric acid and the gas liberated turned lead(II) nitrate paper silvery black. This indicates that the compound was
A a carbonate
B a sulphite
C a sulphate
D a sulphide
E an oxide.

Question 16.4

Use grid 1 on page 2 to choose an answer **A–E**.
Arrangements for drying a gas with concentrated sulphuric acid could include:

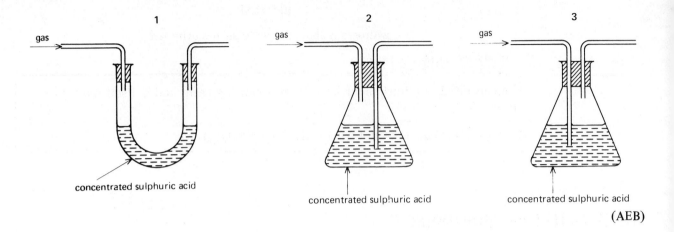

(AEB)

16.14 Answers to Self-Test Questions

16.1 **A.**

Aluminium, zinc and lead hydroxides are all amphoteric.

16.2 **A.**

In each case a precipitate of the metal sulphide is formed from the metal salt leaving the corresponding acid in solution (i.e. 1 gives sulphuric acid, 2 gives nitric acid and 3 gives hydrochloric acid).

16.3 **D.**

16.4 **E.**

17 The Halogens

17.1 Hydrogen Chloride, HCl

Hydrogen chloride is prepared in the laboratory by the action of concentrated sulphuric acid on rock salt (impure sodium chloride). The gas is dried by passing it through concentrated sulphuric acid and collected by downward delivery.

$$H_2SO_4(l) + NaCl(s) \rightarrow NaHSO_4(s) + HCl(g)$$

It is manufactured by burning hydrogen in chlorine, both materials being obtained by the electrolysis of brine in the mercury cathode cell (see Section 18.2).

(a) Tests for Hydrogen Chloride

Hydrogen chloride forms steamy fumes in moist air. It will turn moist universal indicator paper red and gives a thick white precipitate of silver chloride with silver nitrate solution.

$$HCl(g) + AgNO_3(aq) \rightarrow AgCl(s) + HNO_3(aq)$$

(b) Properties of Hydrogen Chloride

1. Hydrogen chloride is a colourless gas with a pungent, choking smell.
2. It gives steamy fumes in moist air.
3. It is slightly more dense than air.
4. Hydrogen chloride is very soluble in water, forming hydrochloric acid. This is a strong acid (see Section 12.2 and also Example 17.1).
5. Hydrogen chloride reacts with ammonia to form thick white fumes of ammonium chloride.

   $$NH_3(g) + HCl(g) \rightleftharpoons NH_4Cl(s)$$

6. Concentrated hydrochloric acid is easily oxidised to chlorine, e.g. by potassium manganate(VII) or manganese(IV) oxide (see Example 17.2).

(c) Uses of Hydrogen Chloride and Hydrochloric Acid

1. Hydrogen chloride is used in the manufacture of organic chlorine compounds such as chloroethene (vinyl chloride), the starting material for polyvinyl chloride (PVC).
2. Hydrochloric acid is used to 'pickle' metals, i.e. clean the surface prior to electroplating or galvanising.

17.2 Chlorides

All of the common metallic chlorides are soluble in water, except those of silver and lead. They are prepared as described in section 12.6 (see also Examples 17.2 and 17.4).

$$Pb(NO_3)_2(aq) + 2NaCl(aq) \rightarrow PbCl_2(s) + 2NaNO_3(aq)$$
$$CuO(s) + 2HCl(aq) \rightarrow CuCl_2(aq) + H_2O(l)$$

(a) Tests for Chlorides

Chlorides react when warmed with concentrated sulphuric acid to give steamy fumes of hydrogen chloride. They react with silver nitrate solution in the presence of dilute nitric acid to give a white precipitate of silver chloride (see Example 17.1).

$$NaCl(aq) + AgNO_3(aq) \rightarrow AgCl(s) + NaNO_3(aq)$$

17.3 Chlorine, Cl_2

Chlorine is prepared in the laboratory by the oxidation of concentrated hydrochloric acid by a strong oxidising agent such as potassium manganate(VII) or manganese(IV) oxide. The gas is passed through water to remove unchanged hydrogen chloride, dried by means of concentrated sulphuric acid and collected by downward delivery (see Example 17.2).

$$MnO_2(s) + 4HCl(aq) \rightarrow MnCl_2(aq) + Cl_2(g) + 2H_2O(l)$$

Chlorine is manufactured by the electrolysis of sodium chloride solution using titanium anodes and a flowing mercury cathode (see Section 18.2).

(a) Test for Chlorine

Chlorine bleaches moist universal indicator paper.

(b) Properties of Chlorine

1. Chlorine is a greenish-yellow gas with a characteristic pungent, choking smell.
2. It is poisonous.
3. It is about twice as dense as air.
4. Chlorine is slightly soluble in water. It reacts with water to give a mixture of hydrochloric and chloric(I) acids (see Example 17.3). Hence, chlorine water is acidic.
5. Chlorine combines with most metals, non-metals and with hydrogen to give the corresponding chloride, particularly on heating (see Examples 17.2 and 17.8).

$$2Na(s) + Cl_2(g) \rightarrow 2NaCl(s)$$
$$H_2(g) + Cl_2(g) \rightarrow 2HCl(g)$$

6. Chlorine is an extremely powerful oxidising agent (see Examples 17.3, 17.5 and 17.6).

(c) Uses of Chlorine

1. In the manufacture of plastics (e.g. PVC), anaesthetics, insecticides (e.g. DDT), solvents and aerosol propellants, all of which are chlorinated organic compounds.
2. As a bleach in the pulp and textile industries.
3. In the treatment of sewage and in the purification of water.
4. In the manufacture of hydrogen chloride and hydrochloric acid.

17.4 A Comparison of the Halogens

Atoms of the halogens all have 7 electrons in their outermost shells and therefore behave similarly (see Example 17.8).

Chlorine, bromine and iodine can all be obtained by the oxidation of the corresponding hydrogen halide.

The melting points and boiling points increase down the group so that fluorine is a yellow gas, chlorine a greenish-yellow gas, bromine a reddish-brown liquid and iodine a black solid. All the halogens combine with a large number of metals and non-metals and with hydrogen.

$$2Fe\,(s) + 3Br_2\,(g) \rightarrow 2FeBr_3\,(s)$$

In general, the reactions of fluorine are the most vigorous and those of iodine are the least vigorous. For example, bromine water like chlorine water is acidic but only about 1% of the dissolved bromine actually reacts with the water. Iodine is virtually insoluble in water but does show slight acidic properties by dissolving in sodium hydroxide solution.

The size of the atoms increases from fluorine to iodine (see Question 17.1). Thus fluorine which has the smallest atoms is the best electron attractor (i.e. oxidising agent) of these four elements and iodine the feeblest. Once the extra electron has been gained it will be more firmly held in a small ion such as fluorine than in a large ion. Thus it is possible for a change such as

$$Cl_2\,(g) + 2I^-\,(aq) \rightarrow I_2\,(aq) + 2Cl^-\,(aq)$$

to occur (see Example 17.7).

17.5 A Comparison of the Hydrogen Halides

Hydrogen fluoride (see Example 17.8) in some respects behaves differently from other hydrogen halides. It is a colourless liquid dissolving in water to produce a weak acid. The other hydrogen halides are colourless gases dissolving in water to produce strong acids (see Question 17.3).

The stability of these compounds decreases with increase in atomic number of the halogen whilst the reducing power increases, e.g. hydrogen chloride is unaffected by concentrated sulphuric acid but hydrogen iodide is almost completely oxidised to iodine whilst the sulphuric acid is reduced to sulphur dioxide and hydrogen sulphide.

An aqueous solution of a halide precipitates the corresponding silver salt from silver nitrate solution acidified with dilute nitric acid (see Example 17.1). If excess ammonia solution is added, silver chloride dissolves, silver bromide dissolves slightly but silver iodide is insoluble.

17.6 Worked Examples

Example 17.1

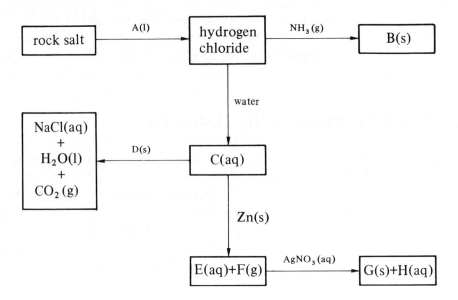

(a) Name the compounds A to H. **(8 marks)**
(b) What would you observe if silver nitrate solution were added to a solution of zinc iodide? **(1 mark)**
(c) Describe a test by which you could identify gas F. **(1 mark)**

(a) A is concentrated sulphuric acid.

$$H_2SO_4(l) + NaCl(s) \rightarrow NaHSO_4(s) + HCl(g)$$

Hydrogen chloride gas reacts with ammonia to give white fumes of ammonium chloride (B).

$$NH_3(g) + HCl(g) \rightleftharpoons NH_4Cl(s)$$

C is hydrochloric acid.
D is sodium carbonate.

$$Na_2CO_3(s) + 2HCl(aq) \rightarrow 2NaCl(aq) + H_2O(l) + CO_2(g)$$

Zinc reacts with hydrochloric acid to give zinc chloride (E) and hydrogen (F).

$$Zn(s) + 2HCl(aq) \rightarrow ZnCl_2(aq) + H_2(g)$$

Silver nitrate solution reacts with zinc chloride solution to give a white precipitate of silver chloride (G) and a solution of zinc nitrate (H).

$$ZnCl_2(aq) + 2AgNO_3(aq) \rightarrow 2AgCl(s) + Zn(NO_3)_2(aq)$$

(b) A yellow precipitate of silver iodide is observed.

$$2AgNO_3(aq) + ZnI_2(aq) \rightarrow Zn(NO_3)_2(aq) + 2AgI(s)$$

(c) Hydrogen 'pops' when a flame is applied (see Section 11.4).

Example 17.2

(a) The diagram shows the apparatus for the preparation of an anhydrous salt.

     (i) Name the gas prepared in flask A.
    (ii) What is the purpose of wash bottles B, C and D?
   (iii) Write the equation for the reaction in E.
   (iv) Name the crystals formed in F.
    (v) What is the purpose of tube G?   **(11 marks)**

(b) How would you distinguish between a solution in water of the salt prepared in (a) and the product formed when iron filings are added to dilute sulphuric acid? Write an appropriate equation for any one reaction you use.   **(4 marks)**
                                                           (SUJB)

(a) (i) Chlorine.

The equation is
$$2KMnO_4(s) + 16HCl(aq) \rightarrow 2KCl(aq) + 2MnCl_2(aq) + 8H_2O(l) + 5Cl_2(g)$$

   (ii) The water in B removes any hydrogen chloride that is carried over.
         The concentrated sulphuric acid in D is used to dry the chlorine.
         Wash bottle C is used to trap any sulphuric acid that may suck back and thus prevent it combining with the water in B.
  (iii) $2Fe(s) + 3Cl_2(g) \rightarrow 2FeCl_3(s)$
  (iv) Iron(III) chloride.
   (v) The anhydrous calcium chloride prevents water from the atmosphere entering the apparatus and reacting with the product.

(b) Sodium hydroxide solution produces a precipitate of red/brown iron(III) hydroxide with iron(III) chloride solution but a precipitate of green iron(II) hydroxide when added to iron(II) sulphate solution.

$$FeCl_3(aq) + 3NaOH(aq) \rightarrow 3NaCl(aq) + Fe(OH)_3(s)$$
$$\text{red/brown}$$
$$FeSO_4(aq) + 2NaOH(aq) \rightarrow Na_2SO_4(aq) + Fe(OH)_2(s)$$
$$\text{green}$$

Example 17.3

(a) Outline the manufacture of chlorine in an electrolytic cell.   **(6 marks)**
(b) What reactions take place when chlorine is
  (i) bubbled into cold water;
  (ii) bubbled into cold sodium hydroxide solution;
  (iii) bubbled into water saturated with hydrogen sulphide;
  (iv) passed over heated iron wool;
  (v) mixed with hydrogen and exposed to diffused sunlight?

Write appropriate equations   **(9 marks)**
(SUJB)

(a) See Example 18.4.
(b) (i) When chlorine is passed into cold water, some of it simply dissolves but some of it reacts to give hydrochloric acid and chloric(I) acid.

$$Cl_2(g) + water \rightleftharpoons Cl_2(aq)$$
$$Cl_2(aq) + H_2O(l) \rightleftharpoons HCl(aq) + HOCl(aq)$$

(ii) If sodium hydroxide solution is used instead of water, solutions of the sodium salts of hydrochloric acid and chloric(I) acid are formed, i.e. sodium chloride and sodium chlorate(I).

$$Cl_2(g) + 2NaOH(aq) \rightarrow NaCl(aq) + NaOCl(aq) + H_2O(l)$$

(iii) Chlorine is a powerful oxidising agent and will oxidise hydrogen sulphide to a yellow precipitate of sulphur.

$$Cl_2(g) + H_2S(aq) \rightarrow 2HCl(aq) + S(s)$$

(iv) Iron wool inflames in chlorine to give thick brown fumes of iron(III) chloride.

$$2Fe(s) + 3Cl_2(g) \rightarrow 2FeCl_3(s)$$

(v) The two gases combine to produce hydrogen chloride.

$$H_2(g) + Cl_2(g) \rightarrow 2HCl(g)$$

Example 17.4

Which one of the following methods would be most suitable for preparing a sample of anhydrous iron(II) chloride?
A Dissolving iron filings in aqueous hydrochloric acid followed by evaporating to dryness
B Dissolving iron(II) oxide in aqueous hydrochloric acid followed by evaporating to dryness
C Passing dry chlorine gas over heated iron
D Passing dry hydrogen chloride gas over heated iron
E Precipitation by mixing aqueous iron(II) sulphate and aqueous barium chloride.   (AEB)
The answer is **D**.

$$Fe(s) + 2HCl(g) \rightarrow FeCl_2(s) + H_2(g)$$
C would give iron(III) chloride.

Example 17.5

Use grid 1 on page 2 to choose an answer **A–E**.
The addition of chlorine water to aqueous iron(II) sulphate results in the appearance of a yellow colour and the disappearance of the chlorine smell. In this reaction:

1 iron(II) ions are oxidised to iron(III) ions
2 chlorine molecules are reduced to chloride ions
3 sulphate ions are unchanged.

The answer is **A**.

The ionic equation is
$$2Fe^{2+}(aq) + Cl_2(aq) \rightarrow 2Fe^{3+}(aq) + 2Cl^-(aq)$$

Example 17.6

What would you observe when a burning wax taper is plunged into a jar of chlorine?

(2 marks)
(SUJB)

The wax taper continues to burn in the chlorine with a red flame, producing black particles of carbon and steamy fumes of hydrogen chloride.

Example 17.7

(a) Chlorine is obtained commercially by the electrolysis of fused sodium chloride.
   (i) Write down the equation for the production of chlorine at the appropriate electrode and name the type of chemical reaction taking place. **(5 marks)**
   (ii) Give **two** important uses of chlorine. **(2 marks)**
(b) Explain the chemistry of the bleaching action of moist chlorine. **(4 marks)**
(c) Describe a reaction of chlorine with (i) a metallic element, (ii) a non-metallic element. Your descriptions should include a statement of the conditions under which each reaction occurs. **(8 marks)**
(d) Bromine and iodine are members of the same group of the periodic table as chlorine. Describe tests by which these three elements could be arranged in an order of activity.

(11 marks)
(OLE)

(a) (i) $2Cl^-(l) - 2e \rightarrow 2Cl(g)$

$$\downarrow$$

$$Cl_2(g)$$

Chlorine is liberated at the anode (see Section 7.2). Since electrons are lost, oxidation is taking place.

   (ii) Choose any two uses in Section 17.3 as your answer.

(b) When chlorine is passed into water, a yellow-green solution consisting of dissolved chlorine, hydrochloric acid and chloric(I) acid is formed.

$$Cl_2(g) + water \rightleftharpoons Cl_2(aq)$$
$$Cl_2(aq) + H_2O(l) \rightleftharpoons HCl(aq) + HOCl(aq)$$

The chloric(I) acid is unstable and readily gives up its oxygen to dyes, thereby converting them to colourless products.

dye + HOCl(aq) $\rightarrow$ (dye+oxygen) + HCl(aq)
coloured   colourless

(c) (i) Chlorine reacts with strongly heated iron to give brown fumes of iron(III) chloride (see Example 17.2).
   (ii) Red phosphorus combines with chlorine on gentle heating to give white fumes of phosphorus trichloride and phosphorus pentachloride.

$$P_4(s) + 6Cl_2(g) \rightarrow 4PCl_3(l)$$
$$P_4(s) + 10Cl_2(g) \rightarrow 4PCl_5(s)$$

(d) If chlorine water is added to an aqueous solution of sodium bromide, containing a little 1,1,1-trichloroethane, then the chlorine being more reactive than bromine will displace it from the solution. The bromine produces an orange coloration with 1,1,1-trichloroethane. A similar experiment using bromine water and an aqueous solution of sodium iodide produces a violet coloration in the 1,1,1-trichloroethane due to the displacement of iodine.

Thus the order of activity is:

chlorine
bromine
iodine.

Example 17.8

(a) Chlorine, bromine and iodine are all in Group VII of the Periodic Table. What does this tell you about:
   (i) the electronic structures of atoms of bromine and iodine;
   (ii) the molecular formula of bromine and iodine;
   (iii) the formula of sodium bromide;
   (iv) the solubility of silver iodide? **(4 marks)**
(b) Fluorine is the first member of the group. From your knowledge of the chemistry of chlorine and its compounds, write an equation for a reaction by which you might prepare hydrogen fluoride gas in the laboratory. **(2 marks)**
(c) If chlorine is passed over iodine in a U-tube the first product is a brown sludge of iodine monochloride, ICl. If the flow of chlorine is continued this brown compound is converted into diiodine hexachloride, I_2Cl_6, whose yellow crystals appear on the sides of the U-tube as in the figure.

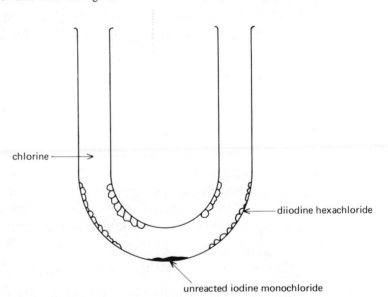

(i) Name the reagents you would use to make chlorine in the laboratory. State briefly how you would purify and dry the gas. **(6 marks)**
(ii) Write equations for the reactions of chlorine with iodine and with iodine monochloride. **(4 marks)**
The second of these reactions is an equilibrium.
(iii) Explain what you understand by the term *chemical equilibrium* by reference to two other equilibria. **(6 marks)**
(iv) Predict what you would see when the U-tube in the figure is inverted so that the chlorine escapes. **(2 marks)**
(v) Explain why these reactions should be carried out in a fume cupboard. **(1 mark)**
(OLE)

(a) (i) Both atoms will have 7 electrons in their outermost shells.
   (ii) The molecular formulae of bromine and iodine will be similar to that of chlorine, i.e. Br_2 and I_2.
   (iii) NaBr (similar to NaCl).
   (iv) It will be insoluble in water (like silver chloride).
(b) $NaF(s) + H_2SO_4(l) \rightarrow NaHSO_4(s) + HF(g)$

(In fact, calcium fluoride is generally used in preference to sodium fluoride.)

(c) (i) Potassium manganate(VII) and concentrated hydrochloric acid. The gas can be passed through water to remove hydrogen chloride and then through concentrated sulphuric acid to dry it.
   (ii) $I_2(s) + Cl_2(g) \rightarrow 2ICl(l)$
   $2ICl(l) + 2Cl_2(g) \rightleftharpoons I_2Cl_6(s)$

   (iii) Chemical equilibrium is reached in a reversible reaction when the rate of the forward reaction is equal to the rate of the backward reaction (see Section 9.3). For example, nitrogen and hydrogen combine to give ammonia but this splits up to give nitrogen and hydrogen again. Equilibrium is attained when the rate at which ammonia is formed equals the rate at which it decomposes.

   $$N_2(g) + 3H_2(g) \rightleftharpoons 2NH_3(g)$$

   A similar situation occurs when sulphur dioxide and oxygen combine to give sulphur trioxide.

   $$2SO_2(g) + O_2(g) \rightleftharpoons 2SO_3(g)$$

   (iv) If the chlorine escapes from the reaction vessel, the position of equilibrium in the reaction shown above will shift in such a way as to tend to reform the chlorine, i.e. the yellow crystals of diiodine hexachloride will decompose and the brown sludge of iodine monochloride, together with greenish-yellow chlorine gas will be reformed.
   (v) Chlorine and iodine vapour are corrosive and poisonous.

17.7 Self-Test Questions

Question 17.1

Which one of the following statements is true?
A a chlorine atom is larger than a bromine atom
B a chlorine atom is larger than a chloride ion
C a bromide ion is larger than a bromine atom
D a fluorine atom is larger than an iodine atom
E a fluoride ion is larger than an iodide ion.

Question 17.2

What would you observe when chlorine is bubbled into potassium iodide solution?

(2 marks)
(SUJB)

Question 17.3

(a) The element iodine is in the same Group of the Periodic Table as chlorine and bromine. Use this information to complete the following table: **(3 marks)**

	Formula	Solid, liquid or gas at room temperature?	Soluble or insoluble in water?
Potassium iodide	(i)	(ii)	(iii)
Hydrogen iodide	(iv)	(v)	(vi)

(b) For the reaction

$$Cl_2 + 2I^- \rightarrow 2Cl^- + I_2$$

state which species has been oxidised and explain your answer. **(2 marks)**
(OLE)

17.8 Answers to Self-Test Questions

17.1 **C.**

As a group in the periodic table is descended, further shells of electrons are added and so the atoms become bigger. Halide ions are larger than the corresponding atoms. When a further electron is added to an atom the attraction of the nucleus for the electrons remains the same but the mutual repulsion between the electrons increases; hence the radius becomes larger.

17.2 A brown coloration would develop in the solution.

Chlorine is more reactive than iodine so it will displace it from solutions containing its ions.

$$Cl_2(aq) + 2I^-(aq) \rightarrow 2Cl^-(aq) + I_2(aq)$$

Iodine is soluble in potassium iodide solution, producing a brown solution.

17.3 (a) (i) KI
(ii) solid
(iii) soluble
(iv) HI
(v) gas
(vi) soluble.
(b) The I^- ions have been oxidised since they have each lost an electron to form an iodine atom.

18 Some Industrial Processes

18.1 Extraction of Metals

The method of extracting a metal from its compounds depends upon the position of the metal in the reactivity series. Electrolysis is the only economic way of reducing ions of metals near the top of the series: for example, sodium is manufactured by electrolysing its molten chloride.

$$Na^+(l) + e^- \rightarrow Na(l)$$

Aluminium is obtained by electrolysing a solution of aluminium oxide in molten cryolite (see Example 18.2).

For metals lower down in the series, chemical reduction is used. The commonest reducing agent is coke (impure carbon, made by heating coal in the absence of air). Iron is manufactured by heating its ore, often impure iron(III) oxide, with limestone and coke in a blast furnace (see Example 18.3).

The blast furnace produces *cast iron,* which is hard and brittle owing to the presence of impurities such as carbon, sulphur and phosphorus. Steel is stronger and more flexible than iron. It is made by removing the impurities from cast iron and then adding carbon and other elements such as chromium in the correct proportions to give the required product.

Oxygen is blown on to the surface of molten cast iron in a converter of the type shown in Fig. 18.1. It oxidises the non-metallic impurities to acidic oxides, which escape as gases or combine with the basic lining of the converter to form slag. Other elements are then added to give the type of steel required.

Fig. 18.1

18.2 Manufacture of Sodium Hydroxide and Chlorine

These two important chemicals are manufactured by the electrolysis of brine (sodium chloride solution) in a mercury cell (see Example 18.4).

18.3 Manufacture of Sodium Carbonate

In the Solvay process, sodium carbonate is formed from brine, limestone and ammonia (see Example 18.4).

18.4 Manufacture of Sulphuric Acid

Sulphuric acid is manufactured from sulphur, air and water in the Contact process (see Example 18.5).

18.5 Manufacture of Ammonia

Nitrogen from the air and hydrogen from water and natural gas (methane) are combined under special conditions in the Haber process to make ammonia (see Example 18.6).

18.6 Manufacture of Nitric Acid

Nitric acid is made in the Ostwald process, where ammonia is catalytically oxidised by the oxygen of the air (see Example 18.7).

18.7 Worked Examples

Example 18.1

Which of the metals listed below is most likely to be extracted by electrolysis of its molten chloride?
A Calcium
B Copper
C Iron
D Silver
E Zinc

(AEB)

The answer is **A**

Calcium is high up in the reactivity series.

Example 18.2

The diagram on the next page represents a modern aluminium smelter.
The United Kingdom has no natural supply of the ore (empirical formula $Al_2O_3.2H_2O$) from which aluminium is normally extracted. At one time the entire treatment and extraction

fresh electrolyte

ANODE

ANODE

molten electrolyte

molten aluminium

steel cell case

CATHODE

processes were carried out after the importation of the ore but nowadays it is at least calcined (heated strongly) before shipment.

(a) What is the common name for the ore? **(1 mark)**

Bauxite

(b) What is the effect of *calcining* the ore? **(1 mark)**

It drives off the water from the $Al_2O_3.2H_2O$, leaving Al_2O_3.

(c) What economic advantage is there (i) for the exporter, (ii) for the importer in calcining the ore at source? **(1 mark each)**

(i) The exporter can charge more per tonne for the ore as there is no water present, thus saving transport costs.

(ii) The importer has less to do before extracting the aluminium, thus saving processing costs.

(d) The refined ore (pure aluminium oxide) is dissolved in molten electrolyte in the smelter.

(i) Name the electrolyte used as solvent. **(1 mark)**

Cryolite.

The formula for cryolite is Na_3AlF_6

(ii) Why is the refined ore not used on its own? **(1 mark)**

Electrolysis occurs only in liquids, not in solids. Aluminium oxide has too high a melting point to be used on its own, so it is dissolved in molten cryolite at about 900°C.

(e) Describe the chief pollutant produced by an aluminium smelter. **(2 marks)**

The chief pollutant is gaseous carbon dioxide, formed at the anodes as described in (f) (ii).

(f) (i) Of what material are the electrodes constructed? **(1 mark)**

Carbon.

(ii) Why must the anodes be constantly replaced? **(2 marks)**

Oxygen is produced by the discharge of oxide ions at the anodes.
$$2O^{2-}(l) - 4e^- \rightarrow O_2(g)$$
The oxygen oxidises the anodes to carbon dioxide and so they have to be replaced.

    (g) Give the equation for the reaction that occurs at the cathode during electrolysis.
                                                                               (2 marks)

$$Al^{3+}(l) + 3e^- \rightarrow Al(l)$$

    (h) Why is aluminium usually used in the form of an alloy rather than as a pure metal?
                                                                             (1 mark)

Pure aluminium is soft. It is alloyed with other metals to give it more strength.

    (i) What are the products of the reaction between aluminium and aqueous sodium hydroxide?
                                                                (2 marks)
                                                                 (AEB)

Sodium aluminate and hydrogen are produced.

See Section 12.3.

Example 18.3

    (a) Name the starting materials used in the production of iron in the blast furnace. Describe the chemistry of the production explaining the purposes of those starting materials and giving equations where possible.   **(19 marks)**
    (b) Describe three properties of steel which make it more useful than the iron produced in the blast furnace.   **(6 marks)**
                                                                (NISEC)

(a) The starting materials are air, coke, limestone and iron ore (e.g. haematite, Fe_2O_3).

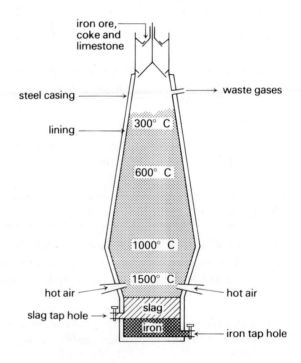

    At the top of the furnace the raw materials are fed in by means of a double cup and cone device to prevent the escape of dust and gas. A blast of hot air at the base of the furnace causes the coke to burn at white heat to form carbon dioxide.

$$C(s) + O_2(g) \rightarrow CO_2(g)$$

As it rises through the furnace the carbon dioxide is reduced by more hot coke to carbon monoxide.

$$CO_2(g) + C(s) \rightarrow 2CO(g)$$

In the upper part of the furnace, at 750°C, the carbon monoxide reduces the iron(III) oxide to give iron in the form of a porous solid.

$$Fe_2O_3(s) + 3CO(g) \rightleftharpoons 2Fe(s) + 3CO_2(g)$$

As the iron reaches the lower part of the furnace it melts and flows down to the bottom. The gas which reaches the top of the furnace contains about one-third carbon monoxide by volume and is piped off and burned to heat the air for the hot air blast.

   The purpose of the limestone is to remove the infusible sandy impurities (mainly silicon(IV) oxide). Firstly the limestone decomposes at a temperature of 850°C to form calcium oxide.

$$CaCO_3(s) \rightarrow CaO(s) + CO_2(g)$$

The calcium oxide (basic) then reacts with the silicon(IV) oxide (acidic) to form a *fusible* slag (calcium silicate) which flows to the bottom of the furnace and floats on the molten iron.

$$CaO(s) + SiO_2(s) \rightarrow CaSiO_3(l)$$

The iron and slag are tapped off periodically and the furnace continually recharged.
(b) Steel is more flexible than cast iron and so can be bent into various shapes. It can withstand greater stress than cast iron without breaking and so can be used in thin sheets. It can be made rust-proof in the form of stainless steel, which contains about 15% chromium.

Example 18.4

   (a) Describe how sodium chloride is extracted from underground deposits other than by digging it out.
       Discuss the environmental problem caused by the method of extraction you have described and explain why it is difficult to control. **(5 marks)**
   (b) In more than one region the occurrence of sizeable workable deposits of sodium chloride has led to the establishment of large chemical industries in the area. These industries depend on sodium chloride as raw material.
       The scheme below represents a small part only of such a development.

(i) Describe the conversions **A**, **B**, **C** and **D**.

(ii) Name **one** product that is manufactured from chlorine and give **one** use of it.

(18 marks)

(AEB)

(a) Water is pumped underground, the sodium chloride dissolves and the resulting solution is pumped to the surface.

Underground caverns are formed and collapse of these can cause the land to sink. It is difficult to fill the caverns with other material and therefore difficult to prevent the land from sinking. Serious damage to buildings can result from this.

(b) (i) Conversion A is carried out in the mercury cell (Fig. 18.2).

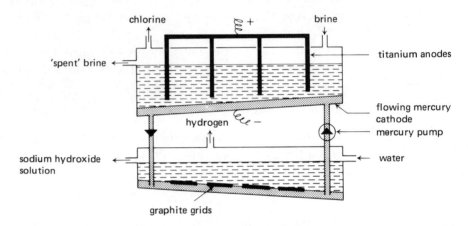

Fig. 18.2

Chlorine is liberated at titanium anodes and is piped off as shown. The use of a mercury cathode results in the discharge of sodium ions, *not* hydrogen ions as would be expected from the relative positions of the two elements in the reactivity series.

At anode $\qquad$ At cathode

$$2Cl^-(aq) \longrightarrow 2Cl(g) + 2e^- \quad \vdots \quad 2e^- + 2Na^+(aq) \longrightarrow 2Na(s)$$

$$\downarrow$$

$$Cl_2(g)$$

(oxidation) $\qquad$ (reduction)

The sodium dissolves in the mercury and the resulting sodium amalgam drops into water where it reacts to form sodium hydroxide solution and hydrogen, the mercury being regenerated. The decomposition of the amalgam is speeded up by the presence of graphite grids.

$$2Na(s) + 2H_2O(l) \rightarrow 2NaOH(aq) + H_2(g)$$

The mercury is pumped back to the top cell and used again. The sodium hydroxide solution is evaporated to dryness and some of the hydrogen burned in some of the chlorine to make hydrogen chloride.

Conversion B is carried out by reacting vegetable oils, which are unsaturated compounds containing double bonds (see Section 19.3), with hydrogen in the presence of a finely divided nickel catalyst at 200°C. An addition reaction takes place.

$$\begin{array}{ccccc} & \text{H} & \text{H} & & \text{H} \quad \text{H} \\ & | & | & & | \quad | \\ \cdots - \text{C} & = & \text{C} - \cdots \ + \ \text{H}_2 \longrightarrow \ \cdots - \text{C} - \text{C} - \cdots \\ & & & & | \quad | \\ & & & & \text{H} \quad \text{H} \end{array}$$

Conversion C is described in Section 19.9.

Conversion D is the manufacture of sodium carbonate by the Solvay process.

Limestone is heated in a kiln to give calcium oxide and carbon dioxide.

$$CaCO_3(s) \rightarrow CaO(s) + CO_2(g)$$

The carbon dioxide is reacted with sodium chloride solution which has been saturated with ammonia. A precipitate of sodium hydrogencarbonate forms and is filtered off.

$$NaCl(aq) + NH_3(aq) + H_2O(l) + CO_2(g) \rightarrow NaHCO_3(s) + NH_4Cl(aq) - A$$

The sodium hydrogencarbonate is heated to convert it to the required product, sodium carbonate.

$$2NaHCO_3(s) \rightarrow Na_2CO_3(s) + H_2O(g) + CO_2(g)$$

The carbon dioxide formed here passes back to react with fresh sodium chloride/ammonia solution in equation A.

The calcium oxide from the limekiln is slaked with water to produce calcium hydroxide.

$$CaO(s) + H_2O(l) \rightarrow Ca(OH)_2(s)$$

When this is heated with the ammonium chloride solution formed in equation A, ammonia is regenerated to be used again.

$$Ca(OH)_2(s) + 2NH_4Cl(aq) \rightarrow CaCl_2(aq) + 2H_2O(l) + 2NH_3(g)$$

(ii) Polyvinyl chloride (PVC) is made from chlorine. It is used for guttering and drainpipes.

Example 18.5

(a) Outline briefly the manufacture of sulphuric acid starting from sulphur and air (details of industrial plant are **not** required). **(6 marks)**

(b) Explain what is observed if

(i) concentrated sulphuric acid is heated with hydrated copper(II) sulphate crystals, **(3 marks)**

(ii) dilute sulphuric acid is heated with small lumps of calcium carbonate. **(3 marks)**

(c) What mass of pure sulphuric acid is needed to prepare 1 dm^3 of 2M sulphuric acid? This diluted acid (i.e. 1 dm^3 of 2M strength) is treated with 100 g of magnesium metal. How much metal is left at the end of the reaction? **(8 marks)**

(OLE)

(a) Sulphur is burned in *excess* air to form sulphur dioxide.

$$S(s) + O_2(g) \rightarrow SO_2(g)$$

The gases are cleaned to remove catalyst poisons and dried by passing them through concentrated sulphuric acid. They are then heated in a heat exchanger by hot gases leaving the catalyst chamber.

In the catalyst chamber sulphur dioxide combines with oxygen from the air in the presence of a complex catalyst based on vanadium(V) oxide. The

193

catalyst is spread out on silica gel to give a greater surface area on which reaction can take place.

$$2SO_2(g) + O_2(g) \rightleftharpoons 2SO_3(g)$$

The forward reaction is exothermic and the rate of flow of gases is adjusted to keep the temperature at $450°C$ without external heating. The various factors affecting the position of equilibrium in a reversible reaction are described in Section 9.3. Although a high pressure would move the equilibrium to the right, a very good yield of sulphur trioxide is obtained at atmospheric pressure. A pressure slightly above atmospheric is used to force the gases through the plant.

The hot sulphur trioxide is passed back to the heat exchanger to heat the incoming gases and then dissolved in concentrated sulphuric acid. It is not dissolved in water because the reaction is too violent and inefficient. The resulting product, fuming sulphuric acid (oleum), is then diluted with water to give the ordinary concentrated acid.

$$H_2SO_4(l) + SO_3(g) \rightarrow H_2S_2O_7(l) \quad \text{(oleum)}$$
$$H_2S_2O_7(l) + H_2O(l) \rightarrow 2H_2SO_4(l)$$

(b) (i) The blue hydrated crystals are dehydrated by the concentrated sulphuric acid to give white anhydrous copper(II) sulphate.
   (ii) Very little reaction occurs because the lumps of calcium carbonate become coated almost immediately with insoluble calcium sulphate.

$$CaCO_3(s) + H_2SO_4(aq) \rightarrow CaSO_4(s) + H_2O(l) + CO_2(g)$$

(c) 1 dm^3 of 2M sulphuric acid contains 2 mol of H_2SO_4 (see Section 20.3)
    i.e. $2 \times 98 = 196$ g of H_2SO_4

$$Mg(s) + H_2SO_4(aq) \rightarrow MgSO_4(aq) + H_2(g)$$

$$\text{mol } H_2SO_4 : \text{mol } Mg = 1 : 1 \quad . . . . . . \quad A$$
$$\text{mol } H_2SO_4 = 2$$
$$\therefore \text{mol } Mg \text{ used} = 2 \text{ (from A)}$$
$$\therefore \text{ g } Mg \text{ used} = 2 \times 24 = 48$$
$$\therefore \text{ g } Mg \text{ left} = (100 - 48)$$
$$= 52$$

Example 18.6

(a) Ammonia is manufactured from hydrogen and nitrogen by the Haber process.
   (i) How are the hydrogen and nitrogen obtained from the raw materials of air, water and natural gas? **(5 marks)**
   (ii) Write an equation for the synthesis of ammonia, and state the three essential conditions for an acceptable yield of ammonia. Explain the point of using each of these conditions. **(7 marks)**
(b) (i) Describe, with a diagram, how ammonia may be safely dissolved in water in the laboratory. **(3 marks)**
   (ii) Aqueous ammonia (ammonium hydroxide solution) is a *weak electrolyte*, while sodium hydroxide solution is a *strong electrolyte*. Explain the meaning of this statement. **(2 marks)**
(c) (i) The fertiliser 'Growmore' contains nitrogen in the form of ammonium compounds and not in the form of nitrates. How would you prove the truth of this statement? **(6 marks)**
   (ii) To what general class of compounds are nitrates converted in plants? **(2 marks)**
   (OLE)

(a) (i) Natural gas (methane) and steam are heated under pressure in a limited air supply in the presence of a nickel catalyst to give nitrogen, hydrogen, carbon monoxide and carbon dioxide. This mixture is passed over an iron(III) oxide catalyst with more steam to oxidise the carbon monoxide and produce more hydrogen.

$$H_2O(g) + CO(g) \rightleftharpoons H_2(g) + CO_2(g)$$

The carbon dioxide is removed chemically, as is any residual carbon monoxide.

(ii) $N_2(g) + 3H_2(g) \rightleftharpoons 2NH_3(g)$

High pressure (250 atm) is used so that the equilibrium is moved to the right and the yield of ammonia maximised (see Section 9.3).

The forward reaction is exothermic and so a low temperature would favour a high equilibrium yield of ammonia. However, the reaction would be too slow at low temperatures and so the plant operates at about 500°C – the equilibrium yield is lower but the rate of reaction is more acceptable.

A catalyst of iron is used to speed up the reaction and remove the need for even higher temperatures and lower yields.

(b) (i)

Fig. 18.3

Ammonia is so soluble in water that precautions have to be taken to prevent sucking back. In the funnel arrangement water rises in the funnel but the level in the beaker drops. Air enters under the rim of the funnel and equalises the pressure inside and outside the apparatus so that the water drops back again. The funnel must be almost as wide as the beaker if the system is to work efficiently.

(ii) A weak electrolyte is a poor conductor of electricity. Aqueous ammonia contains mainly unionised water and ammonia molecules with just a few ions to carry an electric current.

$$NH_3(aq) + H_2O(l) \rightleftharpoons NH_4^+(aq) + OH^-(aq)$$

Sodium hydroxide is an ionic solid, made up of Na^+ and OH^- ions. When it dissolves in water the ions separate and their large numbers mean that the solution conducts electricity well, i.e. is a strong electrolyte.

(c) (i) Carry out tests for ammonium ions and nitrate ions as described in Section 20.2. The first should be positive and the second negative.

(ii) Nitrates are converted to proteins in plants.

Example 18.7

Nitric acid, HNO_3, is made from ammonia in three stages.

Stage 1 A mixture of ammonia and air is passed over a platinum gauze catalyst when nitrogen oxide is formed by an exothermic reaction.

$$4NH_3(g) + 5O_2(g) \rightleftharpoons 6H_2O(g) + 4NO(g)$$

Stage 2 The nitrogen oxide is cooled and mixed with air to give nitrogen dioxide.

$$4NO(g) + 2O_2(g) \rightarrow 4NO_2(g)$$

Stage 3 The nitrogen dioxide forms nitric acid when dissolved in water in the presence of air.

$$4NO_2(g) + 2H_2O(l) + O_2(g) \rightarrow 4HNO_3(aq)$$

(a) Air is used to provide the necessary oxygen for the process. Give the names of TWO other gases which must inevitably be present in the reaction vessel from this source.
(1 mark)

Nitrogen, carbon dioxide

(b) What percentage of the air is oxygen? **(1 mark)**

See Section 10.1.

(c) Suggest ONE reason why the platinum catalyst used is in the form of a gauze. **(1 mark)**

The gauze has a greater surface area than a lump of platinum of the same mass and is thus more effective.

(d) When the reaction vessel is first being brought into service, the catalyst is heated electrically. Explain why this heating is stopped once the reactor is in full operation.
(1 mark)

The chemical reaction in Stage 1 takes place on the catalyst surface and is exothermic, so it keeps the catalyst hot.

(e) Why is the temperature used in Stage 1 reasonably *high*? **(1 mark)**
So that the reaction proceeds at a reasonable rate.

(f) What volume of ammonia, measured at room temperature and atmospheric pressure, is needed to produce 63 kg of nitric acid? (1 mole of molecules of any gas occupies 24 dm^3 at room temperature and atmospheric pressure. Relative atomic masses: H = 1, N = 14, O = 16) **(2 marks)**

1 mole of nitric acid is made from 1 mole of ammonia (see equations)
∴ 63 g of nitric acid is made from 24 dm^3 of ammonia at room temperature and pressure
∴ 63 kg of nitric acid is made from 24 000 dm^3 of ammonia at room temperature and pressure.

(g) A pressure of up to 10 atmospheres is often used in Stage 1, although an increase in pressure favours the *left* hand side of the equilibrium. Suggest a reason for compressing the gases. **(1 mark)**
Compressing the gases increases their concentrations and therefore increases the rate of reaction.

(h) State ONE large-scale use of nitric acid. **(1 mark)**
To make fertilisers such as ammonium nitrate.

(i) Complete the following equation to show how pure nitric acid reacts with water to produce an acidic solution. **(1 mark)**
$HNO_3 + H_2O \rightarrow$
$HNO_3 + H_2O \rightarrow H_3O^+ + NO_3^-$

(j) Electrolysis of a dilute solution of nitric acid produces gases at *both* electrodes. Which gas is likely to be produced at the cathode if inert electrodes are used? **(1 mark)**

(L)

Hydrogen

H_3O^+ ions give hydrogen and water when discharged.

18.8 Self-Test Questions

Question 18.1

In the manufacture of aluminium, the reaction occurring at the cathode of the cell is:

A $Al^+ + e^- \rightarrow Al$
B $Al^{3+} - 3e^- \rightarrow Al$
C $Al^{3+} + 3e^- \rightarrow Al$
D $Al \rightarrow Al^{3+} + 3e^-$
E $Al + 3e^- \rightarrow Al^{3+}$

Question 18.2

The production of iron in the blast furnace requires an iron ore and
A coke, limestone and calcium silicate only
B air, limestone and calcium silicate only
C air, coke and limestone only
D air, coke and calcium silicate only
E air, coke, limestone and calcium silicate

(NISEC)

Question 18.3

Use grid 2 on page 2 to choose an answer **A–E**.

The Haber process was developed to make ammonia from nitrogen in the air

BECAUSE

Nitrogen occurs only in the air.

(L)

18.9 Answers to Self-Test Questions

18.1 C.

18.2 C.

18.3 C

Nitrogen occurs in ammonium salts, nitrates and many other compounds.

19 Organic Chemistry

19.1 Introduction

Organic chemistry is the chemistry of carbon compounds, excluding carbonates and the oxides of carbon. There are a very large number of organic compounds since carbon atoms can join together in many different ways to form rings and chains of atoms. These compounds can be divided into families known as **homologous** series, in which all the members can be represented by the same general formula. The members have similar chemical properties and the physical properties change gradually as the relative molecular mass changes (see Example 19.2).

Isomerism is the existence of two or more compounds with the same molecular formula but different structures, the different forms being called *isomers* (see Question 19.1). For example, butane and methylpropane, whose structures are given below, are isomers.

butane   methylpropane

19.2 The Alkanes

The alkanes are hydrocarbons, i.e. compounds containing hydrogen and carbon only. They form a homologous series of general formula, C_nH_{2n+2}, their molecules containing only single covalent bonds.
Examples include

methane   ethane   propane   butane

Compounds which have molecules containing only single covalent bonds are said to be **saturated**.

Alkanes are obtained commercially from petroleum but may be prepared in the laboratory by heating soda lime with the sodium salt of the appropriate carboxylic acid.

198

$$CH_3COONa(s) + NaOH(s) \rightarrow CH_4(g) + Na_2CO_3(s)$$

The simplest alkanes are colourless gases or liquids which are insoluble in water but readily dissolve in organic solvents. Like all hydrocarbons, alkanes burn in a plentiful air supply to form carbon dioxide and water (see Example 19.1). In a limited air supply, carbon monoxide or even carbon may be produced because of incomplete combustion. Alkanes take part in *substitution* reactions, e.g. methane reacts with chlorine or bromine in the presence of light.

$$CH_4(g) + Cl_2(g) \rightarrow HCl(g) + CH_3Cl(g)$$
chloromethane

Further substitution may occur to give a mixture of products (see Example 19.2).

Alkanes are used as fuels and as the starting materials in the manufacture of a number of other substances, e.g. plastics and soapless detergents.

19.3   The Alkenes

The alkenes form a homologous series of general formula C_nH_{2n}, their molecules containing a double bond, e.g.

ethene   and   propene

Compounds which have molecules containing double or triple covalent bonds are said to be **unsaturated**.

Ethene can be prepared by the catalytic dehydration of ethanol in the apparatus shown in Fig. 19.1. The catalyst of aluminium oxide is heated strongly and sufficient heat is conducted down the tube to vaporise the ethanol.

![Apparatus diagram showing rocksil soaked in ethanol, aluminium oxide, HEAT, ethene collection over water]

aluminium oxide

rocksil soaked in ethanol

ethene

HEAT

water

Fig. 19.1

$$C_2H_5OH(g) \rightarrow C_2H_4(g) + H_2O(g)$$

Ethene is a colourless gas which is practically insoluble in water but readily soluble in organic solvents.

199

One of the two bonds in a double bond is easily broken and as a result alkenes are very reactive. They take part in *addition* reactions (see Examples 19.2 and 19.5). When ethene is shaken with a solution of bromine in 1,1,1-trichloroethane the reddish-brown colour of the bromine disappears almost immediately and 1,2-dibromoethane is obtained as the organic product.

$$
\begin{array}{c}
H \\
^{\diagdown}C{=}C^{\diagup} \\
H H
\end{array}
\quad + \quad Br_2 \quad \longrightarrow \quad
\begin{array}{c}
H \quad H \\
| \quad | \\
H{-}C{-}C{-}H \\
| \quad | \\
Br \quad Br
\end{array}
$$

An acidified solution of potassium manganate(VII) is decolorised by alkenes and an alkaline solution is turned green, finally depositing a brown precipitate.

Polymerisation is the process in which many small molecules join together to make one large one, e.g.

$$
\cdots + \quad
\begin{array}{c}
H \qquad H \\
^{\diagdown}C{=}C^{\diagup} \\
H \qquad H
\end{array}
\ +\
\begin{array}{c}
H \qquad H \\
^{\diagdown}C{=}C^{\diagup} \\
H \qquad H
\end{array}
\ + \cdots \longrightarrow \cdots
\begin{array}{c}
H \ \ H \ \ H \ \ H \\
| \ \ | \ \ | \ \ | \\
{-}C{-}C{-}C{-}C{-} \\
| \ \ | \ \ | \ \ | \\
H \ \ H \ \ H \ \ H
\end{array}
\cdots
$$

$$
nC_2H_4 \xrightarrow{\hspace{4cm}} (C_2H_4)n
$$

Molecules of ethene (the monomer) join together in chains to form polythene (the polymer). One of the bonds in the C=C bond breaks and the molecules undergo an addition reaction. This process is called *addition polymerisation* (see Example 19.3).

Condensation polymerisation occurs when a small molecule such as water or hydrogen chloride is eliminated when the monomer units link together, e.g.

$$
\cdots + \quad
\begin{array}{c}
HO \\
^{\diagup}C{-}C_6H_4{-}C^{\diagdown} \\
_{O} _{O}
\end{array}
\begin{array}{c}
OH \\

\end{array}
\quad + \quad
\begin{array}{c}
H \quad H \\
| \quad | \\
H{-}O{-}C{-}C{-}O{-}H \\
| \quad | \\
H \quad H
\end{array}
\quad + \cdots
$$

$$
\text{acid} \qquad\qquad\qquad\qquad \text{alcohol}
$$

$$
\downarrow
$$

$$
\cdots {-}
\begin{array}{c}
 \\
C{-}C_6H_4{-} \\
\| \\
O
\end{array}
\begin{array}{c}
 \\
C{-}O{-} \\
\| \\
O
\end{array}
\begin{array}{c}
H \ \ H \\
| \ \ | \\
C{-}C{-}O{-} \\
| \ \ | \\
H \ \ H
\end{array}
\cdots \quad + \quad 2H_2O
$$

Terylene – a polyester

Plastics can be divided into two main classes according to their behaviour when heated – thermoplastics or thermosetting plastics (see Example 19.4).

Alkenes are converted into a wide range of products, e.g. plastics, ethanol, 1,2-dibromoethane (a petrol additive) and ethane-1,2-diol (antifreeze).

19.4 The Alkynes

The alkynes are members of a homologous series of general formula C_nH_{2n-2}. Each molecule contains a carbon carbon triple bond. Ethyne, C_2H_2, is prepared by adding water to calcium dicarbide (see Question 19.2). The gas is collected over water.

$$CaC_2(s) + 2H_2O(l) \rightarrow Ca(OH)_2(aq) + H-C\equiv C-H(g)$$

The reactions of ethyne are similar to those of ethene.

19.5 Petroleum and Coal

Petroleum was produced underground by the combined effects of heat, pressure and bacteria on the remains of marine animals and plants which died many millions of years ago. It is composed chiefly of hydrocarbons. Liquid petroleum is fractionally distilled in tall fractionating towers. Each fraction contains groups of hydrocarbons with boiling points within a particular range, rather than pure samples of individual compounds.

There is little demand for the heavier oils and they are usually converted to more useful products by cracking (see Example 19.6).

Cracking is the thermal decomposition of alkanes of high relative molecular mass to give a mixture of alkanes and alkenes of lower relative molecular mass.

Coal was formed in a similar way to petroleum by the underground compression of vegetable matter. It consists mainly of carbon, together with compounds containing hydrogen, oxygen, nitrogen and sulphur. Burning coal pollutes the atmosphere with smoke and harmful gases such as sulphur dioxide. However, *destructive distillation* of coal (heating coal in the absence of air) gives useful products from which many organic chemicals can be obtained.

19.6 Carbohydrates

Carbohydrates are compounds composed of carbon, hydrogen and oxygen where the hydrogen and oxygen atoms are present in the same ratio as in water, e.g. glucose, $C_6H_{12}O_6$, sucrose, $C_{12}H_{22}O_{11}$ and starch, $(C_6H_{10}O_5)_n$.

Glucose has molecules made up of single six-membered rings and is an example of a monosaccharide. A molecule of glucose and one of its isomers, fructose, can join together and eliminate a water molecule to form sucrose. Sucrose is a disaccharide since its molecules contain two rings. Starch is a polysaccharide – its molecules are formed by the joining together of many monosaccharide units.

(a) Tests for Carbohydrates

Glucose and fructose give a red precipitate of copper(I) oxide with Fehling's solution. Starch gives a blue–black colour when added to an aqueous solution of iodine in potassium iodide solution.

(b) Hydrolysis of Carbohydrates

Hydrolysis of sucrose produces a mixture of glucose and fructose.

$$C_{12}H_{22}O_{11}(aq) + H_2O(l) \rightleftharpoons \underset{glucose}{C_6H_{12}O_6(aq)} + \underset{fructose}{C_6H_{12}O_6(aq)}$$

Starch can also be hydrolysed but the products of the reaction depend upon the nature of the catalyst used (see Example 19.8).

19.7   The Alcohols

The alcohols form a homologous series of general formula $C_nH_{2n+1}OH$, e.g.

$$
\begin{array}{ccc}
& H & \\
& | & \\
H-&C-O-H& \\
& | & \\
& H &
\end{array}
\qquad
\begin{array}{ccc}
& H \quad H & \\
& | \quad | & \\
H-&C-C-O-H& \\
& | \quad | & \\
& H \quad H &
\end{array}
$$

methanol   ethanol

Ethanol is manufactured by the hydration of ethene.

$$C_2H_4(g) + H_2O(g) \xrightarrow[\text{phosphoric(V) acid catalyst}]{300°C,\ 65\ atm,} CH_3CH_2OH(g)$$

It is also prepared by fermentation of aqueous glucose solution using yeast which contains the enzyme zymase. After filtering, the solution can be concentrated using fractional distillation (see Example 19.7).

$$C_6H_{12}O_6(aq) \rightarrow 2C_2H_5OH(aq) + 2CO_2(g)$$

Fermentation is the slow decomposition of an organic substance brought about by micro-organisms and usually accompanied by the evolution of heat and a gas.
   The simple alcohols are colourless liquids which are miscible with water.

(a) Chemical Properties of the Alcohols

1. The alcohols burn in air to form carbon dioxide and water.

   $$C_2H_5OH(l) + 3O_2(g) \rightarrow 2CO_2(g) + 3H_2O(g)$$

2. They react quietly with sodium to give sodium ethoxide and hydrogen (c.f. the behaviour of water).

   $$2C_2H_5OH(l) + 2Na(s) \rightarrow 2C_2H_5ONa(s) + H_2(g)$$

3. They react with phosphorus pentachloride to produce steamy fumes of hydrogen chloride.

   $$C_2H_5OH(l) + PCl_5(s) \rightarrow C_2H_5Cl(g) + POCl_3(l) + HCl(g)$$

4. Alcohols react with organic acids to produce esters and water. They are oxidised to aldehydes and acids with acidified potassium dichromate(VI) (see Example 19.7) and can be dehydrated to alkenes by passing them over heated aluminium oxide (see Section 19.3).

(b) Uses of the Alcohols

1. As solvents.
2. To make other organic compounds.
3. As fuels.
4. In beers, wines and spirits.

19.8 Carboxylic Acids

The carboxylic acids form a homologous series of general formula $C_nH_{2n+1}COOH$ e.g.

methanoic acid   ethanoic acid

Carboxylic acids are prepared by the oxidation of the corresponding alcohol using acidified potassium dichromate(VI) solution (see Example 19.7), e.g.

$$CH_3CH_2OH(l)\ 2[O]\ CH_3COOH(l) + H_2O(l)$$

The simple acids are colourless liquids which are completely miscible with water. A 5% solution of ethanoic acid is used as vinegar.

(a) Chemical Properties of Carboxylic Acids

1. They are weak acids.
2. Anhydrous carboxylic acids react quietly with sodium to produce hydrogen and the sodium salt of the acid.

$$2CH_3COOH(l) + 2Na(s) \rightarrow 2CH_3COONa(s) + H_2(g)$$

3. They combine with alcohols to give esters and water (see Example 19.7 and below).

19.9 Esters and Detergents

Organic acids react reversibly with alcohols to form esters and water, the process being known as *esterification* (see Example 19.7).

$$CH_3COOH(l) + C_2H_5OH(l) \rightleftharpoons CH_3COOC_2H_5(l) + H_2O(l)$$
ethanoic acid   ethanol   ethyl ethanoate   water

The reaction is speeded up by heat and by the addition of a catalyst of concentrated sulphuric acid.

The simple esters are colourless liquids which are immiscible with water and have characteristic pleasant smells. They are hydrolysed by warming with dilute sulphuric acid to give an acid and an alcohol (i.e. the reverse of esterification). Sodium hydroxide solution may be used to catalyse the hydrolysis but in this case the reaction goes to completion.

$$CH_3COOC_2H_5(l) + NaOH(aq) \rightarrow CH_3COONa(aq) + C_2H_5OH(l)$$

Soaps are the sodium or potassium salts of long-chained carboxylic acids (e.g. octadecanoic acid) which are prepared by boiling animal fats or vegetable oils (which are esters) with sodium hydroxide solution (see Example 7.4). This process is called saponification. Soapless detergents are made from petroleum and consist of molecules which are similar in form and action to those of soap. Unlike soap, their calcium and magnesium salts are soluble in water and thus do not form scum (see Example 19.9).

19.10 Worked Examples

Example 19.1

(a) (i) What is understood by the term *unsaturated hydrocarbon*? Name **one** unsaturated hydrocarbon and draw its structural formula.

(ii) Name the product formed when bromine and the unsaturated hydrocarbon combine and write an equation for the reaction.

(iii) Name **one** *saturated* hydrocarbon and draw its structural formula. What would be the products of the reaction between 1 mol of this hydrocarbon and 1 mol of bromine? Write an equation for the reaction.

(iv) Which of the two named hydrocarbons can be converted to a polymer? Name the polymer, draw its structure and explain what is meant by *polymerisation*.

(16 marks)

(b) 10 cm³ of a hydrocarbon, C_xH_y, was burned with 50 cm³ of oxygen in a suitable apparatus. When the reaction was complete, it was found that the residual gas consisted of 15 cm³ of oxygen, 20 cm³ of carbon dioxide and some water vapour. (All gas volumes were measured under the same conditions of temperature and pressure.)

Deduce from this data the formula of the hydrocarbon, showing clearly how you arrive at your answer, and write an equation for its combustion in oxygen.   **(8 marks)**

(AEB)

(a) (i) Hydrocarbons are compounds containing carbon and hydrogen only. If the compound is unsaturated, its molecules contain double or triple covalent bonds.

Ethene

(ii) 1,2-dibromoethane

i.e C_2H_4 + Br_2 ⟶ CH_2BrCH_2Br

In this reaction two bromine atoms add on across the double bond.

(iii) Ethane.

i.e. C_2H_6 + Br_2 ⟶ C_2H_5Br + HBr

One of the hydrogen atoms in ethane is substituted by a bromine atom to give bromoethane and hydrogen bromide.

In both (ii) and (iii) the colour of the bromine disappears and colourless products are obtained but (ii) is much quicker than (iii).

(iv) Unsaturated hydrocarbons can be converted to polymers, i.e. ethene can be polymerised to give polythene,

$$\cdots -\underset{\underset{H}{|}}{\overset{\overset{H}{|}}{C}}-\underset{\underset{H}{|}}{\overset{\overset{H}{|}}{C}}-\underset{\underset{H}{|}}{\overset{\overset{H}{|}}{C}}-\underset{\underset{H}{|}}{\overset{\overset{H}{|}}{C}}- \cdots$$

Polymerisation is the process in which many small molecules join together to make one large one. One of the bonds in each carbon to carbon double bond breaks and then the molecules add together to make the polymer.

(b) First of all write down the equation for the combustion of the hydrocarbon in oxygen. Since the formula of the hydrocarbon is $C_x H_y$, there must be x molecules of carbon dioxide produced from 1 molecule of hydrocarbon. Similar reasoning leads to the conclusion that there must be $y/2$ molecules of water produced and $x + y/4$ molecules of oxygen used up, so the equation is

$$C_x H_y + (x + y/4)O_2 \rightarrow x CO_2 + y/2 H_2O.$$

Volume of oxygen used up = $50 - 15 = 35$ cm^3

	$C_x H_y$	O_2	CO_2
Ratio of volumes =	10 :	35 :	20
=	1 :	3.5 :	2

By Avogadro's principle,

ratio of molecules = 1 : 3.5 : 2

From the equation,

number of molecules of carbon dioxide = x
$x = 2$

number of molecules of oxygen = $x + y/4$
$= 3.5$

$3.5 = 2 + y/4$
$y/4 = 1.5$
$y = 6$

Formula of hydrocarbon = $C_2 H_6$.

The equation is thus

$$C_2 H_6 (g) + 3\tfrac{1}{2} O_2 (g) \rightarrow 2CO_2 (g) + 3H_2O (g)$$
$$\text{or} \quad 2C_2 H_6 (g) + 7 O_2 (g) \rightarrow 4CO_2 (g) + 6H_2O (g)$$

Example 19.2

(a) Methane is the first member of the *homologous series* of hydrocarbons called the *alkanes*. Explain what is meant by the terms printed in italics. **(6 marks, 2 marks)**

(b) 7 g of a gaseous hydrocarbon, X, is found to have the same volume, at the same temperature and pressure, as 4 g of methane. Calculate the relative molecular mass of the hydrocarbon X and then write down its molecular and structural formulae.

(4 marks, 2 marks, 2 marks)

(c) Write an equation for, and name the products of the reaction between (i) chlorine and ethane, (ii) chlorine and ethene. **(5 marks)**

(d) Use the reactions in (c) to explain what is meant by a *substitution* and an *addition* reaction. **(4 marks)**

(OLE)

(a) A homologous series is a group of compounds in which
1 all members possess the same general formula,
2 each member differs from the next by the group $-CH_2-$,
3 the physical properties of members change gradually as the relative molecular mass changes,
4 all members have similar chemical properties and
5 all members can be made by general methods.

The alkanes form a homologous series of general formula C_nH_{2n+2}.

(b) Relative molecular mass of CH_4 = 16

$$\text{Moles of } CH_4 \text{ in } 4\text{ g} = \frac{4}{16} = \frac{1}{4}$$

Moles of X in 7 g   = 1/4 (Avogadro's principle, Section 6.1)
Relative molecular mass of X = 7 × 4 = 28

∴ The only reasonable molecular formula is C_2H_4
and the structural formula is

(c) (i) $C_2H_6(g) + Cl_2(g) \rightarrow HCl(g) + C_2H_5Cl(g)$
hydrogen chloride   chloroethane

The reaction does not stop here but successive hydrogen atoms in the chloroethane will be replaced by chlorine atoms to give eventually hexachloroethane

---

(ii)

1,2-dichloroethane

(d) The reaction between ethane and chlorine is an example of a substitution reaction.

206

A substitution reaction is a reaction in which one atom or group of atoms in a molecule is replaced by another. In this example, successive hydrogen atoms are replaced by chlorine atoms.

The reaction between ethene and chlorine is an example of an addition reaction.

An addition reaction is a reaction in which two or more molecules react to give a single product.

Example 19.3

Buta-1,3-diene is a gas at s.t.p. and forms a polymer according to the equation

$$n\ CH_2=CH-CH=CH_2 \longrightarrow \{CH_2-CH=CH-CH_2\}_n$$

(a) Is this a condensation or addition polymerisation process?
   Briefly explain your answer. **(3 marks)**

This is an addition polymerisation process. In this process, the molecules of the monomer (buta-1,3-diene) join together to form the polymer. The empirical formula of the polymer is the same as that of the monomer.

(b) What does the n on the left-hand side of the equation stand for? **(1 mark)**

n is a large whole number, usually several hundred.

(c) Give one chemical test which would show that the product still contains double bonds.

(3 marks)
(OLE)

One of the following tests for unsaturation will show the presence of a double bond:

1. a solution of bromine in 1,1,1-trichloroethane is rapidly decolorised,
2. an acidified solution of potassium manganate(VII) is decolorised or
3. an alkaline solution of potassium manganate(VII) turns green and finally gives a brown precipitate.

Example 19.4

(a) Rewrite in a balanced form the equation given below.

$$CH_2 = CH_2 + O_2 + HCl \rightarrow \underset{A}{Cl-CH = CH_2} + H_2O$$

   Name the chlorinated gaseous product A and show by means of an equation how it may be converted into a polymeric product B. How could it be demonstrated that B is a thermoplastic rather than a thermosetting polymer? **(12 marks)**

(b) Calculate the volume of A (measured at s.t.p.) which would be necessary to produce 125 g of polymer B, assuming 100% yield. **(8 marks)**
(OLE)

(a)

$$2CH_2 = CH_2 + O_2 + 2HCl \rightarrow 2Cl - CH = CH_2 + 2H_2O$$

A is chloroethene (vinyl chloride).

$$n \quad \mathrm{C=C} \xrightarrow{\text{catalyst}} \left[\begin{matrix} \mathrm{Cl} & \mathrm{H} \\ | & | \\ \mathrm{C} - \mathrm{C} \\ | & | \\ \mathrm{H} & \mathrm{H} \end{matrix} \right]_n$$

B = poly(chloroethene),
polyvinylchloride, PVC

Thermoplastics are those which soften on heating and harden on cooling, the process being repeatable any number of times. Thermosetting plastics soften on being heated the first time after manufacture and thus can be moulded. This heating causes cross-linking to occur between the long chained macromolecules and results in the setting up of a rigid three-dimensional network which cannot be softened by subsequent reheating. Thus, studying the effect of heat on B will demonstrate that B is a thermoplastic rather than a thermosetting polymer.

(b) Relative molecular mass of B = $n(3 + 24 + 35.5)$
$$= n \times 62.5$$

2 moles of A are needed to produce 125 g of B.
Volume of A = 2×22.4 dm^3 (molar volume = 22.4 dm^3 mol^{-1}
$$= 44.8 \text{ dm}^3 \quad \text{at s.t.p.})$$

Example 19.5

Give the name or molecular formula for the product of reaction of ethene (ethylene) with each of the following:

(i) bromine;   **(1 mark)**

$C_2H_4Br_2$ or 1,2-dibromoethane

(ii) steam in the presence of a hot phosphoric acid catalyst;   **(1 mark)**

C_2H_5OH or ethanol

(iii) hydrogen with a suitable catalyst;   **(1 mark)**

C_2H_6 or ethane

The conditions needed are a nickel catalyst and a temperature of 200°C.

(iv) more ethene.   **(1 mark)**

$(C_2H_4)_n$ or polythene.   (OLE)

Example 19.6

Domestic paraffin, which is a mixture of alkanes, is passed over strongly heated broken porcelain in the apparatus shown on the next page.

(a) (i) What is the purpose of the broken porcelain?   **(1 mark)**

The porcelain enables the paraffin vapour to be heated to a high temperature in order to decompose. It ensures maximum contact between the vapour and the hot surface.

(ii) What is the name given to this type of thermal decomposition?   **(1 mark)**

Cracking.

(b) If propane is heated under suitable conditions, it decomposes into methane and ethene.
(i) Write an equation for this reaction.   **(1 mark)**

$C_3H_8(g) \rightarrow CH_4(g) + C_2H_4(g)$

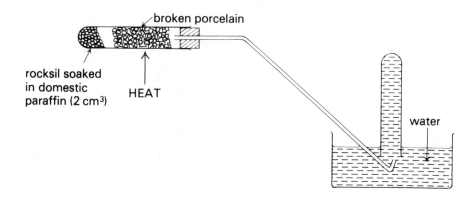

broken porcelain

rocksil soaked
in domestic
paraffin (2 cm³)   HEAT

water

N.B. Cracking always produces an unsaturated compound as one of the products. products.

      (ii) How would you prove that ethene is formed?   **(2 marks)**

Any of the tests for unsaturation given in Example 19.3 will show that an alkene is produced.

  (c) Using different conditions, propane can be decomposed into propene and hydrogen.

      (i) Write an equation for this reaction.   **(1 mark)**

$$C_3H_8(g) \rightarrow C_3H_6(g) + H_2(g)$$

      (ii) What volume of hydrogen, measured at the same temperature and pressure, is obtained from the decomposition of 100 cm^3 of propane.   **(2 marks)**

From the equation,

   1 molecule of propane → 1 molecule of hydrogen

By Avogadro's principle,

   1 volume of propane → 1 volume of hydrogen

i.e. 100 cm^3 of propane → 100 cm^3 of hydrogen.

  (d) Why are these reactions of importance in the petrochemical industry?   **(2 marks)**

There is little demand for the higher alkanes but the demand for the alkanes with fewer numbers of carbon atoms in their molecules is far greater than can be obtained directly from petroleum. The alkanes are converted into simpler alkanes and alkenes by cracking.

Example 19.7

  Fermentation of sucrose by yeast may be carried out in apparatus such as shown in the figure overleaf.

  (a) What ingredients are required in mixture **Y** for successful fermentation? Give any other essential conditions.   **(4 marks)**

  (b) A dye Janus Green is added to mixture **Y**. It is blue in the presence of dissolved oxygen and pink in its absence. What colour would you expect it to go as fermentation takes place? Explain your answer.   **(4 marks)**

  (c) The gaseous product of fermentation bubbles out through the airlock containing solution **X**. Name this product and say how you would prove its identity using a suitable solution **X**.   **(4 marks)**

  (d)   (i) The organic product of fermentation may be concentrated by distillation. Name the compound and give its structural formula.   **(3 marks)**

      (ii) Describe how you would convert the concentrated product into the corresponding carboxylic acid.   **(3 marks)**

      (iii) Describe the preparation of a **named** ester from this acid, giving the structural and empirical formulae of the ester.   **(7 marks)**

                                          (OLE)

(a) Sugar solution and yeast are required for fermentation. The solution must be kept warm.

(b) Initially I would expect the dye to go blue. As fermentation proceeds, carbon dioxide is produced. This will carry the dissolved oxygen out of solution and hence the dye will gradually go pink.

(c) The gaseous product is carbon dioxide. This can be identified using limewater as solution X. The limewater will turn milky.

(d)　(i) Ethanol is obtained by fermentation.

$$H-\underset{\underset{H}{|}}{\overset{\overset{H}{|}}{C}}-\underset{\underset{H}{|}}{\overset{\overset{H}{|}}{C}}-O-H$$

(ii) Carboxylic acids are made by oxidation of the corresponding alcohols. The alcohol is refluxed with acidified potassium dichromate(VI) solution using the apparatus shown in Fig. 19.2.

cold water →

alcohol + acidified potassium dichromate(VI) solution

Fig. 19.2

The reflux condenser ensures that the aldehyde which is first formed is returned to the flask and is oxidised further to the carboxylic acid. The orange potassium dichromate(VI) is reduced to green chromium(III) sulphate. The condenser is then placed in the normal position and the acid is distilled off.

$$CH_3CH_2OH\,(l) \xrightarrow{\text{oxidation}} CH_3COOH\,(l) + H_2O\,(l)$$
$$\text{ethanoic acid}$$

(iii) Ethanol is refluxed with anhydrous ethanoic acid in the presence of concentrated sulphuric acid. The ester, ethyl ethanoate, is separated by fractional distillation.

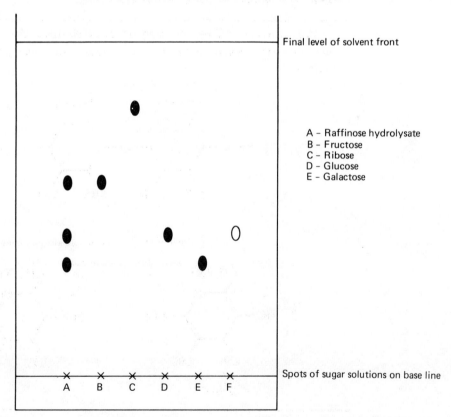

The molecular formula is $C_4H_8O_2$ and therefore the empirical formula, showing the ratio of the numbers of atoms, is C_2H_4O.

Example 19.8

This question concerns the compound RAFFINOSE, a carbohydrate of formula $C_{18}H_{32}O_{16}$, which occurs in many plants. Like many carbohydrates, raffinose can be broken down into simpler sugars by hydrolysis. An aqueous solution of raffinose was hydrolysed by boiling with an equal volume of 8 M hydrochloric acid. The hydrolysate obtained was analysed by paper chromatography using simple sugars as standards for comparison.

Final level of solvent front

A – Raffinose hydrolysate
B – Fructose
C – Ribose
D – Glucose
E – Galactose

Spots of sugar solutions on base line

A   B   C   D   E   F

When a dry sample of solid raffinose was heated in a dry tube with copper(II) oxide, two products of the reaction were driven out of the tube.

(a) Give the **names** of these two volatile products. (1 mark)

Name of product 1: *carbon dioxide*. Name of product 2: *water*.

(b) What information about raffinose can be deduced from the formation of these two products? (1 mark)

211

Raffinose contains carbon and hydrogen. These two elements are oxidised by the copper(II) oxide to give the products in (a).

(c) What is meant by the term 'hydrolysis'. **(1 mark)**

Hydrolysis is the reaction of a compound with water such that the hydroxyl group of the water remains intact.

(d) The hydrolysis can only be achieved by prolonged boiling of the raffinose solution with the hydrochloric acid.
Draw a labelled diagram of a suitable apparatus for carrying out this reaction **without** the addition of any liquid during boiling. **(2 marks)**

The apparatus shown in Fig. 19.2 is suitable but the flask will contain raffinose solution and hydrochloric acid instead of the ethanol and acidified dichromate(VI) solution.

(e) Assuming that the substances in the hydrolysate have been separated completely by the solvent used, what does the chromatogram show about the composition of raffinose? **(2 marks)**

Raffinose can be hydrolysed to give fructose, glucose and galactose.

(f) A concentrated solution from the acid hydrolysis of starch was placed on the point labelled F on the chromatogram.
Mark the position where the product (or products) of this hydrolysis would appear. **(1 mark)**
(L)

Acid hydrolysis of starch produces glucose: thus on the chromatogram, the product will appear in the position marked o.

The products of the hydrolysis depend upon the catalyst used. If amylase (an enzyme present in saliva) had been used, the product would have been maltose.

part of a starch molecule

acid reflux   amylase at room temperature

glucose   maltose

Example 19.9

Below is a simple representation of a detergent molecule.

Covalent tail ⸺⸺⸺◯ Ionic head

(a) Using representations like the one on the previous page, fill in the diagram below to show how you would expect detergent molecules to interact with grease and water.

(2 marks)

Water

Grease

Material

The hydrophobic (water-hating) tails of the detergent molecules enter the grease but the hydrophilic (water-loving) heads stay in the water. The grease is broken up into small particles and carried off into solution.

Water

Grease

Material

(b) Describe one similarity in structure between the above detergent molecule and a soap molecule. **(1 mark)**
Detergent molecules and soap molecules are similar in that they both have a long covalent tail and an ionic head.

(c) Most detergents produced today are biodegradable.
    (i) Explain what this term means. **(1 mark)**
Biodegradable materials are acted upon by bacteria and decomposed into simpler substances.

    (ii) Why is it necessary that detergents should be biodegradable? **(2 marks)**
A large build-up of detergents in our rivers is undesirable since vast quantities of foam are unsightly and marine life is harmed.

(d) (i) What happens when soap is dissolved in water containing calcium ions in solution?
(2 marks)
The soap reacts with the calcium ions to give a precipitate of calcium octadecanoate (scum).

$$2C_{17}H_{35}COONa(aq) + Ca^{2+}(aq) \rightarrow (C_{17}H_{35}COO)_2Ca(s) + 2Na^+(aq)$$
          soap   scum

    (ii) Give the name of one calcium compound commonly found in solution in natural waters. **(1 mark)**
Either calcium sulphate or calcium hydrogencarbonate is a suitable answer. (AEB)

213

19.11 Self-Test Questions

Question 19.1

(i) Name the straight-chain compound having the formula C_5H_{12}.
Is it an alkane or an alkene? **(2 marks)**
(ii) Draw the structural formulae of the two isomers of this compound. **(2 marks)**

Question 19.2

From the information given below, deduce the identities of the unknown substances, giving a brief explanation in support of your answer, and writing balanced equations for the reactions which take place.

(a) (i) A colourless liquid **A**, molecular formula C_2H_6O, was vaporised and passed over a heated catalyst. A colourless gas **B** was formed which decolorised bromine water when shaken with it.

(ii) Liquid **A** was heated with acidified potassium dichromate(VI) and the product of the reaction was isolated; this product **C** was a sharp-smelling liquid with a molecular formula $C_2H_4O_2$.

(iii) When **A** and **C** were heated together in the presence of a few drops of concentrated sulphuric acid, and the reaction mixture was poured into water, a fruity-smelling oily liquid **D** was observed floating on the surface.

(iv) When gas **B** was subjected to a very high pressure and a catalyst, a colourless solid **E** was obtained. **E** was inert to most chemical reagents and had a very high relative molecular mass. **(18 marks)**

(b) A grey solid **F** imparted a brick-red colour to a flame. On adding water to **F**, a vigorous reaction occurred liberating a colourless gas **G**, which had an empirical formula CH and a relative molecular mass of 26. **(6 marks)**

(AEB)

Question 19.3

Use grid 1 on page 2 to choose an answer **A–E**.
Ethyl ethanoate (acetate) is an organic liquid which
1 is made by warming ethanoic acid and ethanol in the presence of concentrated sulphuric acid
2 is hydrolysed by hot sodium hydroxide solution
3 is a pleasant smelling ester.

19.12 Answers to Self-Test Questions

19.1 (i) Pentane. An alkane.

(ii) Pentane has the structural formula:

The question requires you to draw the structural formulae of the other two isomers which are:

```
    H   H   H   H                                    H
    |   |   |   |                                    |
H — C — C — C — C — H                             H — C — H
    |   |   |   |                         H          |          H
    H   |   H   H                         |          |          |
        |                             H — C — C — C — H
    H — C — H                             |   |   |
        |                                 H   |   H
        H                                     |
                                          H — C — H
                                              |
                                              H
```

19.2 (a)   (i)   Since **B** decolorises bromine water **B** must contain a double bond. **B** is ethene, C_2H_4. **B** is obtained by the dehydration of **A**: **A** is ethanol.

$$C_2H_5OH(g) - H_2O(g) \rightarrow C_2H_4(g)$$
$$\mathbf{A}\mathbf{B}$$
$$C_2H_4(g) + Br_2(aq) \rightarrow C_2H_4Br_2(l)$$

    (ii)   Alcohols are oxidised to acids on heating with acidified potassium dichromate(VI) solution. Hence **C** is ethanoic acid.

$$C_2H_5OH(l) \xrightarrow{\text{oxidation}} CH_3COOH(l) + H_2O(l)$$

    (iii)   Alcohols and acids react together to give esters which are insoluble in water. Thus **D** is ethyl ethanoate.

$$CH_3COOH(l) + C_2H_5OH(l) \rightleftharpoons CH_3COOC_2H_5(l) + H_2O(l)$$

    (iv)   Gas **B** is ethene which will polymerise at high pressure in the presence of a catalyst to give **E**, polythene.

$$nC_2H_4(g) \rightarrow (C_2H_4)_n(s)$$

```
          H   H   H   H
          |   |   |   |
··· — C — C — C — C — ···
          |   |   |   |
          H   H   H   H
```

  (b) **F** must be a calcium compound since it imparts a brick-red colour to the flame. **G** has a molecular formula C_2H_2 (since $M_r = 26$). **G** is ethyne which can be obtained by adding water to calcium dicarbide. **F** is thus calcium dicarbide.

$$CaC_2(s) + 2H_2O(l) \rightarrow Ca(OH)_2(aq) + C_2H_2(g)$$

19.3 **A.**

Ethyl ethanoate is prepared from ethanoic acid and ethanol. The reaction is reversible. When sodium hydroxide is used to catalyse the hydrolysis, the reaction goes to completion.

$$CH_3COOC_2H_5(l) + NaOH(aq) \rightarrow CH_3COONa(aq) + C_2H_5OH(l)$$
$$\text{sodium ethanoate}$$

20 Chemical Analysis

20.1 Introduction

There are two types of chemical analysis, *qualitative analysis*, in which the various elements in a substance are identified, and *quantitative analysis*, where their relative masses are found.

20.2 Qualitative Analysis

This section has been restricted to the detection of the following ions: NH_4^+, K^+, Na^+, Li^+, Ca^{2+}, Al^{3+}, Zn^{2+}, Fe^{2+}, Fe^{3+}, Pb^{2+}, Cu^{2+}, CO_3^{2-}, HCO_3^-, S^{2-}, SO_3^{2-}, SO_4^{2-}, NO_3^-, Cl^-, Br^-, and I^-.

The preliminary tests give an indication of the identity of the substance and the further tests are used to confirm the results where possible.

(a) Preliminary Tests

Tests 1, 2, 3 and 4 are carried out on a small quantity of the *solid* substance, Tests 5 and 6 on a *solution* of the substance in water or acid and Test 7 on *either* solid or solution.

Experiment	Observation	Conclusion
1 Note appearance of solid	(a) Blue or bright green (b) Pale green (c) Yellow or brown	Possibly Cu^{2+} Possibly Fe^{2+} Possibly Fe^{3+}
2 Heat in an ignition tube	(a) O_2 (glowing splint relit), no brown fumes of NO_2 (b) O_2 (glowing splint relit), + brown fumes of NO_2 (c) CO_2 (lime water milky) (d) Sublimation (e) Steam (f) Yellow when hot, white when cold (g) Red when hot, yellow when cold	Nitrate of K or Na Nitrate (not of K or Na) CO_3^{2-} or HCO_3^- Possibly NH_4^+ Water of crystallisation ZnO *residue* PbO *residue*
3 Add dil. HCl. Warm if no reaction.	(a) Immediate effervescence (CO_2 — lime water milky) (b) SO_2 (smell, potassium dichromate(VI) paper green)	CO_3^{2-} or HCO_3^- (Go on to FT2*) SO_3^{2-}

*FT is used here as an abbreviation for 'further test'.

	(c) H_2S (smell, lead(II) ethanoate paper black)	S^{2-}
4 Add 2 cm^3 conc. H_2SO_4. Warm *gently* if no reaction. Do not pour hot mixture into water. Add a little Cu powder if no reaction	(a) Same gases as in test 3 (b) HCl (colourless, fuming, acidic gas) (c) $HBr + Br_2$ (colourless, fuming, acidic gas + reddish-brown vapour) (d) I_2 (black solid + purple vapour) + SO_2 + H_2S (e) NO_2 (acidic brown fumes)	Anions as in 3 Cl^- (Go on to FT3) Br^- (Go on to FT3) I^- (Go on to FT3) NO_3^- (Go on to FT4)
5 Add NaOH solution until *just* alkaline (test with indicator paper), then fill up the tube and tip its contents into a second tube. Heat if no precipitate.	(a) White precipitate, insoluble in excess alkali ($Ca(OH)_2$) (b) White precipitate, soluble in excess alkali ($Al(OH)_3$, $Zn(OH)_2$ or $Pb(OH)_2$). Keep solution for FT5 (c) Pale blue precipitate ($Cu(OH)_2$) (d) Dirty-green precipitate ($Fe(OH)_2$) (e) Red-brown precipitate ($Fe(OH)_3$) (f) NH_3 (smell, alkaline gas)	Ca^{2+} (Go on to test 7) Al^{3+}, Zn^{2+} or Pb^{2+} Cu^{2+} Fe^{2+} Fe^{3+} NH_4^+
6 Repeat test 5 using NH_3 solution in place of the NaOH solution.	(a) White precipitate, insoluble in excess alkali ($Ca(OH)_2$, $Al(OH)_3$ or $Pb(OH)_2$) (b) White precipitate, soluble in excess alkali ($Zn(OH)_2$) (c) Pale blue precipitate ($Cu(OH)_2$), giving royal blue solution with excess alkali (d) Dirty-green precipitate ($Fe(OH)_2$) (e) Red-brown precipitate ($Fe(OH)_3$)	Ca^{2+}, Al^{3+} or Pb^{2+} (Go on to FT5) Zn^{2+} Cu^{2+} Fe^{2+} Fe^{3+}
7 Dip a platinum wire into conc. HCl in a watch glass and then heat the *end* of the wire in a flame. Repeat if necessary until the wire does not colour the flame. Then dip the wire into the acid again, touch it on the powdered solid and replace it in the flame. Clean the wire after use.	(a) Lilac flame (red through blue glass) (b) Golden yellow flame (c) Crimson flame (d) Brick-red flame (e) Green-blue flame	K^+ Na^+ Li^+ Ca^{2+} Cu^{2+}

(b) Further Tests

Experiment	Observation	Conclusion
1 Dissolve in distilled water (dil. HCl if insoluble in water). Acidify with dil. HCl and add a little $BaCl_2$ solution.	Thick white precipitate (of $BaSO_4$)	SO_4^{2-}
2 If preliminary test 3(a) is positive, dissolve original solid in water and add 3 drops of universal indicator.	(a) Original solid insoluble (b) Purple colour (c) Green colour, turning purple on boiling	CO_3^{2-} CO_3^{2-} HCO_3^-
3 Dissolve in distilled water (dil. HNO_3 if insoluble in water). Acidify with dil. HNO_3 and add a few drops of $AgNO_3$ solution.	(a) Thick white precipitate (of AgCl), soluble in excess ammonia solution (b) Pale cream precipitate (of AgBr), slightly soluble in ammonia solution (c) Yellow precipitate (of AgI), insoluble in ammonia solution	Cl^- Br^- I^-
4 Dissolve in distilled water and add freshly made $FeSO_4$ solution. Pour 1 cm^3 of conc. H_2SO_4 *carefully* into tilted tube.	(a) Insoluble in water (b) Brown ring at junction of layers	NO_3^- absent NO_3^-
5 Pass H_2S into *solution* from preliminary test 5(b).	(a) No precipitate (b) White precipitate (of ZnS) (c) Black precipitate (of PbS)	Al^{3+} Zn^{2+} Pb^{2+}

20.3 Quantitative Analysis

In this chapter we shall limit ourselves to the branch of quantitative analysis known as *volumetric analysis*, where a solution of the substance under investigation is titrated with a standard solution of a suitable reagent. (A **standard solution** is one whose concentration is known). Only titrations between acids and alkalis will be considered. (See Examples 20.6 and 20.7, and Question 20.8.)

(a) Concentrations of solutions

Since compounds react in mole ratios it is usual to quote concentrations of solutions in mol dm^{-3}. An abbreviation which is often employed for mol dm^{-3} is the letter 'M'. Thus a 0.1 M solution of a given substance has a concentration of 0.1 mole of solute per dm^3 of solution. Strictly speaking, this abbreviation is now obsolete.

20.4 Worked Examples

Example 20.1

Two experiments were carried out on a substance X.

Experiment 1   Experiment 2

(a) Which gas is turning the lime water (calcium hydroxide solution) cloudy?

(b) **From experiment 1 alone** what can be learned about the identity of X?
(c) **From experiment 2 alone** what can be learned about the identity of X?   **(3 marks)**
(SEB)

(a) Carbon dioxide.
(b) X is a carbonate or hydrogencarbonate.

See preliminary test 3.

(c) X is a compound of potassium.

See preliminary test 7.

Example 20.2

In **each** case below give **ONE** simple test which would enable you to distinguish between the two substances named, stating clearly what would happen when you performed the test on each substance of the pair. (No equations are required.)
(a) Magnesium oxide and calcium oxide.   **(3 marks)**
Add a small quantity of water to each solid. Magnesium oxide will not react but calcium oxide will react violently, giving out a great deal of heat and swelling up to give a fine powder of calcium hydroxide.

(b) Calcium hydroxide and calcium carbonate.   **(5 marks)**
Add a spatula measure of each solid to dilute hydrochloric acid. Calcium hydroxide will dissolve, forming a solution of calcium chloride and water (acid + base → salt + water). Calcium carbonate will fizz, giving off carbon dioxide (turns lime water milky) and leaving a solution of calcium chloride and water.

See preliminary test 3.

(c) Magnesium sulphate and magnesium chloride. **(5 marks)**

Add dilute hydrochloric acid, followed by barium chloride solution, to an aqueous solution of each substance. Magnesium sulphate will give a white precipitate of barium sulphate but magnesium chloride will not react.

See Further Test 1.

(d) Zinc hydroxide and magnesium hydroxide. **(5 marks)**

(NISEC)

To each solid add excess sodium hydroxide solution and shake well. Zinc hydroxide is amphoteric (see Section 12.5) and will dissolve, forming a solution of sodium zincate. Magnesium hydroxide will not react.

Example 20.3

In each of the experiments described below, suggest a probable identity for each substance indicated by a letter and write equations for the reactions which take place.

(a) A colourless gas **A** was passed over a heated yellow solid **B**. The products were a shiny solid and a gas **C**, which formed a white precipitate **D** when passed through aqueous calcium hydroxide. **(6 marks)**

(b) When excess zinc powder was added to a blue solution **E** and stirred, a red-brown solid **F** was formed and the solution became colourless. The addition of acidified aqueous silver nitrate to the colourless solution resulted in the formation of a white precipitate **G**. **(5 marks)**

(c) A white solid **H** was warmed with aqueous hydrochloric acid and a pungent smelling, colourless gas **J** was evolved. When this gas was shaken with aqueous iron(III) chloride, a green solution **K** was formed. **(5 marks)**

(AEB)

(a) C is carbon dioxide and D is calcium carbonate.

$$Ca(OH)_2(aq) + CO_2(g) \rightarrow CaCO_3(s) + H_2O(l)$$

A must be oxidised to carbon dioxide and B reduced to a metal. Therefore A is carbon monoxide and B is lead(II) oxide.

$$PbO(s) + CO(g) \rightarrow Pb(s) + CO_2(g)$$

(b) G is silver chloride, so E must be a chloride of some kind.

See Further test 3.

F is copper, displaced from E by zinc. Therefore E is copper(II) chloride.

$$Zn(s) + CuCl_2(aq) \rightarrow ZnCl_2(aq) + Cu(s)$$
$$2\,AgNO_3(aq) + ZnCl_2(aq) \rightarrow 2AgCl(s) + Zn(NO_3)_2(aq)$$

(c) J reduces iron(III) chloride solution to green iron(II) chloride solution, K. Therefore J is sulphur dioxide, produced from a sulphite H and warm dilute hydrochloric acid. H could be sodium sulphite.

$$Na_2SO_3(s) + 2HCl(aq) \rightarrow 2NaCl(aq) + H_2O(l) + SO_2(g)$$
$$2FeCl_3(aq) + 2H_2O(l) + SO_2(g) \rightarrow 2FeCl_2(aq) + 2HCl(aq) + H_2SO_4(aq)$$

Example 20.4

Suggest a name and formula for each of the compounds **A** to **H** below. Write equations for the reactions mentioned. Structural formulae are required for the compounds **F**, **G** and **H**.

(a) The green crystalline solid **A** dissolved in water to give a pale green solution. One portion of this solution was treated with aqueous ammonia (ammonium hydroxide solution) and a green precipitate **B** was formed. A second portion of the solution of **A** gave a white precipitate **C** with barium chloride solution that was not soluble in dilute hydrochloric acid. **(8 marks)**

(b) A white deliquescent solid **D** dissolved in water exothermically to give a strongly alkaline solution. When the solution of **D** was added to copper(II) sulphate solution a blue precipitate **E** was formed. Substance **D** gave a golden yellow flame colour. **(8 marks)**

(c) When the colourless flammable liquid **F** is treated with sodium there is fizzing as the sodium reacts and a colourless solution is formed. Careful evaporation of this solution leaves a white solid **G**. When **F** is boiled with a concentrated acidified potassium dichromate solution and the resulting mixture distilled, an acidic liquid **H** with a sharp vinegary smell is produced. **(9 marks)**

(OLE)

(a) C is barium sulphate, $BaSO_4$, so A is a sulphate.

See further test 1.

B is iron(II) hydroxide, $Fe(OH)_2$.

See preliminary test 6.

So A must be iron(II) sulphate, $FeSO_4$.

$$FeSO_4(aq) + 2NH_4OH(aq) \rightarrow Fe(OH)_2(s) + (NH_4)_2SO_4(aq)$$
$$FeSO_4(aq) + BaCl_2(aq) \rightarrow BaSO_4(s) + FeCl_2(aq)$$

(b) D is sodium hydroxide, NaOH, and E is copper(II) hydroxide, $Cu(OH)_2$

See preliminary tests 7 and 5.

$$CuSO_4(aq) + 2NaOH(aq) \rightarrow Cu(OH)_2(s) + Na_2SO_4(aq)$$

(c) F is ethanol, G is sodium ethoxide and H is ethanoic acid.

F   G   H

$$2C_2H_5OH + 2Na \longrightarrow 2C_2H_5ONa + H_2 \qquad C_2H_5OH \xrightarrow{2[\ddot{O}]} CH_3COOH + H_2O$$

See Section 19.7.

Example 20.5

(a) Describe what you would observe when each of the following pairs of substances is mixed, and write an ionic equation for each reaction.
  (i) sodium chloride and silver nitrate solutions;
  (ii) iron(III) chloride and ammonium hydroxide solutions;
  (iii) lead(II) nitrate and sodium iodide solutions;
  (iv) copper(II) sulphate solution and zinc. **(4 × 3 marks)**

221

(b) State how you would distinguish between the two substances in each of the following pairs; one test for each pair is sufficient, but you should state how each substance will behave under the test you describe:
  (i) chlorine and sulphur dioxide;
  (ii) potassium carbonate and potassium hydrogencarbonate;
  (iii) hydrogen sulphide and hydrogen.   (13 marks)

(a) (i) A white precipitate of silver chloride would form.   (OLE)

Further test 3.

$$Ag^+(aq) + Cl^-(aq) \rightarrow AgCl(s)$$

(ii) A brown precipitate of iron(III) hydroxide would form.

Preliminary test 6.

$$Fe^{3+}(aq) + 3OH^-(aq) \rightarrow Fe(OH)_3(s)$$

(iii) A bright yellow precipitate of lead(II) iodide would form.

$$Pb^{2+}(aq) + 2I^-(aq) \rightarrow PbI_2(s)$$

(iv) A reddish-brown precipitate of copper would form and the blue colour of the solution would fade.

$$Cu^{2+}(aq) + Zn(s) \rightarrow Cu(s) + Zn^{2+}(aq)$$

(b) (i) Bubble each gas into sodium bromide solution. Chlorine displaces bromine and the solution turns reddish-brown. Sulphur dioxide has no effect.

$$Cl_2(g) + 2Br^-(aq) \rightarrow 2Cl^-(aq) + Br_2(aq)$$

(ii) Dissolve the substances separately in distilled water and add universal indicator. Potassium carbonate solution turns the indicator purple but potassium hydrogencarbonate solution turns it green.

Further test 2.

(iii) Bubble each gas into sodium bromide solution. Chlorine displaces bromine and the solution turns reddish-brown. Sulphur dioxide has no effect.

See further test 5.

$$Pb(NO_3)_2(aq) + H_2S(g) \rightarrow PbS(s) + 2HNO_3(aq)$$

Example 20.6

(a) Describe precisely how you would estimate the concentration of a solution of sulphuric acid, using normal laboratory glassware and 0.1 M sodium hydroxide solution (containing 0.1 mole per dm^3). You should name or draw the glassware that you need, and state your indicator with its colour change.   (9 marks)

(b) In a similar experiment an average volume of 22.0 cm^3 of 0.1 M sodium hydroxide solution neutralised 25.0 cm^3 of sulphuric acid.

$$H_2SO_4 + 2NaOH \rightarrow Na_2SO_4 + 2H_2O$$

Calculate
  (i) the number of moles of sodium hydroxide solution used;   (3 marks)

(ii) the number of moles of sulphuric acid in the 25.0 cm^3 samples; **(4 marks)**
(iii) the concentration of the sulphuric acid in moles per dm^3; **(3 marks)**
(iv) the concentration of the acid in grams per dm^3. **(3 marks)**

(c) Give the name and formula of the salt that would be formed if you used only 11.0 cm^3 of the sodium hydroxide solution. State the method by which you could obtain this compound from its solution in water. **(3 marks)**

(OLE)

(a) Rinse a 25.0 cm^3 pipette with distilled water and then with the sodium hydroxide solution. Rinse a burette, including the jet, with distilled water and then with the dilute sulphuric acid. Fill the burette with the acid, open the tap and allow the acid to run out until all air bubbles have been expelled from the jet. Wash the flask with distilled water *only*.

Transfer 25.0 cm^3 of the alkali to a conical flask by means of the pipette. Add 2–3 drops of screened methyl orange indicator to the alkali and then read the level of the acid in the burette. Run 1 cm^3 portions of the acid into the alkali, swirling the flask after each addition until the indicator changes from green to red, showing that the acid is just in excess. Note the new burette reading and subtract the initial reading from this to give the volume, to the nearest 1 cm^3, of the acid required to neutralise the alkali. Empty the flask, rinse it with distilled water and repeat the titration, this time adding the acid in a continuous stream until the volume is within 1 cm^3 of the end-point. Carry out the final additions dropwise, with swirling, until the indicator turns buff coloured, showing that the solution is exactly neutral. Perform further accurate titrations until two results within 0.1 cm^3 of one another are obtained. Calculate the results as in part (b).

It is quicker to name the pieces of glassware than to draw them – the question gives you the choice of either course of action.

(b) (i) mol of NaOH per dm^3 = 0.1
$\therefore$ mol of NaOH per 22.0 cm^3 = $0.1 \times \dfrac{22}{1000}$ = 0.0022

(ii) mol NaOH : mol H$_2$SO$_4$ = 2 : 1 = 1 : $\frac{1}{2}$ (from equation)
$\therefore$ mol of H$_2$SO$_4$ per 25.0 cm^3 = $0.0022 \times \frac{1}{2}$ = 0.0011

(iii) mol of H$_2$SO$_4$ per dm^3 = $0.0011 \times \dfrac{1000}{25}$ = 0.044

(iv) g of H$_2$SO$_4$ per dm^3 = 0.044×98 (M_r (H$_2$SO$_4$) = 98)

= 4.31

(c) Sodium hydrogensulphate, NaHSO$_4$, would be formed. It could be obtained from its solution by crystallisation.

Example 20.7

The equation for the reaction between sodium carbonate and an aqueous solution of hydrogen chloride is:

$$Na_2CO_3(aq) + 2HCl(aq) \rightarrow 2NaCl(aq) + CO_2(g) + H_2O(l)$$

In an experiment it was found that 10 cm^3 of a solution of hydrogen chloride reacted completely with 20 cm^3 of 0.025 M sodium carbonate solution. What is the concentration of hydrogen chloride in the original solution (in mol dm^{-3})?
A 0.1
B 0.5

(L)

The answer is **A**.

mol Na_2CO_3 : mol HCl	= 1 : 2 . . . . A
mol Na_2CO_3 per dm^3	= 0.025
mol Na_2CO_3 per 20 cm^3	$= 0.025 \times \dfrac{20}{1000}$
mol HCl per 10 cm^3	$= 0.025 \times \dfrac{20}{1000} \times 2$ (from A)
mol HCl per dm^3	$= 0.025 \times \dfrac{20}{1000} \times 2 \times \dfrac{1000}{10}$
	= 0.1

N.B. Always begin line A with the substance whose concentration is *known*. (Compare with method in Example 5.8).

20.5 Self-Test Questions

Question 20.1

Describe briefly a simple chemical or physical test which would distinguish between the ions in each of the following pairs:
(a) Br^-(aq) and NO_3^-(aq)   (4 marks)
(b) SO_3^{2-}(aq) and CO_3^{2-}(aq)   (5 marks)
(c) Li^+(aq) and Na^+(aq)   (2 marks)
(d) NH_4^+(aq) and Mg^{2+}(aq)   (5 marks)

The result of the test on **each ion** should be stated and **ionic** equations should be given wherever possible.   (AEB)

Question 20.2

A pale blue precipitate is formed when equal volumes of aqueous X and aqueous Y are mixed. The pale blue precipitate dissolves when an excess of aqueous Y is added to the mixture. X and Y could be

X	Y
A ammonia	copper(II) sulphate
B ammonia	iron(II) sulphate
C copper(II) sulphate	ammonia
D copper(II) sulphate	sodium hydroxide
E iron(II) sulphate	sodium hydroxide

(AEB)

Question 20.3

Which of the following metals forms a hydroxide which is insoluble in water but soluble in aqueous sulphuric acid or sodium hydroxide?

A aluminium
B calcium
C copper
D lead
E magnesium

Question 20.4

Sodium hydroxide solution produces a reddish-brown precipitate when added to a solution of

A aluminium sulphate
B copper(II) sulphate
C iron(II) sulphate
D iron(III) sulphate
E magnesium sulphate

Question 20.5

When solid X is heated, it gives off a brown gas. X could be

A Ammonium chloride
B Lead(II) nitrate
C Lead(IV) oxide
D Potassium nitrate
E Sodium bromide

Question 20.6

The gas evolved when concentrated sulphuric acid is added to ammonium chloride will

A bleach moist litmus paper
B form a white solid near the top of the test tube
C form steamy fumes when it comes into contact with moist air
D turn acidified aqueous potassium dichromate(VI) green
E turn moist red litmus paper blue.

Question 20.7

Use grid 1 on page 2 to choose an answer A-E.
A WHITE precipitate is formed when solutions of X and Y are mixed. X and Y could be

1 copper(II) sulphate and sodium hydroxide
2 copper(II) sulphate and barium chloride
3 sodium chloride and silver nitrate

Question 20.8

Which of the following procedures is NOT correct when preparing to titrate sulphuric acid solution into sodium hydroxide solution?

A Rinse the burette with the acid and then fill it with the acid.
B Run a few cm^3 of the acid out through the burette jet.
C Rinse the titration flask with alkali and then add exactly 25 cm^3 of the alkali solution.

D Put a few drops of indicator in the titration flask.
E Read the level at which the acid stands in the burette.   (NISEC)

20.6   Answers to Self-Test Questions

20.1 (a) Add chlorine water. Reddish-brown bromine will be displaced from the Br^-(aq) but no change will occur in the NO_3^-(aq).

$$2Br^-(aq) + Cl_2(aq) \rightarrow Br_2(aq) + 2Cl^-(aq)$$

Further test 3 could be used here.

(b) Add *cold* dilute hydrochloric acid. CO_3^{2-}(aq) will give an effervescence of carbon dioxide (turns lime water milky) but SO_3^{2-}(aq) will not effervesce. A pungent smell of sulphur dioxide (turns a moist potassium dichromate(VI) paper from orange to green) may be detected from the SO_3^{2-}(aq) in the cold. On warming it will become much more noticeable.

$$2H^+(aq) + CO_3^{2-}(aq) \rightarrow H_2O(l) + CO_2(g)$$
$$2H^+(aq) + SO_3^{2-}(aq) \rightarrow H_2O(l) + SO_2(g)$$

See preliminary test 3.

(c) Carry out a flame test. Li^+(aq) gives a crimson flame and Na^+(aq) a golden yellow one.

See preliminary test 7.

(d) Add sodium hydroxide solution. Mg^{2+}(aq) will give a white precipitate of magnesium hydroxide.

$$Mg^{2+}(aq) + 2OH^-(aq) \rightarrow Mg(OH)_2(s)$$

From the NH_4^+(aq) a smell of ammonia (turns moist red litmus paper blue) may be detected in the cold. On warming, more ammonia will be evolved.

$$NH_4^+(aq) + OH^-(aq) \rightarrow NH_3(g) + H_2O(l)$$

See preliminary test 5.

20.2 **C.**

See preliminary test 6.

20.3 **A.**

Aluminium hydroxide is amphoteric; lead(II) hydroxide is amphoteric but does not dissolve in dilute sulphuric acid because lead(II) sulphate is insoluble in water.

20.4 **D**

See preliminary test 5.

20.5 **B**.

See preliminary test 2.

20.6 **C**.

See preliminary test 4.

20.7 **C**.

See preliminary test 5 and further tests 1 and 3.

20.8 **C**.

The flask should be rinsed with distilled water, not alkali.

Table of Relative Atomic Masses

Element	Symbol	Atomic number	Relative atomic mass	Element	Symbol	Atomic number	Relative atomic mass
Actinium	Ac	89	227	Holmium	Ho	67	165
Aluminium	Al	13	27	Hydrogen	H	1	1
Americium	Am	95	243	Indium	In	49	115
Antimony	Sb	51	122	Iodine	I	53	127
Argon	Ar	18	40	Iridium	Ir	77	192
Arsenic	As	33	75	Iron	Fe	26	56
Astatine	At	85	210	Krypton	Kr	36	84
Barium	Ba	56	137	Lanthanum	La	57	139
Berkelium	Bk	97	249	Lawrencium	Lr	103	257
Beryllium	Be	4	9	Lead	Pb	82	207
Bismuth	Bi	83	209	Lithium	Li	3	7
Boron	B	5	11	Lutetium	Lu	71	175
Bromine	Br	35	80	Magnesium	Mg	12	24
Cadmium	Cd	48	112	Manganese	Mn	25	55
Caesium	Cs	55	133	Mendelevium	Md	101	256
Calcium	Ca	20	40	Mercury	Hg	80	201
Californium	Cf	98	251	Molybdenum	Mo	42	96
Carbon	C	6	12	Neodymium	Nd	60	144
Cerium	Ce	58	140	Neon	Ne	10	20
Chlorine	Cl	17	35.5	Neptunium	Np	93	237
Chromium	Cr	24	52	Nickel	Ni	28	59
Cobalt	Co	27	59	Niobium	Nb	41	93
Copper	Cu	29	63.5	Nitrogen	N	7	14
Curium	Cm	96	247	Nobelium	No	102	254
Dysprosium	Dy	66	162.5	Osmium	Os	76	190
Einsteinium	Es	99	254	Oxygen	O	8	16
Erbium	Er	68	167	Palladium	Pd	46	106
Europium	Eu	63	152	Phosphorus	P	15	31
Fermium	Fm	100	253	Platinum	Pt	78	195
Fluorine	F	9	19	Plutonium	Pu	94	242
Francium	Fr	87	223	Polonium	Po	84	210
Gadolinium	Gd	64	157	Potassium	K	19	39
Gallium	Ga	31	70	Praseodymium	Pr	59	141
Germanium	Ge	32	73	Promethium	Pm	61	147
Gold	Au	79	197	Protactinium	Pa	91	231
Hafnium	Hf	72	178.5	Radium	Ra	88	226
Helium	He	2	4	Radon	Rn	86	222

Rhenium	Re	75	186		Terbium	Tb	65	159
Rhodium	Rh	45	103		Thallium	Tl	81	204
Rubidium	Rb	37	85.5		Thorium	Th	90	232
Ruthenium	Ru	44	101		Thulium	Tm	69	169
Samarium	Sm	62	150		Tin	Sn	50	119
Scandium	Sc	21	45		Titanium	Ti	22	48
Selenium	Se	34	79		Tungsten	W	74	184
Silicon	Si	14	28		Uranium	U	92	238
Silver	Ag	47	108		Vanadium	V	23	51
Sodium	Na	11	23		Xenon	Xe	54	131
Strontium	Sr	38	88		Ytterbium	Yb	70	173
Sulphur	S	16	32		Yttrium	Y	39	89
Tantalum	Ta	73	181		Zinc	Zn	30	65
Technetium	Tc	43	99		Zirconium	Zr	40	91
Tellurium	Te	52	128					

Note: (1) The relative atomic masses are based on a scale where the mass of $^{12}C = 12$.
(2) For many of the radioactive elements the relative atomic mass given is the mass number of the most stable or the most common isotope.

The Periodic Table

Key:
Atomic Number — Relative Atomic Mass

Groups	I	II	Transition Metals											III	IV	V	VI	VII	O
Period 1	H 1 1																		He 2 4
Period 2	Li 3 7	Be 4 9												B 5 11	C 6 12	N 7 14	O 8 16	F 9 19	Ne 10 20
Period 3	Na 11 23	Mg 12 24												Al 13 27	Si 14 28	P 15 31	S 16 32	Cl 17 35.5	Ar 18 40
Period 4	K 19 39	Ca 20 40	Sc 21 45	Ti 22 48	V 23 51	Cr 24 52	Mn 25 55	Fe 26 56	Co 27 59	Ni 28 59	Cu 29 63.5	Zn 30 65		Ga 31 70	Ge 32 73	As 33 75	Se 34 79	Br 35 80	Kr 36 84
Period 5	Rb 37 85.5	Sr 38 88	Y 39 89	Zr 40 91	Nb 41 93	Mo 42 96	Tc 43 99	Ru 44 101	Rh 45 103	Pd 46 106	Ag 47 108	Cd 48 112		In 49 115	Sn 50 119	Sb 51 122	Te 52 128	I 53 127	Xe 54 131
Period 6	Cs 55 133	Ba 56 137	La 57 139	Hf 72 178.5	Ta 73 181	W 74 184	Re 75 186	Os 76 190	Ir 77 192	Pt 78 195	Au 79 197	Hg 80 201		Tl 81 204	Pb 82 207	Bi 83 209	Po 84 210	At 85 210	Rn 86 222
Period 7	Fr 87 223	Ra 88 226	Ac 89 227																

Lanthanide Series:

Ce 58 140	Pr 59 141	Nd 60 144	Pm 61 147	Sm 62 150	Eu 63 152	Gd 64 157	Tb 65 159	Dy 66 162.5	Ho 67 165	Er 68 167	Tm 69 169	Yb 70 173	Lu 71 175

Actinide Series:

Th 90 232	Pa 91 231	U 92 238	Np 93 237	Pu 94 242	Am 95 243	Cm 96 247	Bk 97 249	Cf 98 251	Es 99 254	Fm 100 253	Md 101 256	No 102 254	Lr 103 257

Index